Rum and Coconut
Crème Brûlée,
page 52

Sausage-Beef Enchiladas, page 102

Chunky Tofu Guacamole, page 13

Pineapple-Coconut Upside Down Cake, page 36

Weight Watchers®
ANNUAL RECIPES *for* SUCCESS
2001

Oxmoor House®

ISBN: 0-8487-1967-0
ISSN: 1526-1565
Printed in the United States of America
First Printing 2000

Be sure to check with your health-care provider before making any changes in your diet.

OXMOOR HOUSE, INC.
EDITOR-IN-CHIEF: Nancy Fitzpatrick Wyatt
SENIOR FOODS EDITOR: Katherine M. Eakin
SENIOR EDITOR, COPY AND HOMES: Olivia Kindig Wells
ART DIRECTOR: James Boone

WEIGHT WATCHERS® ANNUAL RECIPES FOR SUCCESS 2001

EDITORS: Suzanne Henson, M.S., R.D.; Patricia Wilens
COPY EDITOR: Donna Baldone
EDITORIAL ASSISTANT: Heather Averett
INTERN: Libby Monteith
ASSOCIATE ART DIRECTOR: Cynthia R. Cooper
DESIGNER: Clare T. Minges
DIRECTOR, TEST KITCHENS: Elizabeth Tyler Luckett
ASSISTANT DIRECTOR, TEST KITCHENS: Julie Christopher
RECIPE EDITOR: Gayle Hays Sadler
TEST KITCHENS STAFF: Rebecca Mohr Boggan; Gretchen Feldtman, R.D.; Jan A. Smith
PHOTOGRAPHER: Brit Huckabay
PHOTO STYLIST: Virginia R. Cravens
PUBLISHING SYSTEMS ADMINISTRATOR: Rick Tucker
DIRECTOR, PRODUCTION AND DISTRIBUTION: Phillip Lee
BOOKS PRODUCTION MANAGER: Theresa L. Beste
PRODUCTION ASSISTANT: Faye Porter Bonner

WE'RE HERE FOR YOU!

We at Oxmoor House are dedicated to serving you with reliable information that expands your imagination and enriches your life. We welcome your comments and suggestions. Please write us at:

Oxmoor House, Inc.
Weight Watchers® Annual Recipes for Success
2100 Lakeshore Drive
Birmingham, AL 35209

To order additional publications, call 1-205-877-6560.

COVER: Individual Lime Tarts, page 40
BACK COVER: Lemon and Rosemary Roasted Chicken With Potatoes, page 110

CONTENTS

INTRODUCTION

RECIPES

SUCCESSES

WEEKLY MENU PLANNERS

Welcome! Let this book be your guide to nourishing and nurturing a healthy, active lifestyle.

Living a healthy lifestyle is about so much more than what you weigh. It's about finding a balance in your life. You'll discover the tools to achieve that balance in *Weight Watchers Annual Recipes for Success 2001*. In this cookbook, you'll find great-tasting food and fitness guides. Plus, you'll find weight-loss success stories that will inspire you to make healthy living a habit.

We've compiled more than 250 wonderfully delicious recipes that are reliable and satisfying. No matter what your schedule, your grocery list, or your mood, you'll find a recipe that meets your needs. Some recipes are designed to help you get a homemade meal on the table in a hurry. Others are ideal when you want to linger a bit longer in the kitchen and enjoy the craft of cooking. Either way, you can count on every recipe for delicious results.

We know you don't like uncertainty in the kitchen. So throughout the book we've included charts, helpful hints, and step-by-step photos that take the guesswork out of cooking. And, with many recipes, we've answered the age-old question "What's for dinner?" with ideas for rounding out your family's meal.

NUTRITION KNOW-HOW

Accurate information is an important tool in the pursuit of healthful living. So that you know where you stand nutritionally, you'll find guides with every recipe. Each recipe has a ***POINTS*** value calculated through the ***POINTS***® Food System, an integral part of the new weight-loss program, Weight Watchers **Winning Points.** We've also included the diabetic exchanges for individuals who may have special dietary considerations, as well as a complete nutrient analysis (for more information, see About Our Recipes on page 10).

And, throughout the book, look for our Nutrition columns with sound food and health-related advice from our registered dietitians.

Here's just a sample of the nutrition news you'll find to help you stay in balance:

- THE FATS YOU NEED (page 60): Yes, some fat is good for you, particularly if you choose heart-healthy types. Discover how fitting certain fats into your diet can be a delicious proposition.
- CALCIUM COUNTS (page 83): How strong are your bones? Read these smart strategies to learn how to get the calcium you need to keep your bones healthy for life.
- PUMPING IRON (page 86): Feeling fatigued? A lack of iron may be the answer. Discover the best way to get this essential mineral.
- WHAT'S IN FOR TAKEOUT (page 104): You don't have to forsake healthy eating with fast food. Use these tips the next time you pull up to a drive-through to order food.
- PERFECT PORTIONS (page 147): Just how much is enough? You'll find the answer with this guide to good eating.

QUICK & EASY MENUS

We know that a crammed calendar often makes healthy eating a challenge. So we created nine weeks of superfast and simple menus that do the planning for you. With every menu, you'll find the ***POINTS*** and diabetic exchanges calculated for each day. Use these menus to prepare meals for the week ahead, for one day, or for even one meal. Or, use them as guides for planning your own menus, substituting your favorite recipes.

OUR FAVORITE RECIPES

We judge the merits of every recipe, and only the best make the cut. But a few have an indefinable quality that can only be described as the "yum factor." These are the recipes that are so outstanding, they've become our personal favorites. We think they'll become yours and your family's as well.

- **Chocolate Cake With Mocha Glaze** (page 36). The tender texture and simple goodness of this cake earned our judges' highest praises. We consider this cake, and its yummy glaze, the new standard by which we'll compare all future cakes.
- **Peanut Butter and Jelly Muffins** (page 18). We've transformed the lunchbox staple sandwich into a treat that both kids and their moms on the run will love.
- **Sausage-Beef Enchiladas** (page 102). This hearty meat-and-cheese meal is bound to be a family favorite.
- **Pasta With Fresh Garlic Oil** (page 145). This easy-but-elegant side dish will instantly dress up beef, chicken, or fish.
- **Lemon-Buttermilk Pound Cake** (page 38). No one will ever guess—or believe—that this luscious cake is light.
- **Cincinnati Four-Way Chili** (page 155). Even the hungriest appetite will be satisfied with this extraordinary chili. This hearty weeknight meal starts out with a bed of pasta; then is built with beef, beans, and an array of spices including cocoa, coffee, and cinnamon.
- **Citrus-Salmon Salad** (page 127). Bored with the same old greens? A mouthwatering combination of fruit, seasonings, and succulent salmon makes this salad an appetizing change of pace.
- **Chunky Tofu Guacamole** (page 13). We cut calories and fat from the traditional guacamole recipe. But, thanks to tofu, we kept the classic creamy texture and buttery richness.
- **Grilled Grouper With Cilantro-Lime Sauce** (page 57). A tangy marinade of sweet soy sauce, and brown sugar, blended with ginger and tart lime makes this fish dish a low-calorie, low-fat taste sensation.
- **Lemon and Rosemary Roasted Chicken With Potatoes** (page 110). This distinctive medley of lemon and herbs transforms ordinary chicken into an elegant feast that's a cinch to make. To cut your time in the kitchen, red potatoes roast right with the bird.
- **Individual Lime Tarts** (page 40). A crispy graham cracker crust holds the cool, delicate lime filling in this refreshing dessert. For an impressive presentation, bake a larger size tart.

PICTURES OF HEALTH

Weight loss and maintenance don't have to be a do-it-yourself situation. Read the inspiring stories of 11 people who found help and encouragement in Weight Watchers programs. For people like Susan Lopez (page 65), losing weight meant regaining control of their lives.

"I feel great, and my kids see that in me. I'm passing on to them healthful habits and the happiness I feel every day."

Take the tips from folks like Susan and other weight-loss winners and use them as motivation for your own success story, and then tell us about it. Read on to see how your story could inspire someone else.

SHARE YOUR SUCCESS

If you have a Weight Watchers weight-loss success story that you would like to share with us, please send a brief account of your personal experience to:

Weight Watchers Annual Recipes for Success
2100 Lakeshore Drive
Birmingham, AL 35209

Tell us your name, address, daytime telephone number, and e-mail address (if applicable). If possible, please include before and after snapshots.

About Our Recipes

Weight Watchers Annual Recipes for Success gives you the nutrition facts you want to know. To make your life easier, we've provided the following useful information with every recipe:

- A number calculated through ***POINTS***® Food System, an integral part of the new weight-loss program from Weight Watchers International, Inc., **Winning Points**
- Diabetic exchange values for those who use them as a guide for planning meals
- A complete nutrient analysis per serving

POINTS FOOD SYSTEM

Every recipe in the book includes a number assigned through ***POINTS*** value. This system uses a formula based on the calorie, fat, and fiber content of the food. Foods with more calories and fat (like a slice of pepperoni pizza) receive high numbers, while fruits and vegetables receive low numbers. For more information about **Winning Points** and the Weight Watchers meeting nearest you, call 1-800-651-6000.

DIABETIC EXCHANGES

Recipes include diabetic exchanges, which are calculated from the *Exchange Lists for Meal Planning* developed by the American Diabetes Association and The American Dietetic Association. Exchange information is designated as follows: starch, fruit, skim milk, low-fat milk, whole milk, vegetable, very lean meat, lean meat, medium-fat meat, high-fat meat, and fat.

NUTRIENT ANALYSIS

Each recipe has a complete list of nutrients, including CAL (calories), PRO (protein), FAT (total fat), sat (saturated fat), CARB (carbohydrate), FIB (dietary fiber), CHOL (cholesterol), IRON, SOD (sodium), and CALC (calcium). Measurements are abbreviated g (grams) and mg (milligrams). Numbers are based on these assumptions:

- Unless otherwise indicated, meat, poultry, and fish refer to skinned, boned, and cooked servings.
- When we give a range for an ingredient (3 to 3½ cups flour, for instance), we calculate using the lesser amount.
- Some alcohol calories evaporate during heating; the analysis reflects that.
- Only the amount of marinade absorbed by the food is used in calculation.
- Garnishes and optional ingredients are not included in an analysis.

Nutritional values used in our calculations come from either a computer program by Computrition, Inc., or are provided by food manufacturers.

Appetizers & Beverages

ROASTED CORN SALSA

5 ears yellow corn
Cooking spray
2 cups diced seeded tomato (about 2 small)
½ cup finely chopped green bell pepper
½ cup finely chopped red bell pepper
⅓ cup diced peeled jicama
¼ cup peeled diced avocado
⅓ cup finely chopped red onion
3 tablespoons finely chopped fresh cilantro
1 garlic clove, minced
1 jalapeño pepper, seeded and minced
2 tablespoons fresh lime juice
2½ teaspoons extra-virgin olive oil

1. Preheat oven to 475°.
2. Remove husks from corn. Scrub silks from corn.
3. Cut kernels from ears of corn. Place corn in a single layer on a jelly-roll pan coated with cooking spray. Bake 15 minutes or until slightly charred, stirring every 5 minutes. Remove corn from pan; let cool.
4. Combine corn, tomato, and remaining ingredients, stirring well. **YIELD:** 9 servings (serving size: ½ cup).
NOTE: Plum tomatoes are a good substitute if you don't have ripe summer tomatoes.

POINTS: 1; **EXCHANGES:** 1 Starch, ½ Fat;
PER SERVING: CAL 81 (30% from fat); PRO 2g; FAT 2.7g (sat 0.4g); CARB 14.8g; FIB 2.8g; CHOL 0mg; IRON 0.8mg; SOD 12mg; CALC 9mg

THE SAFE WAY TO SEED PEPPERS

You don't have to remove the seeds from hot peppers such as jalapeños, but sauces and salsas are more attractive without them. Removing the seeds and membranes also tempers the heat. Handling hot peppers can burn your skin, so wear rubber gloves when preparing them.

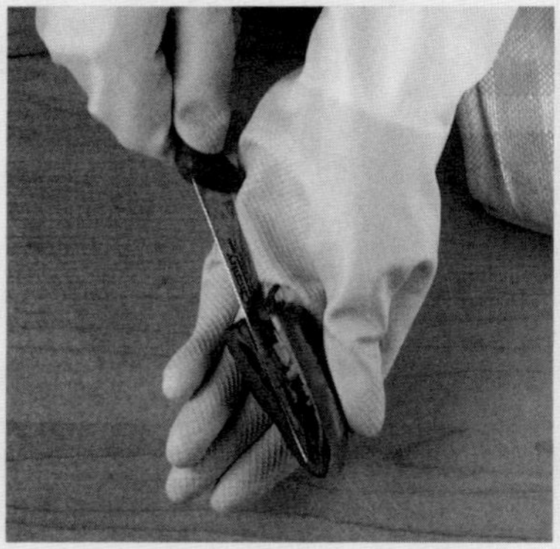

1. Split the jalapeño lengthwise with a small sharp knife.

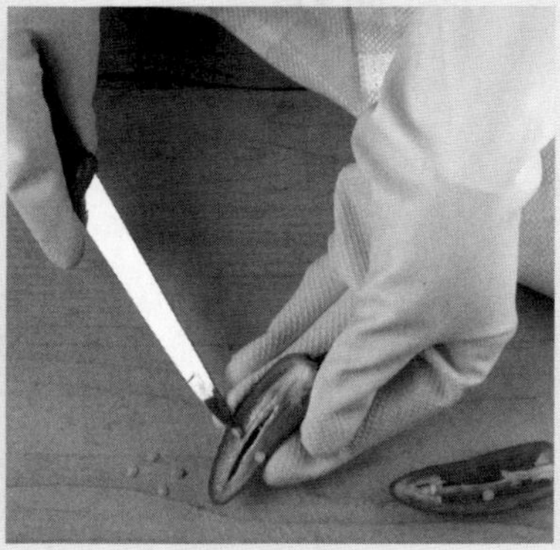

2. Use the knife tip to scrape the seeds from the pepper cavity.

ROASTED GARLIC AND PORTOBELLO CROSTINI

2 whole garlic heads
1 (6-ounce) package presliced portobello mushrooms
2 tablespoons balsamic vinegar
Olive oil-flavored cooking spray
15 (½-inch-thick) slices French bread baguette (about 5 ounces)
¾ cup (3 ounces) crumbled goat cheese

1. Preheat oven to 350°.
2. Remove white papery skin from garlic heads (do not peel or separate cloves). Wrap each head separately in foil. Bake at 350° for 1 hour; let cool 10 minutes. Separate cloves; squeeze to extract garlic pulp. Discard skins. Set pulp aside.
3. Combine mushrooms and balsamic vinegar in a shallow dish, turning mushrooms to coat. Let stand 15 minutes.
4. Coat a large nonstick skillet with cooking spray; place over medium-high heat until hot. Add mushrooms and vinegar; cook 5 minutes or until mushrooms are tender, stirring occasionally.
5. Spread roasted garlic pulp on 1 side of each bread slice; divide mushrooms evenly among bread. Spoon 2 teaspoons cheese onto each crostini. Place crostini on a baking sheet; broil 2 minutes or until toasted. Serve immediately. **YIELD:** 15 servings (serving size: 1 slice).

POINTS: 1; **EXCHANGE:** ½ Starch;
PER SERVING: CAL 52 (28% from fat); PRO 2.2g; FAT 1.6g (sat 0.9g); CARB 7.3g; FIB 0.5g; CHOL 5mg; IRON 0.5mg; SOD 122mg; CALC 44mg

AVOCADO 101

Slice the avocado in half lengthwise, working around the seed. If necessary, twist the halves a little to get them to separate, leaving the seed in one half.

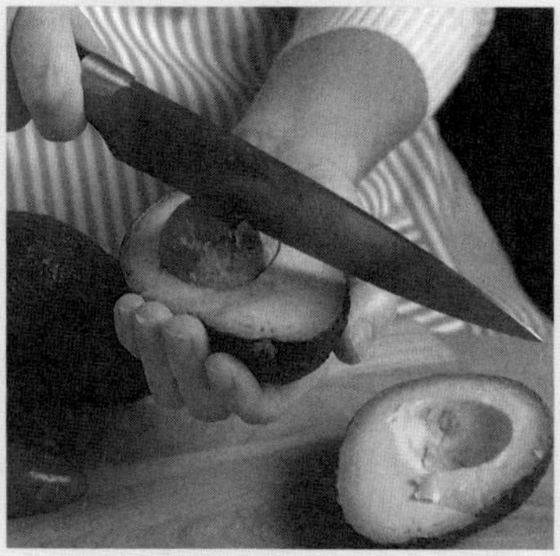

1. Hold the avocado in the palm of one hand; stab the seed with the blade of a sharp knife. Gently twist the knife to remove the seed.

2. Scoop out buttery-soft pulp with a spoon. Once exposed to the air, avocado pulp discolors quickly. Lemon or lime juice helps to minimize that effect.

CHUNKY TOFU GUACAMOLE

(pictured on page 3)

- 1 medium avocado
- 1 (12.3-ounce) package firm silken-style tofu (such as Mori-Nu), drained
- 1 (7-ounce) can salsa verde (such as Herdez) or ¾ cup other tomatillo salsa
- 2 garlic cloves, peeled
- 2 tablespoons fresh lemon juice
- ½ teaspoon salt
- 1¼ cups diced seeded tomato (about 1 medium)
- ½ cup finely diced red onion

1. Slice avocado in half. Scoop pulp from 1 half of avocado; set remaining half aside.
2. Place tofu, avocado pulp, salsa verde, and next 3 ingredients in a food processor; process until smooth, scraping down sides of bowl occasionally. Transfer to a medium bowl.
3. Dice remaining avocado. Add diced avocado, tomato, and onion to tofu mixture, stirring well. **YIELD:** 12 servings (serving size: about ¼ cup).

POINTS: 1; **EXCHANGES:** ½ Vegetable, ½ Fat;
PER SERVING: CAL 45 (24% from fat); PRO 2g; FAT 2g (sat 0.3g); CARB 3g; FIB 0.8g; CHOL 0mg; IRON 0.5mg; SOD 291mg; CALC 11mg

CRANBERRY-JALAPEÑO CHEESE

This cheese spread is great served with crackers.

- ½ cup fresh cranberries
- 2 tablespoons water
- 2 tablespoons hot jalapeño jelly
- 1 teaspoon chopped fresh cilantro
- 2 teaspoons lime juice
- 1 (8-ounce) block fat-free cream cheese

1. Combine cranberries and water in a medium saucepan. Place over medium heat; cook until cranberries pop, stirring occasionally. Add jelly; cook until jelly melts, stirring frequently. Remove from heat; stir in cilantro and lime juice. Cool to room temperature.
2. Place cheese on a serving plate; pour cranberry mixture over cheese. **YIELD:** 8 servings (serving size: 2 tablespoons cream cheese and about 2 teaspoons cranberry mixture).

POINTS: 1; **EXCHANGE:** ½ Fruit;
PER SERVING: CAL 37 (0% from fat); PRO 4g; FAT 0g (sat 0g); CARB 4.4g; FIB 0.1g; CHOL 5mg; IRON 0mg; SOD 176mg; CALC 81mg

SMOKED SALMON QUESADILLAS

Don't be tempted to substitute large tomatoes such as the beefsteak for the plum tomatoes. Plum tomatoes are ideal for these quesadillas because they're not as juicy as other varieties.

- ⅓ cup (about 3 ounces) tub-style light cream cheese, softened
- 4 (8-inch) fat-free flour tortillas
- 2 tablespoons chopped fresh dill
- 4 ounces smoked salmon
- Cooking spray
- ¾ cup finely chopped plum tomato

1. Spread cream cheese on 1 side of 2 tortillas; top with dill, salmon, and remaining tortillas.
2. Coat a large nonstick skillet with cooking spray; place over medium-high heat until hot. Add 1 quesadilla; cook 3 minutes on each side or until golden. Remove quesadilla from skillet; keep warm. Repeat procedure with remaining quesadilla.
3. Cut each quesadilla into 8 wedges; top each wedge with about 2 teaspoons tomato. **YIELD:** 16 servings (serving size: 1 wedge and 2 teaspoons tomato).

POINTS: 1; **EXCHANGE:** ½ Starch; **PER SERVING:** CAL 50 (23% from fat); PRO 2.7g; FAT 1.3g (sat 0.6g); CARB 6.8g; FIB 0.4g; CHOL 5mg; IRON 0.4mg; SOD 172mg; CALC 11mg

BEEF AND PINEAPPLE SATAY WITH PEANUT SAUCE

Soak 24 bamboo skewers in water for 1 hour before beginning this recipe.

- 12 ounces lean flank steak
- 2 tablespoons finely chopped green onions
- 2 tablespoons low-salt soy sauce
- 1 tablespoon sugar
- 1 tablespoon dry sherry
- 1½ teaspoons water
- 1½ teaspoons dark sesame oil
- ⅛ teaspoon coarsely ground pepper
- 2 garlic cloves, crushed
- 1 (15¼-ounce) can unsweetened pineapple chunks, undrained
- ¼ cup reduced-fat creamy peanut butter
- 1 teaspoon cornstarch
- ½ teaspoon curry powder
- ¼ teaspoon salt
- ⅛ teaspoon ground red pepper
- 1 tablespoon grated fresh ginger
- Cooking spray

1. Trim fat from steak. Thinly slice steak diagonally across grain into 24 slices. Combine onions and next 7 ingredients in a large zip-top plastic bag. Add steak to bag; seal bag. Marinate in refrigerator 8 hours, turning occasionally. Remove steak from bag, discarding marinade.
2. Drain pineapple, reserving ¾ cup juice and 24 pineapple chunks; reserve remaining pineapple chunks and juice for another use. Combine ¾ cup juice, peanut butter, and next 4 ingredients in a medium saucepan, stirring well. Using cheesecloth or fingertips, squeeze juice from grated ginger into saucepan; discard pulp. Bring to a boil over medium-high heat; reduce heat, and simmer 1 minute, stirring constantly. Remove from heat; let cool.
3. Thread 1 chunk of pineapple and 1 slice of steak onto each skewer. Coat grill pan or nonstick skillet with cooking spray; place over medium-high heat until hot. Add skewers to pan, and cook 1 minute on each side or until desired degree of doneness. Serve with peanut sauce. **YIELD:** 8 servings (serving size: 3 skewers and 1½ tablespoons peanut sauce).

POINTS: 4; **EXCHANGES:** ½ Starch, 1½ Lean Meat, 1 Fat; **PER SERVING:** CAL 154 (47% from fat); PRO 10.6g; FAT 8g (sat 2.5g); CARB 9.8g; FIB 0.9g; CHOL 21mg; IRON 1.2mg; SOD 265mg; CALC 8mg

GRATING GINGER

Those strange looking, knobbly roots in the produce section of the grocery store add divine flavor to a variety of foods. Peel away the brown skin of ginger with a sharp knife.

Rub a piece of peeled ginger across the teeth of a ginger grater. A regular fine-toothed grater works, too.

RUSTIC POTATO PIZZA WITH ROSEMARY

1 pound small red potatoes, thinly sliced (about 7 potatoes)
2½ teaspoons olive oil
6 garlic cloves, coarsely chopped
Olive oil-flavored cooking spray
1 (10-ounce) can refrigerated pizza crust dough
1¼ cups (5 ounces) shredded Gruyère cheese, divided
2 tablespoons finely chopped fresh rosemary
½ teaspoon salt
½ teaspoon cracked pepper

1. Preheat oven to 475°.
2. Place potatoes in a saucepan, and cover with water; bring to a boil. Reduce heat, and simmer 1 minute. Drain well.
3. Heat oil in a small skillet over medium heat; add garlic. Sauté 30 seconds; remove from heat.
4. Coat hands with cooking spray. Press pizza dough into a 15- x 10-inch jelly-roll pan coated with cooking spray. Coat dough with cooking spray. Bake at 475° for 4 minutes or until set.
5. Spread sautéed garlic evenly over crust; top with ¾ cup cheese. Arrange potato slices over cheese, overlapping if necessary. Sprinkle with rosemary, salt, and pepper. Top with remaining ½ cup cheese. Bake at 475° for 8 minutes or until cheese melts and crust is golden. Let cool 10 minutes on a wire rack. Cut into 24 squares. **YIELD:** 24 servings.

POINTS: 2; **EXCHANGES:** 1 Starch, ½ Fat;
PER SERVING: CAL 95 (27% from fat); PRO 3.8g; FAT 2.9g (sat 1.3g); CARB 13.3g; FIB 1g; CHOL 7mg; IRON 0.9mg; SOD 151mg; CALC 68mg

CRAB POT STICKERS

¾ cup (3 ounces) ⅓-less-fat cream cheese (Neufchâtel)
2 tablespoons fat-free milk
2 tablespoons egg substitute
¼ teaspoon salt
Dash of ground red pepper
3 tablespoons finely chopped green onions
1 (6-ounce) can lump crabmeat, rinsed, drained, and shell pieces removed
24 won ton wrappers
Cooking spray
½ cup low-sugar orange marmalade
1 tablespoon hoisin sauce

1. Preheat oven to 325°.
2. Combine first 4 ingredients in a small bowl. Beat at low speed of a mixer until thoroughly combined. Stir in ground red pepper, green onions, and crabmeat.
3. Working with 1 won ton wrapper at a time (cover remaining won ton wrappers with a damp cloth to keep them from drying out), coat with cooking spray. Spoon about 1 teaspoon crab mixture into center of each wrapper. Bring 2 opposite corners of each wrapper to center, pinching points to seal. Bring remaining 2 corners to center, pinching points to seal. Pinch 4 edges together to seal. Coat each pot sticker with cooking spray.
4. Place pot stickers on a baking sheet coated with cooking spray. Bake at 325° for 20 minutes or until golden.
5. Combine orange marmalade and hoisin sauce, stirring well. Serve with pot stickers.

YIELD: 8 servings (serving size: 3 pot stickers and 1 tablespoon sauce).

POINTS: 3; **EXCHANGES:** 1 Starch, ½ Very Lean Meat, ½ Fat; **PER SERVING:** CAL 127 (26% from fat); PRO 6.7g; FAT 3.7g (sat 1.7g); CARB 16.3g; FIB 0.1g; CHOL 21mg; IRON 1.1mg; SOD 337mg; CALC 47mg

CREAMY CHOCOLATE COFFEE

3 fat-free cappuccino crunch biscotti (such as BP Gourmet Cookies)
1 tablespoon chocolate syrup
4 cups boiling water
6 tablespoons fat-free, sugar-free instant French Vanilla coffee (such as International Coffees)
6 tablespoons chocolate-flavored sweetened condensed milk
¾ cup frozen reduced-calorie whipped topping, thawed and divided

1. Place biscotti in a food processor; process until coarsely ground. Place crumbs in a bowl; set aside.
2. Place chocolate syrup in a bowl; dip rims of 4 coffee mugs in syrup, and then in biscotti crumbs to coat rims; set mugs aside.
3. Add water, coffee, condensed milk, and ½ cup whipped topping to chocolate syrup; stir well. Pour into prepared coffee mugs; top each with 1 tablespoon whipped topping. Serve immediately. **YIELD:** 4 servings (serving size: 1 cup).

POINTS: 3; **EXCHANGES:** 1½ Starch, ½ Fat;
PER SERVING: CAL 139 (19% from fat); PRO 1.8g; FAT 2.9g (sat 2.3g); CARB 24.8g; FIB 0g; CHOL 6mg; IRON 0.3mg; SOD 118mg; CALC 56mg

WARM TOMATO SIPPER

4 (5.5-ounce) cans spicy-hot vegetable juice
1 (8-ounce) bottle clam juice
2 tablespoons fresh lemon juice
2 teaspoons Worcestershire sauce
Dash of pepper

1. Combine all ingredients in a medium saucepan; bring to a boil. Pour into cups. Serve immediately.
YIELD: 4 servings (serving size: 1 cup).

POINTS: 1; **EXCHANGE:** 2 Vegetable;
PER SERVING: CAL 39 (0% from fat); PRO 1.3g; FAT 0g (sat 0g); CARB 7.7g; FIB 1g; CHOL 0mg; IRON 0.6mg; SOD 678mg; CALC 27mg

RASPBERRY-LEMON TEA

6¼ cups boiling water
½ cup sugar
3 family-size tea bags
1 (10-ounce) package frozen raspberries in syrup, thawed and undrained
1 (6-ounce) can thawed lemonade concentrate, undiluted

1. Combine first 3 ingredients; stir well. Cover and steep 5 minutes. Remove tea bags, squeezing gently.
2. Place raspberries in a blender. Process until smooth. Pour puréed berries through a fine sieve over a bowl, reserving liquid. Discard seeds.
3. Combine tea, raspberry liquid, and lemonade concentrate in a large pitcher. Chill. Serve over ice.
YIELD: 8 servings (serving size: 1 cup).

POINTS: 2; **EXCHANGE:** 2 Fruit;
PER SERVING: CAL 125 (0% from fat); PRO 0.3g; FAT 0.1g (sat 0g); CARB 32.3g; FIB 1.6g; CHOL 0mg; IRON 0.4mg; SOD 7mg; CALC 7mg

NUTRITION

Focus on Diabetes

One-third of all people with diabetes are unaware they have the disease. Here's how to recognize the warning signs and discern fact from fiction.

The population of Denmark is five million—and you say, so what? But consider that three times that many Americans—15 million—have diabetes.

The statistics may sound grim, but people with diabetes can live healthy lives if they follow a prescribed treatment plan. Knowing the facts about diabetes provides insight into the sixth leading cause of death by disease in this country and clarifies common misconceptions.

TYPE 1. Type 1 diabetes is commonly known as insulin-dependent diabetes. With Type 1, the body destroys the cells in the pancreas that produce insulin, often leading to a total failure to produce insulin. It can begin at any age but typically appears in children or young adults.

TYPE 2. Type 2 diabetes is the most common form, accounting for 9 out of 10 cases. Formerly known as noninsulin-dependent diabetes, it usually occurs in—but is not limited to—overweight people over 45. With Type 2 diabetes, the body either does not make enough insulin or cannot properly use it.

BLOOD SUGARS. With both types of diabetes, the body lacks enough functioning insulin to move blood sugar into its cells. This sugar buildup in the bloodstream can lead to complications, including kidney and heart disease. Diabetes is the leading cause of blindness in people ages 20 to 70.

NUTRITION KNOW-HOW. Food is one tool used to manage diabetes. Individuals with diabetes should focus on eating fresh fruits and vegetables, lean meats, and fish, with fewer calories coming from fat and sugary foods. The appropriate mix of carbohydrates, protein, and fat in a healthful diet and understanding how these nutrients affect your blood sugar are key to managing diabetes successfully.

Planning meals at consistent times is important, so that you eat when your insulin is working the hardest. Spacing meals over the day rather than eating a few large meals also helps maximize insulin function.

SUGAR SENSE. Sugar is no longer off-limits for people with diabetes. Studies show that simple sugars don't raise blood glucose levels any higher or faster than complex carbohydrates.

But sugar becomes glucose in the body, as do other carbohydrates. Eating a piece of cake will raise your blood glucose level, as will eating mashed potatoes or lima beans. Too much of any carbohydrate will increase your blood glucose level.

If you have diabetes, you can salute Valentine's Day with a chocolate kiss. Or indulge in a slice of Thanksgiving pumpkin pie—just save the pasta and bread for another day.

Breads

DILL BISCUITS

2¼ cups reduced-fat biscuit and baking mix (such as Bisquick)
2 teaspoons dried dill
2 tablespoons chilled light stick butter (such as Land O' Lakes), cut into small pieces
½ cup low-fat buttermilk
⅓ cup 30%-less-fat sour cream (such as Breakstone)
Butter-flavored cooking spray

1. Preheat oven to 400°.
2. Combine baking mix and dill in a bowl; stir well. Cut in butter with a pastry blender or two knives until mixture resembles coarse meal. Add buttermilk and sour cream, stirring just until dry ingredients are moistened.
3. Turn dough out onto a lightly floured surface. Knead lightly 4 to 5 times. Roll dough to ½-inch thickness; cut with a 2½-inch biscuit cutter. Place biscuits on a baking sheet lightly coated with cooking spray. Lightly coat tops with cooking spray.
4. Bake at 400° for 8 minutes or until lightly golden. **YIELD:** 9 servings (serving size: 1 biscuit).

POINTS: 3; **EXCHANGES:** 1½ Starch, 1 Fat;
PER SERVING: CAL 139 (32% from fat); PRO 3g; FAT 5g (sat 2g); CARB 22g; FIB 0.8g; CHOL 9mg; IRON 1.2mg; SOD 404mg; CALC 78mg

PARMESAN-CHIVE SCONES

2½ cups reduced-fat biscuit and baking mix (such as Bisquick)
1 cup (4 ounces) preshredded fresh Parmesan cheese
¼ cup chopped fresh or freeze-dried chives
1 (8-ounce) carton plain fat-free yogurt
1 large egg, lightly beaten
Cooking spray

1. Preheat oven to 425°.
2. Combine first 3 ingredients in a large bowl. Combine yogurt and egg in a small bowl; stir well. Add to dry ingredients, stirring just until dry ingredients are moistened.
3. Turn dough out onto a lightly floured surface; with floured hands, knead lightly 4 to 5 times. Pat dough into a 9-inch circle on a baking sheet coated with cooking spray. Using a knife coated with cooking spray, cut dough into 12 wedges, cutting to, but not through, bottom of dough.
4. Bake at 425° for 12 minutes or until lightly golden. Serve warm. **YIELD:** 12 servings (serving size: 1 scone).

POINTS: 3; **EXCHANGES:** 1½ Starch, 1 Fat;
PER SERVING: CAL 147 (30% from fat); PRO 7g; FAT 5g (sat 2g); CARB 20g; FIB 0.8g; CHOL 25mg; IRON 1.3mg; SOD 484mg; CALC 201mg

PEANUT BUTTER AND JELLY MUFFINS

These are kid pleasers! Children will love finding the surprise in the center.

1½ cups self-rising flour
¾ cup firmly packed brown sugar
1 cup low-fat buttermilk
½ cup creamy peanut butter
1 large egg, lightly beaten
2 teaspoons vanilla extract
¼ cup grape jelly
Cooking spray

1. Preheat oven to 400°.
2. Combine flour and sugar in a large bowl; make a well in center of mixture. Combine buttermilk and next 3 ingredients; stir well. Add to dry ingredients, stirring just until dry ingredients are moistened.
3. Spoon about 2 tablespoons batter into each of 12 muffin cups coated with cooking spray. Place 1 teaspoon jelly in center of each; top with remaining batter.
4. Bake at 400° for 16 minutes or until muffins spring back when lightly touched in center.
5. Remove muffins from pan immediately; cool on a wire rack. **YIELD:** 12 servings (serving size: 1 muffin).

POINTS: 5; **EXCHANGES:** 2 Starch, 1 Fat;
PER SERVING: CAL 208 (29% from fat); PRO 5.9g; FAT 6.6g (sat 1.3g); CARB 32.3g; FIB 0.7g; CHOL 18mg; IRON 1.2mg; SOD 275mg; CALC 96mg

CRANBERRY-ORANGE COFFEECAKE

Cooking spray
1 tablespoon all-purpose flour
½ cup butter or stick margarine, softened
1⅓ cups sugar
2 large eggs
2 teaspoons vanilla extract
1 cup 50%-less-fat sour cream (such as Daisy)
2 cups all-purpose flour
1 tablespoon baking powder
¼ teaspoon salt
½ cup dried cranberries
3 tablespoons chopped walnuts
2 tablespoons brown sugar
2 tablespoons grated orange rind
1 teaspoon ground cinnamon
⅔ cup sifted powdered sugar
2 teaspoons fresh orange juice

1. Preheat oven to 350°.
2. Coat a 12-cup Bundt pan with cooking spray; dust with 1 tablespoon flour, and set aside.
3. Beat butter in a large bowl at medium speed of a mixer until creamy; gradually add sugar. Add eggs, one at a time, beating well after each addition. Add vanilla and sour cream, beating just until blended.
4. Combine 2 cups flour, baking powder, and salt; gradually add to sour cream mixture, beating just until smooth.
5. Combine cranberries and next 4 ingredients, stirring well. Spoon ⅓ of batter into prepared pan. Sprinkle cranberry mixture around center of batter. Spoon remaining batter over cranberry mixture, smoothing with a spatula. Bake at 350° for 45 minutes or until a wooden pick inserted in center comes out clean. Let cool in pan on a wire rack 10 minutes. Remove from pan, and let cool completely on a wire rack.
6. Combine powdered sugar and orange juice, stirring well; drizzle over cake. **YIELD:** 16 servings.

POINTS: 6; **EXCHANGES:** 2½ Starch, 1½ Fat;
PER SERVING: CAL 248 (30% from fat); PRO 3.4g; FAT 8.4g (sat 4.4g); CARB 39.5g; FIB 0.8g; CHOL 48mg; IRON 1.1mg; SOD 206mg; CALC 83mg

CARIBBEAN-STYLE JOHNNY CAKES

1 (8½-ounce) box corn muffin mix
¾ cup fat-free milk
¼ cup plus 2 tablespoons fat-free egg substitute
¼ cup thinly sliced green onions

1. Combine all ingredients in a bowl; stir well.
2. Spoon 2 tablespoons batter for each cake onto a hot nonstick griddle or nonstick skillet. Turn cakes when tops are covered with bubbles and edges look cooked. **YIELD:** 4 servings (serving size: 3 cakes).

POINTS: 6; **EXCHANGES:** 3 Starch, 1 Fat;
PER SERVING: CAL 269 (20% from fat); PRO 6.9g; FAT 6.1g (sat 2.3g); CARB 45.1g; FIB 1.7g; CHOL 1mg; IRON 2.1mg; SOD 539mg; CALC 159mg

PECAN CORNBREAD

(pictured on page 22)
If you don't have an iron skillet, use an 8-inch round cake pan or an 8-inch square baking pan, and don't preheat the pan.

⅓ cup finely chopped lean country ham (about 2 ounces)
1 (6.5-ounce) package golden corn muffin and bread mix (such as Betty Crocker)
½ cup fat-free milk
¼ cup fat-free egg substitute
¼ cup coarsely chopped pecans, toasted

1. Preheat oven to 425°.
2. Place an 8-inch cast-iron skillet over medium-high heat until hot. Add ham, and sauté 2 minutes or until lightly browned. Place ham in a large bowl; set aside. Keep skillet hot.
3. Add muffin mix and remaining 3 ingredients to ham, stirring just until moist. Pour batter into preheated skillet. Bake at 425° for 15 minutes or until lightly browned. **YIELD:** 8 servings.

POINTS: 3; **EXCHANGES:** 1½ Starch, 1 Fat;
PER SERVING: CAL 139 (32% from fat); PRO 5g; FAT 5g (sat 0.6g); CARB 20g; FIB 0.3g; CHOL 6mg; IRON 0.9mg; SOD 358mg; CALC 26mg

MARDI GRAS SWEET ROLLS

These rolls are great for Easter, too!

1 package dry yeast
¼ cup warm water (105° to 115°)
3⅔ cups all-purpose flour
½ cup sugar
½ teaspoon salt
1 (8-ounce) carton 50%-less-fat sour cream (such as Daisy)
⅓ cup butter or stick margarine, melted
2 large eggs, lightly beaten
Cooking spray
1¼ cups sifted powdered sugar
3 ounces fat-free cream cheese
½ teaspoon vanilla extract
3 teaspoons yellow sugar sprinkles
3 teaspoons green sugar sprinkles
3 teaspoons purple sugar sprinkles

1. Dissolve yeast in warm water in a small bowl; let stand 5 minutes. Combine flour, ½ cup sugar, and salt in a large mixing bowl, stirring well. Combine sour cream, butter, and eggs, stirring well. Add dissolved yeast and sour cream mixture to dry ingredients. Beat at medium speed of a mixer 2 minutes or until smooth. Cover tightly, and chill 8 hours.
2. Divide dough in half; shape half of dough into 12 (2-inch) balls, smoothing out tops. Place 2 inches apart on a baking sheet coated with cooking spray. Repeat procedure with remaining dough. Cover and let rise 30 minutes or until doubled in bulk.
3. Preheat oven to 350°.
4. Bake rolls at 350° for 12 minutes or until very lightly browned. Let cool on wire racks.
5. Combine powdered sugar, cream cheese, and vanilla in a bowl; beat at medium speed of a mixer until smooth. Combine sugar sprinkles in a small bowl. Spread 2 teaspoons frosting on each roll. Sprinkle each roll with ⅜ teaspoon of sugar sprinkles. **YIELD:** 2 dozen (serving size: 1 roll).

POINTS: 3; **EXCHANGES:** 2 Starch, ½ Fat;
PER SERVING: CAL 161 (22% from fat); PRO 3.5g; FAT 3.9g (sat 2.2g); CARB 27.5g; FIB 0.6g; CHOL 29mg; IRON 1mg; SOD 109mg; CALC 29mg

PEPPERED PARMESAN-TOMATO SPIRALS

Butter-flavored cooking spray
1 (1-pound) loaf refrigerated white bread dough or frozen white bread dough, thawed
½ cup grated Parmesan cheese
¼ cup sun-dried tomato sprinkles
¾ teaspoon coarsely ground pepper
1 tablespoon butter or stick margarine, melted

1. Preheat oven to 350°.
2. Coat 2 (8-inch) round cake pans with cooking spray; set aside.
3. Unroll dough on a large sheet of wax paper. Roll dough into a 19- x 7-inch rectangle; coat with cooking spray. Cut in half crosswise. Sprinkle evenly with cheese, tomato sprinkles, and pepper. Press tomato mixture lightly into dough, and coat with cooking spray.
4. Beginning at short side, roll up one half of dough tightly, jelly-roll fashion; pinch seam to seal (do not seal ends of roll). Place a long piece of dental floss or string under dough 1 inch from the end of roll. Cross ends of string over top of roll; slowly pull ends to cut through the dough. Place roll portion, cut side up, in center of 1 prepared pan. Cut 6 additional portions from roll. Place roll portions around the sides of pan. Set aside. Repeat procedure with remaining half of dough; brush tops of rolls with melted butter.
5. Bake at 350° for 20 minutes or until lightly browned. **YIELD:** 14 rolls (serving size: 1 roll).

POINTS: 3; **EXCHANGES:** 1½ Starch, ½ Fat;
PER SERVING: CAL 154 (20% from fat); PRO 5.9g; FAT 3.5g (sat 1.3g); CARB 24.7g; FIB 1g; CHOL 4mg; IRON 1.4mg; SOD 358mg; CALC 71mg

STUFFED TEX-MEX LOAF

(pictured on page 22)

1 cup salsa
1 (16-ounce) loaf French bread, cut in half lengthwise
1 cup (4 ounces) preshredded reduced-fat Mexican cheese blend (such as Sargento Light)
1 (4.5-ounce) can chopped green chiles, drained
1 (2¼-ounce) can sliced ripe olives, drained

1. Preheat oven to 400°.
2. Spread salsa over bottom half of bread. Top with cheese, chiles, olives, and top half of bread.
3. Wrap in foil; bake at 400° for 20 minutes or until cheese melts and bread is toasted. Let stand 5 minutes. Cut into slices, using a serrated knife. **YIELD:** 10 servings.

POINTS: 3; **EXCHANGES:** 1½ Starch, 1 Fat;
PER SERVING: CAL 168 (21% from fat); PRO 7.6g; FAT 4g (sat 1.6g); CARB 26g; FIB 2g; CHOL 4mg; IRON 1.6mg; SOD 526mg; CALC 127mg

Coming into Her Own

MARY NOEL LUZZI • **HEIGHT** 5'10" • **BEFORE** 230 LBS. • **AFTER** 160 LBS.

Happiest moment: "At my 10-year high school reunion, nobody recognized me. I was the belle of the ball!"

Mary Noel Luzzi grew up competing with seven brothers. "I could run like my brothers, play ball like my brothers, do almost anything like my brothers," she recalls. Unfortunately, the most competitive event was mealtime. "I learned to take as much from that spaghetti bowl as I could or there wouldn't be anything left," explains Mary.

In college, Mary continued to eat unhealthful portions and came home each break a bit heavier. Her family noticed and offered advice, but not much support. "Everyone wants to tell you to lose weight, but no one wants to teach you and be with you every step of the way."

Finally Mary took responsibility for herself. "I realized that nobody else is looking out for me, and it's a cruel world when you don't love yourself," says Mary.

At Weight Watchers, Mary found the guidance and support she needed. "I felt naked walking in there. But the network at Weight Watchers is terrific." Group meetings taught her she was not alone. "You don't realize how many people are dealing with the same thing, whether they want to lose 10 pounds or 60," she says. "Hearing people share their stories was a great help. Their smiles and acceptance made a difference."

Mary's most important weight-loss lesson was in portion size. She learned that quantity matters as much as quality when it comes to weight loss and maintenance. Reducing how much she ate wasn't as difficult as she expected. "I was gorging myself," says Mary. "I could never eat as much now as I used to eat."

Not everything Mary learned from her brothers was bad. Having played sports with the boys growing up, Mary is open-minded about exercise. "I'm the queen of variety: yoga, skiing, aikido, volleyball, hiking—you name it," she says. "I don't like to do one thing for long."

Variety is also important to Mary when it comes to food. When she brings lunch to work, Mary packs fresh veggies for their gratifying crunch, and gets a protein boost from a hummus dip. "I bring salads, but I don't let them get boring," she says. "I add raisins, oranges, coconut, chickpeas, or feta cheese."

"Hearing people share their stories was a great help. Their smiles and acceptance made a difference."

Both food and physical activity, says Mary, are a matter of individual taste. "Find what you like," she says. The best exercise and meal plan is the one that you enjoy. "They say one size fits all," she says, "but when it comes to losing weight, it doesn't."

Pecan Cornbread,
page 19

Stuffed Tex-Mex
Loaf, page 20

Sun-Dried Tomato and Feta Rolls, page 25

Done with Dieting

MICHELLE LITTELL • **HEIGHT** 5'6" • **BEFORE** 186 LBS. • **AFTER** 135 LBS.

Philosophy: Weight-loss programs that label certain food as off-limits are never going to work long-term. "Look at this as a way of life, not a diet."

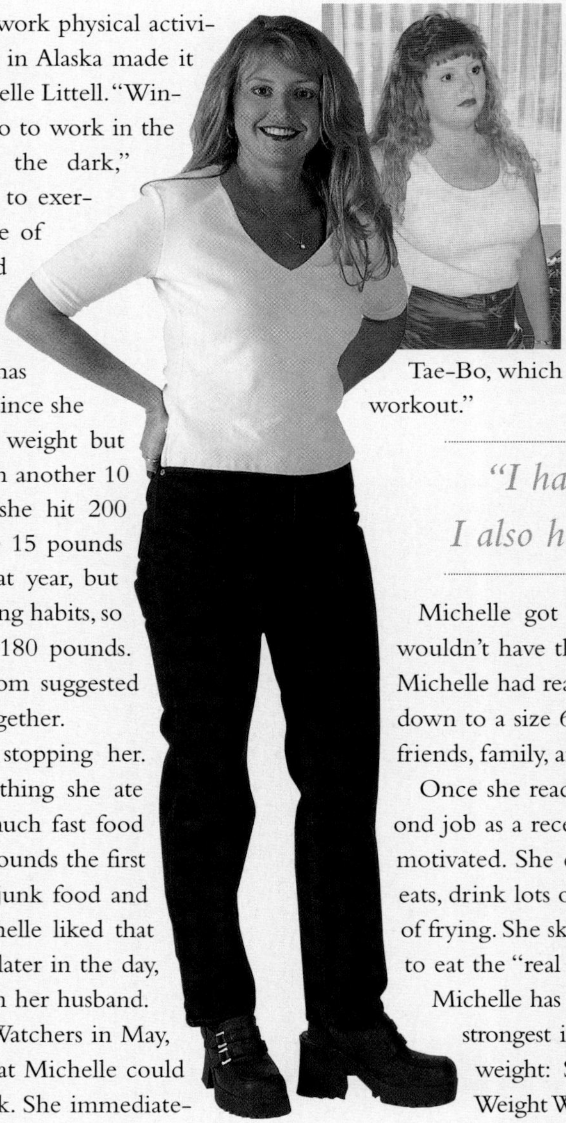

It's hard for any novice to work physical activity into her life, but living in Alaska made it particularly difficult for Michelle Littell. "Winter here lasts five months. I go to work in the dark and come home in the dark," explains Michelle. "I needed to exercise at home but every piece of equipment I bought ended up an expensive coatrack."

Michelle went through diets like exercise gear. She has been on one diet or another since she was a teen. "I'd always lose weight but then gain it back, usually with another 10 pounds," she says. In 1996 she hit 200 pounds. She was able to lose 15 pounds before her wedding later that year, but she didn't have consistent eating habits, so she began to yo-yo around 180 pounds. Then one day, Michelle's mom suggested they join Weight Watchers together.

With that, there was no stopping her. Michelle wrote down everything she ate and was surprised by how much fast food she consumed. She lost 4½ pounds the first week simply by eliminating junk food and eating smaller portions. Michelle liked that she could save ***POINTS*** for later in the day, so she could have dinner with her husband.

When she started Weight Watchers in May, the sun rose early enough that Michelle could walk several mornings a week. She immediately noticed a difference. "I had more energy, and I also had a better attitude," she says.

Michelle was surprised at how easy fitness walking was. When she got bored, she started walking, then running, on a treadmill in front of the TV Now Michelle exercises five days a week: She runs on the treadmill two days a week and does a Tae-Bo video the other three days. "The treadmill prepared me for conditioning like Tae-Bo, which I enjoy because of the overall body workout."

"I had more energy, and I also had a better attitude."

Michelle got rid of her size 16 clothes so she wouldn't have them as a fallback. By Thanksgiving Michelle had reached her goal weight and slimmed down to a size 6. She reveled in compliments from friends, family, and even her 8-year-old stepson.

Once she reached her goal, Michelle took a second job as a receptionist at Weight Watchers to stay motivated. She continues to write down what she eats, drink lots of water, and grill and bake instead of frying. She skips fat-free foods, choosing instead to eat the "real thing" in moderation.

Michelle has started what she believes will be the strongest incentive for maintaining a healthful weight: She has become a leader for her Weight Watchers group. "Becoming a lifetime member was the greatest Christmas present ever," she says, adding that she hopes she can give others that same gift.

SUN-DRIED TOMATO AND FETA ROLLS

(pictured on page 23)
Our Test Kitchens found that light butter works best in these tender rolls. Avoid the temptation to substitute margarine. The end result will not be as good.

1 cup boiling water
½ cup sun-dried tomato sprinkles
1 (16-ounce) box hot roll mix
2 tablespoons light stick butter (such as Land O' Lakes), softened
1 large egg, beaten
1 (4-ounce) package crumbled feta cheese
Cooking spray

1. Pour boiling water over tomato sprinkles in a small bowl; let stand 10 minutes or until soft. Drain in a colander over a 1-cup glass measure, reserving liquid. If necessary, add water to reserved liquid to measure 1 cup; reheat liquid to 120° to 130°.
2. Combine contents of hot roll mix and enclosed yeast packet in a large bowl; stir well. Add very warm reserved liquid, tomato sprinkles, butter, egg, and feta, stirring until dough pulls away from sides of bowl. Turn dough out onto a lightly floured surface; knead dough 2 minutes or until smooth and elastic. Place bowl over dough to cover; let rest 5 minutes.
3. Divide dough into 16 equal portions, shaping each portion into a ball. Place on a baking sheet coated with cooking spray. Cover and let rise in a warm place (85°), free from drafts, 15 minutes or until doubled in bulk.
4. Preheat oven to 375°.
5. Bake at 375° for 19 minutes or until lightly browned. **YIELD:** 16 servings (serving size: 1 roll).

POINTS: 3; **EXCHANGES:** 1½ Starch, 1 Fat;
PER SERVING: CAL 144 (25% from fat); PRO 5g; FAT 4g (sat 1.7g); CARB 22g; FIB 1g; CHOL 22mg; IRON 1.4mg; SOD 299mg; CALC 36mg

QUICK FOCACCIA

1 (10-ounce) can refrigerated pizza crust dough
Cooking spray
1 tablespoon olive oil
1⅓ cups sliced mushrooms
¼ cup (1 ounce) crumbled goat cheese
1 teaspoon dried thyme
½ teaspoon freshly ground pepper
¼ teaspoon salt

1. Preheat oven to 375°.
2. Unroll dough on a baking sheet coated with cooking spray; pat dough into a 10- x 8-inch rectangle. Brush dough with olive oil; sprinkle mushrooms and remaining 4 ingredients evenly over dough.
3. Bake at 375° for 17 minutes or until crust is lightly browned. **YIELD:** 8 servings.

POINTS: 3; **EXCHANGES:** 1 Starch, 1 Fat;
PER SERVING: CAL 127 (28% from fat); PRO 4g; FAT 4g (sat 1g); CARB 18g; FIB 0.6g; CHOL 3mg; IRON 1.4mg; SOD 330mg; CALC 15mg

CHEDDAR BEER BREAD

1 (16-ounce) box hot roll mix
¾ cup warm beer (120° to 130°)
2 tablespoons light stick butter (such as Land O' Lakes), softened
1 large egg, lightly beaten
1 cup (4 ounces) shredded reduced-fat cheddar cheese, divided
Cooking spray

1. Combine contents of roll mix box and enclosed yeast packet in a large bowl; stir well. Add warm beer, butter, egg, and ⅔ cup cheese to flour mixture; stir to form a soft dough. Turn dough out onto a lightly floured surface. Knead until smooth and elastic (about 5 minutes). Place bowl over dough to cover; let rest 5 minutes.
2. Shape dough into a ball; place on a baking sheet coated with cooking spray. Let rise in a warm place (85°), free from drafts, 30 minutes or until dough is doubled in bulk.
3. Preheat oven to 375°.
4. Bake at 375° for 15 minutes. Sprinkle top of bread with remaining ⅓ cup cheese, and bake an additional 5 minutes. Cool slightly; cut into 12 wedges. **YIELD:** 12 servings (serving size: 1 wedge).

POINTS: 4; **EXCHANGES:** 2 Starch, 1 Fat;
PER SERVING: CAL 183 (20% from fat); PRO 7g; FAT 4g (sat 1.8g); CARB 27g; FIB 0.6g; CHOL 27mg; IRON 1.9mg; SOD 338mg; CALC 77mg

GOODS

Machine-Age Bread

The new crop of bread machines makes baking almost effortless.

The smell of freshly baked bread takes us back to Mom's kitchen. But there's a big difference between enjoying fresh bread and baking it yourself—that is, unless you use a bread machine.

With a bread maker, it's easy to make a wholesome loaf—just measure a few ingredients, select a cycle, and press start. Good machines have a dough cycle, crust-color choices, and a specific cycle for whole-wheat bread. But bread makers can do more than that. You can use your machine to make dough, and then shape and bake the machine-made dough in a traditional pan or roll it out for baguettes, bread sticks, or pizza dough. Some machines have extra features, but we suggest using a bread machine for what it does best—making bread.

BEST BUYS. Of the machines we tested, the Breadman Ultimate TR 2200C and the Zojirushi V-20 (both priced under $200) offered the most useful features, made terrific bread dough, and baked a good loaf of whole-wheat bread. Both have horizontal pans, which make loaves shaped like those at the grocery store. Controls on both machines are easy to use.

The Breadman Ultimate's whole-wheat cycle excels because it provides more time for whole-wheat dough to rise between kneading cycles. Another feature unique to the Ultimate is its trapdoor, which automatically adds ingredients (such as raisins for raisin bread or chopped sun-dried tomatoes for focaccia) at the right moment. To add a cinnamon swirl, press the pause button, roll the bread out, top with desired ingredients, roll up, and return to pan to finish baking.

The Zojirushi V-20 has a long, traditionally shaped pan, and a beep that signals when to add ingredients. Unlike the Ultimate, it doesn't have a separate pizza-dough cycle. But the plain dough cycle works well for many doughs, including pizza dough.

GOOD CHOICE. For basic baking, the less-expensive Breadman Plus TR 800 or Toastmaster Corner Bakery (around $100 each) are acceptable. These lack the additional features of higher priced machines, but produce nice loaves of bread.

ROSEMARY-HERB FRENCH BREAD

A bread machine mixes this dough and allows it to rise. You finish the shaping and baking.

- 2¼ cups bread flour
- 1 package dry yeast
- 2 teaspoons sugar
- 1 teaspoon chopped fresh or dried rosemary
- ½ teaspoon dried basil
- ½ teaspoon dried thyme
- ½ teaspoon dried oregano
- ½ teaspoon salt
- 1 cup water
- 1 teaspoon olive oil
- 3 tablespoons preshredded fresh Parmesan cheese
- 1 teaspoon chopped fresh or dried rosemary
- ¼ teaspoon garlic powder

1. Following manufacturer's instructions, place first 9 ingredients into bread pan. Select dough cycle, and start bread machine. Remove dough from machine (do not bake).

RISE TO THE OCCASION

Bread machines are easy to use—just follow instructions (some machines come with a video). If you have a problem, don't give up—everyone bakes a doorstop at least once. These tips will help you put bread on the table.

- Dry ingredients, particularly yeast, should be room temperature before you use them. Liquid ingredients should be slightly warmer (approximately 85 degrees).
- Don't use sugar substitutes in place of sugar in recipes. Sugar reacts with yeast; substitutes don't.
- Spoon flour loosely into a cup measure; use a straight edge to level the flour with the cup top.
- Follow manufacturer's directions for adding ingredients. If you don't, the yeast might not properly mix with the liquid and your loaf could fall flat.

2. Preheat oven to 350°.
3. Turn dough out onto a lightly floured surface; rub with oil. Shape into a 12-inch-long loaf. Place loaf on a baking sheet. Combine cheese, 1 teaspoon rosemary, and garlic powder; sprinkle over top of loaf.
4. Bake at 350° for 45 minutes or until loaf sounds hollow when tapped. Remove from pan; cool on a wire rack. YIELD: 1 (1-pound) loaf (serving size: 1 [1-inch] slice).

POINTS: 2; EXCHANGES: 1½ Starch;
PER SERVING: CAL 110 (13% from fat); PRO 3.9g; FAT 1.6g (sat 0.4g); CARB 19.8g; FIB 0.2g; CHOL 1mg; IRON 1.4mg; SOD 125mg; CALC 26mg

GARLIC-HERB LOAF

- 1 (11-ounce) can refrigerated soft breadstick dough
- 2 teaspoons butter or stick margarine, melted
- 3 garlic cloves, minced
- 1 teaspoon dried Italian seasoning

1. Preheat oven to 350°.
2. Unroll dough (do not separate into breadsticks). Brush top of dough with butter; sprinkle minced garlic and seasoning evenly over dough.
3. Beginning at 1 long edge, roll up jelly-roll fashion. Pinch seam to seal (do not seal ends of dough). Place dough, seam side down, on ungreased baking sheet; cut 6 (1-inch) slits across top. Bake at 350° for 22 minutes or until lightly browned. YIELD: 1 loaf, 8 slices per loaf; serving size: 1 slice.

POINTS: 2; EXCHANGES: 1½ Starch, ½ Fat;
PER SERVING: CAL 116 (23% from fat); PRO 3g; FAT 3g (sat 1g); CARB 19g; FIB 0.4g; CHOL 2.6mg; IRON 1.3mg; SOD 295mg; CALC 8mg

BUTTERNUT-RAISIN BREAD

You can substitute 1⅓ cups canned pumpkin for the butternut squash. For best results, combine 3 cups bread flour with the yeast, and add the remaining 2¾ to 3 cups bread flour with the pumpkin and molasses.

- 1 teaspoon ground cinnamon
- 3 tablespoons sugar
- 5¾ to 6 cups bread flour, divided
- 2 packages rapid-rise yeast
- ¾ cup warm water (120° to 130°)
- ¼ cup warm 1% low-fat milk (120° to 130°)
- 1⅓ cups mashed cooked butternut squash (about 1 small)
- ¼ cup molasses
- 2 tablespoons vegetable oil
- 1 teaspoon salt
- Cooking spray
- 2 tablespoons butter or stick margarine, melted and divided
- ½ cup raisins
- 1 cup sifted powdered sugar
- 3½ teaspoons 1% low-fat milk
- ¼ teaspoon vanilla extract

1. Combine cinnamon and 3 tablespoons sugar; set aside.
2. Combine 5 cups flour and yeast in a mixing bowl. Combine water and milk; gradually add to flour mixture, beating at medium speed of a heavy-duty stand mixer until well blended.
3. Combine squash, molasses, oil, and salt; add to flour mixture, beating well. Add enough of remaining flour, 1 tablespoon at a time, to form a soft dough.
4. Turn dough out onto a lightly floured surface. Knead until smooth and elastic (about 10 minutes), adding enough of remaining flour, 1 tablespoon at a time, to prevent dough from sticking to hands.
5. Place dough in a large bowl coated with cooking spray, turning to coat top. Cover and let rise in a warm place (85°), free from drafts, 25 minutes or until doubled in bulk. Punch dough down; turn dough out onto a lightly floured surface, and knead 5 times. Divide dough in half. Working with 1 portion at a time, (cover remaining dough to keep it from drying out), roll each portion into a 16- x 7-inch rectangle. Brush each with 1 tablespoon melted butter; sprinkle with half of reserved cinnamon-sugar mixture and half of raisins. Roll up each rectangle tightly, starting with short side. Press firmly to eliminate air pockets; pinch seam and ends to seal. Place each roll of dough, seam side down, in a 9- x 5-inch loaf pan coated with cooking spray. Cover and let rise 20 minutes or until doubled in bulk.
6. Preheat oven to 350°.
7. Bake at 350° for 30 minutes or until loaves sound hollow when tapped. Remove from pans immediately, and let cool on wire racks.
8. Combine powdered sugar, milk, and vanilla, stirring well. Drizzle over loaves. YIELD: 2 loaves, 16 servings per loaf (serving size: 1 slice).

POINTS: 3; EXCHANGES: 2 Starch, ½ Fat;
PER SERVING: CAL 141 (13% from fat); PRO 3.3g; FAT 2.1g (sat 0.7g); CARB 27.4g; FIB 0.9g; CHOL 2mg; IRON 1.4mg; SOD 83mg; CALC 16mg

Desserts

CHOCOLATE FONDUE

Pour prepared fondue into a fondue pot for serving, if desired.

- ½ cup fat-free milk
- 2 tablespoons unsweetened cocoa
- 2½ (1.55-ounce) milk chocolate candy bars (such as Hershey's)
- 1 (7-ounce) jar marshmallow creme
- ½ cup 50%-less-fat sour cream (such as Daisy Light)
- 1 teaspoon vanilla extract
- ½ (10-ounce) package reduced-fat, reduced-calorie pound cake (such as Sara Lee Free and Light), cut into 24 cubes
- 3 medium bananas, each cut into 8 slices
- 24 fresh strawberries (about 1 pound)

1. Combine first 3 ingredients in a medium saucepan. Bring to a boil over medium-high heat, stirring constantly with a whisk. Reduce heat to medium; cook 3 minutes or until chocolate melts, stirring constantly. Reduce heat to medium-low; add marshmallow creme, stirring until creme melts. Bring mixture to a simmer over medium heat, and remove from heat.
2. Add sour cream and vanilla, stirring until well blended. Serve warm with cake, bananas, and strawberries. **YIELD:** 8 servings (serving size: about ¼ cup fondue, 3 cake cubes, 3 banana slices, and 3 strawberries).

POINTS: 6; **EXCHANGES:** 2½ Starch, 1 Fruit, 1 Fat; **PER SERVING:** CAL 286 (22% from fat); PRO 4.2g; FAT 6.9g (sat 4g); CARB 52g; FIB 2.4g; CHOL 9mg; IRON 1.6mg; SOD 109mg; CALC 84mg

CANDIED APPLESAUCE

Serve this applesauce as a dessert or side dish.

- ⅔ cup cinnamon decorator candies
- ½ cup apple juice
- ¼ cup firmly packed brown sugar
- 1 teaspoon lemon juice
- 2½ pounds Granny Smith apples (about 8), peeled, cored, and quartered

1. Combine candies and apple juice in a 2-cup glass measure. Microwave at HIGH 5 minutes, stirring after 2½ minutes. Stir mixture until candies melt. Pour into a 4-quart electric slow cooker; stir in sugar and lemon juice. Add apples, stirring to coat. Cover with lid; cook on low heat-setting 8 hours or until very tender. Stir well. Serve warm or chilled. **YIELD:** 13 servings (serving size: ½ cup).

POINTS: 2; **EXCHANGES:** 1 Starch, 1 Fruit; **PER SERVING:** CAL 111 (2% from fat); PRO 0.1g; FAT 0.2g (sat 0g); CARB 28.2g; FIB 0.2g; CHOL 0mg; IRON 0.2mg; SOD 2mg; CALC 7mg

STRAWBERRIES WITH CRÈME ANGLAISE

You can substitute a whole vanilla bean for the vanilla extract in the crème anglaise. Drop a split vanilla bean into the milk before heating; discard bean before adding milk to egg mixture.

- 3 pints (6 cups) fresh strawberries, rinsed and hulled
- ¼ cup sugar
- 1 teaspoon vanilla extract
- ½ teaspoon fresh lemon juice
- 2 cups 1% low-fat milk
- 2 large eggs, lightly beaten
- ⅓ cup sugar
- 2 teaspoons vanilla extract

1. Chop and mash 1 pint (2 cups) strawberries in a large bowl. Stir in ¼ cup sugar, 1 teaspoon vanilla, and lemon juice. Halve remaining 2 pints (4 cups) strawberries; add to mashed strawberries. Set aside.
2. Heat milk in a medium saucepan over medium heat until hot (do not boil). Combine eggs and ⅓ cup sugar in a medium saucepan; stir well with a whisk. Gradually add hot milk, stirring well. Cook, stirring constantly, over medium heat 6 minutes or until mixture coats back of a spoon (do not boil). Remove from heat, and let cool.
3. Stir in 2 teaspoons vanilla extract. Cover and chill thoroughly. Spoon crème anglaise over berries to serve. **YIELD:** 6 servings (serving size: ½ cup strawberry mixture, ½ cup crème anglaise).

POINTS: 3; **EXCHANGES:** 1½ Starch, 1 Fruit, ½ Fat; **PER SERVING:** CAL 288 (14% from fat); PRO 5.8g; FAT 3.2g (sat 1.1g); CARB 35.5g; FIB 3.9g; CHOL 77mg; IRON 0.9mg; SOD 63mg; CALC 130mg

SUMMER FRUIT WITH ZABAGLIONE SAUCE

Omit the Marsala for a nonalcoholic sauce, if desired.

- 2 tablespoons brown sugar
- 2 teaspoons cornstarch
- ¾ cup fat-free milk
- ¼ cup fat-free egg substitute
- ⅛ teaspoon salt
- ⅓ cup low-fat sour cream
- 1 tablespoon sweet Marsala
- ¼ teaspoon vanilla extract
- 1 cup sliced strawberries
- 1 cup sliced fresh plums
- 1 cup sliced fresh nectarines

1. Combine brown sugar and cornstarch in a small saucepan; stir well. Gradually stir in milk. Cook over medium heat, stirring constantly, until mixture comes to a boil and thickens; reduce heat, and simmer 1 minute. Remove from heat. Gradually stir about one-fourth of hot mixture into egg substitute; add to remaining hot mixture, stirring constantly. Cook over low heat 10 to 15 seconds, stirring constantly (do not boil).
2. Remove from heat; stir in salt and next 3 ingredients. Pour into a bowl; cover surface with plastic wrap. Chill 24 hours.
3. Combine fruit, and spoon into 4 dessert dishes; spoon sauce evenly over fruit. **YIELD:** 4 servings (serving size: ¾ cup fruit and ¼ cup sauce).

POINTS: 2; **EXCHANGES:** ½ Starch, 1 Fruit, ½ Fat;
PER SERVING: CAL 130 (21% from fat);
PRO 4.6g; FAT 3.1g (sat 1.6g); CARB 22.5g;
FIB 2.7g; CHOL 8mg; IRON 0.7mg;
SOD 127mg; CALC 95mg

STRAWBERRIES 'N' CREAM PIE

(pictured on page 46)
Top the pie with strawberries right before serving or they will water out and soften the filling.

- ¼ cup spoonable sugar substitute (such as Equal Spoonful)
- ¼ teaspoon water
- 1 (8-ounce) tub light cream cheese, softened
- 2 cups frozen fat-free whipped topping, thawed
- 1 (6-ounce) ready-made reduced-fat graham cracker piecrust
- 3 cups halved fresh strawberries
- Mint sprigs (optional)

1. Combine first 3 ingredients in a large bowl; stir with a whisk until well blended. Fold in whipped topping. Spread mixture into crust; cover and chill 1 hour or until firm.
2. Arrange strawberries evenly over cream cheese mixture just before serving. Garnish with mint sprigs, if desired; serve pie immediately.
YIELD: 8 servings.

POINTS: 4; **EXCHANGES:** 1 Starch, 1 Fruit, 1½ Fat;
PER SERVING: CAL 208 (34% from fat);
PRO 4.3g; FAT 8g (sat 3.9g); CARB 27.6g;
FIB 1.7g; CHOL 17mg; IRON 0.6mg;
SOD 266mg; CALC 46mg

BANANA SPLIT PIE

(pictured on page 42)
During testing, we tried this pie both chilled and slightly frozen. Chilling produces a soft, creamy filling while freezing creates a firmer pie.

- ¾ cup sliced banana
- 1 (6-ounce) ready-made reduced-fat graham cracker piecrust
- 1 (8-ounce) can crushed pineapple in juice, well drained
- 1⅓ cups water
- 1 (1-ounce) package vanilla fat-free, sugar-free instant pudding mix
- 2 cups frozen fat-free whipped topping, thawed and divided
- 6 maraschino cherries (optional)

1. Arrange banana slices in bottom of piecrust, and spread crushed pineapple over banana. Combine water and pudding mix in a medium bowl; stir with a whisk until mixture is well blended. Fold in ½ cup whipped topping.
2. Spread pudding mixture evenly over fruit; cover and chill at least 2 hours or freeze 45 minutes. Spread remaining whipped topping over pudding mixture. Garnish pie with cherries, if desired. **YIELD:** 6 servings.

POINTS: 5; **EXCHANGES:** 2½ Starch, ½ Fruit, 1 Fat;
PER SERVING: CAL 224 (16% from fat);
PRO 2g; FAT 4g (sat 1.4g); CARB 42g;
FIB 1.2g; CHOL 0mg; IRON 0.7mg;
SOD 361mg; CALC 5mg

CHOCOLATE-PEANUT BUTTER PIE

- ¾ cup nutlike cereal nuggets (such as Grape-Nuts), divided
- 2 cups chocolate low-fat ice cream, slightly softened
- 1 (2.1-ounce) package chocolate sugar-free instant pudding mix
- ¼ cup creamy peanut butter
- 1 cup frozen fat-free whipped topping, thawed

1. Sprinkle ½ cup cereal nuggets evenly in an 8-inch round cake pan. Combine remaining ¼ cup cereal nuggets, chocolate ice cream, pudding mix, and peanut butter in a large bowl; stir until mixture is well blended. Fold in whipped topping. Spoon ice cream mixture into prepared pan, spreading gently with a spatula. Cover and freeze 2 hours or until firm. Let stand at room temperature 15 minutes before serving. **YIELD:** 8 servings.

POINTS: 4; **EXCHANGES:** 2 Starch, 1 Fat;
PER SERVING: CAL 177 (25% from fat); PRO 5g; FAT 5g (sat 1.7g); CARB 28g; FIB 2g; CHOL 5mg; IRON 1.1mg; SOD 386mg; CALC 47mg

CRISPY PEANUT BUTTERSCOTCH PIE

(pictured on page 46)

- ¼ cup creamy peanut butter
- 1 tablespoon honey
- 1½ cups oven-toasted rice cereal (such as Rice Krispies)
- 1 (1-ounce) package butterscotch fat-free, sugar-free instant pudding mix
- 2 cups fat-free milk
- 1½ cups frozen fat-free whipped topping, thawed and divided
- Ground cinnamon (optional)
- Additional oven-toasted rice cereal (optional)

1. Combine peanut butter and honey in a medium microwave-safe bowl; microwave at HIGH 30 seconds, stirring until mixture melts. Stir in rice cereal. Using wax paper, press cereal mixture into bottom of an 8-inch round cake pan.
2. Prepare pudding mix according to package directions for pudding, using 2 cups milk; fold in 1 cup whipped topping. Spoon pudding mixture into prepared pan. Cover and freeze until firm. Let pie stand at room temperature 15 minutes before serving. Spoon remaining whipped topping over each serving. If desired, sprinkle with ground cinnamon and additional cereal. **YIELD:** 6 servings.

POINTS: 3; **EXCHANGES:** 1½ Starch, 1 Fat;
PER SERVING: CAL 149 (30% from fat); PRO 4g; FAT 5g (sat 0.9g); CARB 21.2g; FIB 0.7g; CHOL 0mg; IRON 0.7mg; SOD 375mg; CALC 5mg

BLACK BOTTOM PEPPERMINT ICE CREAM PIE

For the holidays, substitute candy canes for the peppermint candies.

- 1 (7¾-ounce) package reduced-fat chocolate sandwich cookies (such as Snack Well's), crushed
- 1 tablespoon fat-free milk
- 4 cups chocolate or vanilla low-fat ice cream, slightly softened
- ¼ cup coarsely crushed hard peppermint candies (such as Starlight Mints; about 10 candies)
- 1 tablespoon semisweet chocolate mini-morsels

1. Place crushed cookies in a bowl; sprinkle with milk, and stir well. Press crumb mixture into bottom and up sides of a 9-inch pie plate. Freeze at least 30 minutes.
2. Place ice cream in a large bowl; stir with a wooden spoon until smooth (do not allow ice cream to melt). Stir peppermint and mini-morsels into softened ice cream. Spoon ice cream into pie shell, spreading evenly. Cover and freeze at least 4 hours or until firm.
YIELD: 8 servings.
NOTE: For best results on the piecrust, the cookies should be crushed into large crumbs. During testing, we placed the cookies in a large zip-top plastic bag and crushed them with a rolling pin. You can also use a food processor to crush cookies.

POINTS: 6; **EXCHANGES:** 3 Starch, 1 Fat;
PER SERVING: CAL 262 (22% from fat); PRO 5.1g; FAT 6.4g (sat 2.7g); CARB 47.6g; FIB 0.5g; CHOL 5mg; IRON 0.8mg; SOD 285mg; CALC 173mg

FROZEN RASPBERRY-YOGURT BROWNIES

Watch the yogurt closely as it softens. It needs to be soft enough to stir easily into the raspberry mixture yet firm enough to hold the swirl.

1 (1 lb., 4.5-ounce) package low-fat fudge brownie mix (such as Betty Crocker Sweet Rewards)
1 (14-ounce) package unsweetened frozen raspberries, thawed
½ cup sugar
1 tablespoon cornstarch
1 tablespoon water
1 (½-gallon) carton vanilla fat-free frozen yogurt, slightly softened

1. Preheat oven to 350°.
2. Prepare brownie mix according to package directions, using a 13- x 9-inch baking pan. Bake at 350° for 20 minutes or until just set (brownies will be fudgy). Let cool completely.
3. Press raspberries through a fine sieve over a bowl, reserving 1 cup raspberry purée; discard seeds. Combine raspberry purée, sugar, cornstarch, and water in a saucepan; stir with a whisk until blended. Bring to a boil, and cook 1 minute or until thick, stirring constantly with a whisk. Pour raspberry sauce into a bowl; press plastic wrap onto surface of sauce, and let cool completely.
4. Add yogurt to raspberry sauce; swirl together, using a rubber spatula or spoon. Quickly spread yogurt mixture over brownies in pan. Cover and freeze 4 hours or until firm. Cut into 24 squares. **YIELD:** 24 servings.

POINTS: 3; **EXCHANGES:** 2½ Starch;
PER SERVING: CAL 171 (10% from fat); PRO 3.5g; FAT 1.9g (sat 0.4g); CARB 37.3g; FIB 0.9g; CHOL 0mg; IRON 0.8mg; SOD 133mg; CALC 241mg

TURTLE ICE CREAM PARFAITS

These tasty treats are great for kids. Use the remaining brownie mix to make this dessert again or to make a half-batch of brownies (see note following this recipe).

½ (1 lb., 4.5-ounce) package low-fat fudge brownie mix (about 2 cups)
¼ cup water
1 large egg white
Cooking spray
¼ cup fat-free caramel-flavored sundae syrup
¼ teaspoon vanilla, butter, and nut flavoring
2 tablespoons chopped pecans, toasted
2 cups vanilla fat-free ice cream, softened and divided
6 tablespoons frozen reduced-calorie whipped topping, thawed

1. Preheat oven to 350°.
2. Combine brownie mix, water, and egg white in a large bowl; stir well. Spread batter into an 8-inch square pan coated with cooking spray. Bake at 350° for 20 minutes. Let cool completely on a wire rack. Cut brownie lengthwise 12 times. Then cut brownie crosswise 12 times to equal 144 small cubes.
3. Combine ice cream syrup and flavoring in a microwave-safe bowl. Microwave at HIGH 30 seconds. Let cool slightly. Stir in pecans.
4. Divide half of brownie cubes evenly among 6 (6-ounce) parfait glasses. Spoon 1 cup ice cream evenly over brownie cubes. Top with half of caramel mixture. Repeat layers with remaining brownie cubes, ice cream, and caramel mixture. Freeze 1 hour or until firm.
5. Top each serving with 1 tablespoon whipped topping. **YIELD:** 6 servings.
NOTE: Combine remaining half of brownie mix and ⅓ cup water; stir well. Spread into an 8-inch square pan coated with cooking spray. Bake at 350° for 25 minutes.

POINTS: 7; **EXCHANGES:** 4½ Starch, 1 Fat;
PER SERVING: CAL 334 (16% from fat); PRO 5.2g; FAT 6.1g (sat 2.2g); CARB 67.0g; FIB 1.7g; CHOL 0mg; IRON 1.7mg; SOD 248mg; CALC 64mg

AFTER-DINNER COFFEE CAKE

Cooking spray
24 cream-filled wafer cookies (such as Nabisco Biscos Sugar Wafers with Cream Filling)
3 tablespoons Kahlúa, divided
1 quart low-fat latte ice cream (such as Starbucks Low Fat Latte Ice Cream), divided
2 tablespoons instant coffee granules
2 cups frozen fat-free whipped topping

1. Fold a 12-inch long strip of wax paper in half lengthwise. Coat an 8-inch loaf pan with cooking spray; place wax paper in pan, allowing long ends to extend over the long sides of the pan.

2. Arrange 12 cookies in prepared pan. Drizzle 1½ tablespoons Kahlúa over cookies; set aside.

3. Beat 2 cups ice cream at high speed of a mixer 10 seconds or until smooth and softened. Spread ice cream evenly over Kahlúa-soaked cookies. Freeze 20 minutes.

4. Repeat layering procedure with cookies, Kahlúa, and remaining ice cream. Cover with plastic wrap, and freeze 8 to 24 hours.

5. Discard plastic wrap. Invert cake onto serving platter; remove wax paper. Freeze until ready to frost.

6. Fold instant coffee granules into whipped topping; spread mixture over top and sides of cake. Cut cake into ¾-inch slices, and serve immediately. **YIELD:** 10 servings (serving size: 1 slice).

POINTS: 5; **EXCHANGES:** 2½ Starch, 1 Fat;
PER SERVING: CAL 236 (16% from fat); PRO 4.4g; FAT 4.2g (sat 1.7g); CARB 38.6g; FIB 0g; CHOL 8mg; IRON 0.2mg; SOD 69mg; CALC 83mg

CHOCOLATE MINT STRIPE CAKE

Serve the remaining pound cake with fresh fruit or Chocolate Fondue (page 29) for a quick dessert.

Cooking spray
3¾ cups mint chocolate chip ice cream (such as Blue Bell Mint Chocolate Chip), divided
1 (15-ounce) fat-free chocolate pound cake (such as Entenmann's Chocolate Loaf)
½ cup fat-free fudge ice cream topping, divided

1. Fold a 12-inch piece of wax paper in half lengthwise. Coat an 8-inch loaf pan with cooking spray. Place wax paper lengthwise in loaf pan, leaving excess to extend over long sides of pan. Set aside.

2. Beat 1¼ cups ice cream at high speed of a mixer 10 seconds or until smooth and softened. Spread ice cream in prepared pan. Freeze 20 minutes.

3. Cut 2 slices horizontally from bottom of pound cake, each ⅔ inch thick. Reserve remaining pound cake for another use. Place 1 layer of cake in pan on top of ice cream. Spread ¼ cup fudge topping on cake layer in pan.

4. Repeat procedure with remaining ice cream, cake layer, and fudge topping, ending with ice cream.

5. Cover surface of ice cream with plastic wrap; cover loaf pan with foil. Freeze 8 hours.

6. Let stand 5 minutes before serving. Invert onto serving platter, and remove wax paper. Cut into ¾-inch slices. Serve immediately. **YIELD:** 8 servings (serving size: 1 slice).

NOTE: Before inverting the ice cream cake, dip a thin spatula or knife into hot water. Dry the spatula completely and run it around the edges of the pan to loosen the frozen cake. Use the excess wax paper for leverage when pulling the loaf out of the pan.

POINTS: 6; **EXCHANGES:** 3 Starch, 2 Fat;
PER SERVING: CAL 297 (28% from fat); PRO 4.7g; FAT 9.4g (sat 5.6g); CARB 47.8g; FIB 1.2g; CHOL 33mg; IRON 0.5mg; SOD 321mg; CALC 104mg

CITRUS ANGEL FOOD CAKE

You can substitute a 10.5-ounce loaf angel food cake for a round cake. Slice off top third of loaf, using a serrated knife. Hollow out bottom portion, leaving a ½-inch shell (make sure not to cut through bottom of cake.) Proceed with recipe as directed.

1 (16-ounce) round angel food cake
1¾ cups vanilla low-fat ice cream, slightly softened
¼ cup thawed lemonade concentrate, undiluted
4 teaspoons grated lime rind, divided
2 cups frozen reduced-calorie whipped topping, thawed

1. Slice off top third of angel food cake, using a serrated knife; set aside. Hollow out bottom portion of cake, leaving a 1-inch-thick shell, making sure not to cut through bottom of cake; reserve leftover cake (about 1¾ cups) for another use.

2. Combine ice cream, lemonade concentrate, and 1 teaspoon lime rind. Spoon ice cream mixture into cake shell, pressing firmly with back of spoon; top with remaining third of cake.

3. Combine whipped topping and remaining 3 teaspoons lime rind; spread over top and sides of filled cake. Cover loosely, and freeze 6 hours or until firm. Slice with a serrated knife. **YIELD:** 12 servings (serving size: 1 slice).

POINTS: 3; **EXCHANGES:** 2 Starch, ½ Fat;
PER SERVING: CAL 145 (17% from fat); PRO 2.7g; FAT 2.8g (sat 1.6g); CARB 28.2g; FIB 0.8g; CHOL 2mg; IRON 0mg; SOD 112mg; CALC 78mg

APRICOT SORBET

1 (15.25-ounce) can apricot halves in heavy syrup, undrained and chilled
1½ cups apricot nectar, chilled
¼ cup sugar
1 teaspoon vanilla extract
½ teaspoon almond extract

1. Drain apricots in a sieve over a bowl, reserving ½ cup syrup. Purée apricots and reserved syrup in a food processor.
2. Combine purée, nectar, and remaining ingredients, stirring until sugar dissolves.
3. Pour mixture into freezer can of an ice cream freezer. Freeze according to manufacturer's instructions. Spoon sorbet into a freezer-safe container; cover and freeze 1 hour or until firm. **YIELD:** 7 servings (serving size: ½ cup).

POINTS: 2; **EXCHANGES:** 1 Starch, 1 Fruit;
PER SERVING: CAL 107 (1% from fat);
PRO 0.5g; FAT 0.1g (sat 0g); CARB 26.9g;
FIB 0.5g; CHOL 0mg; IRON 0.4mg;
SOD 2mg; CALC 10mg

STRAWBERRY-ORANGE RUSSE

1 (10-ounce) package 50% fewer calories frozen strawberries in syrup, thawed and undrained
2 tablespoons frozen orange juice concentrate, thawed
22 ladyfingers, split
1 quart orange sherbet
1 quart fat-free vanilla ice cream

1. Place strawberries in a blender; process until almost smooth, leaving some strawberry pieces. Place in a small saucepan, and bring to a boil. Cook over medium heat 10 minutes or until thickened, stirring occasionally. Stir in orange juice concentrate. Pour mixture into a small bowl. Cover and chill.
2. Line a 9-inch springform pan with ladyfingers, cut sides in. Place orange sherbet in a medium bowl. Beat at high speed of a mixer 10 seconds or until softened and smooth. Spoon mixture into prepared springform pan, spreading evenly. Cover and freeze 20 minutes.
3. Place ice cream in a medium bowl. Beat at high speed of a mixer 10 seconds or until softened and smooth. Fold in chilled strawberry mixture, leaving some streaks. Spoon over sherbet layer, spreading evenly. Cover with plastic wrap, pressing plastic wrap directly onto surface of ice cream. Cover with foil; freeze 8 hours or until firm.
4. To serve, uncover and gently remove sides of pan. Cut into wedges. **YIELD:** 12 servings (serving size: 1 slice).

POINTS: 4; **EXCHANGES:** 3 Starch;
PER SERVING: CAL 194 (7% from fat);
PRO 3.1g; FAT 1.6g (sat 0.8g); CARB 42.0g;
FIB 0.3g; CHOL 26mg; IRON 0.5mg;
SOD 105mg; CALC 96mg

SWEET PRALINE FREEZE

Watch the sugar carefully; it caramelizes quickly. Aim for a golden, amber color. The darker the caramel becomes, the more bitter it is.

1 cup sugar
2 cups water
½ cup apple juice
½ cup finely chopped pecans, toasted
¼ teaspoon vanilla, butter, and nut flavoring
⅛ teaspoon salt

1. Place sugar in a large heavy skillet over medium-high heat; cook until sugar dissolves, stirring constantly (do not use a nonstick skillet). Continue cooking an additional 5 minutes or until sugar is golden, stirring constantly. Remove from heat; carefully stir in water (caramelized sugar will harden and stick to spoon). Add apple juice. Place skillet over medium-high heat; cook until caramelized sugar melts.
2. Pour mixture into an 8-inch square baking dish; stir in pecans, flavoring, and salt. Cover and freeze at least 8 hours or until firm. Remove dish from freezer; let stand 5 minutes. Break mixture into large chunks. Place frozen chunks in a food processor; process until smooth. Spoon into chilled individual bowls. **YIELD:** 6 servings (serving size: ½ cup).

POINTS: 4; **EXCHANGES:** 3½ Starch, 1 Fat;
PER SERVING: CAL 204 (30% from fat);
PRO 0.8g; FAT 6.7g (sat 0.5g); CARB 37.5g;
FIB 0.7g; CHOL 0mg; IRON 0.3mg;
SOD 50mg; CALC 5mg

LEMON PUDDING CAKE

- 3 large egg whites
- ⅔ cup sugar, divided
- ¼ cup all-purpose flour
- 1½ cups 1% low-fat milk
- 2 large egg yolks
- 4 teaspoons grated lemon rind
- ¼ cup fresh lemon juice
- 1 tablespoon butter or stick margarine, melted and cooled slightly
- 1 teaspoon vanilla extract
- Cooking spray
- 2 tablespoons sifted powdered sugar

1. Preheat oven to 325°.
2. In a large bowl, beat egg whites at high speed of a mixer until foamy. Gradually add ¼ cup sugar, 1 tablespoon at a time, beating until stiff peaks form. Set aside.
3. Combine flour and remaining sugar in a medium bowl; add milk, egg yolks, and lemon rind, stirring with a whisk until smooth. Stir in lemon juice, butter, and vanilla. (Batter will be very thin.) Add about one-fourth batter to beaten egg whites, stirring well. Stir remaining batter into egg white mixture.
4. Pour mixture into an 8-inch square baking dish coated with cooking spray. Place dish in a 13- x 9-inch baking pan; add hot water to pan to a depth of 1 inch. Bake at 325° for 45 minutes or until lightly browned and sides begin to pull away from the pan. Let stand in pan 5 minutes. Remove dish from pan; let cool 15 minutes. Sprinkle top with powdered sugar; serve warm. **YIELD:** 6 servings.

POINTS: 4; **EXCHANGES:** 2 Starch, 1 Fat;
PER SERVING: CAL 192 (21% from fat); PRO 5.2g; FAT 4.5g (sat 2.2g); CARB 33g; FIB 0.2g; CHOL 80mg; IRON 0.5mg; SOD 78mg; CALC 86mg

BOURBON-PECAN PUDDING CAKE

You'll find a rich, gooey pudding layer underneath the cake—don't mistake it for being underdone; that layer is a feature of pudding cakes.

- 1 tablespoon butter or margarine
- ¼ cup chopped pecans
- ¾ cup firmly packed brown sugar
- 2 tablespoons butter or stick margarine, softened
- ½ cup 1% low-fat milk
- 3 tablespoons bourbon, divided
- 1½ cups all-purpose flour, divided
- 1½ teaspoons baking powder
- ½ teaspoon ground cinnamon
- ⅛ teaspoon salt
- Cooking spray
- ⅔ cup firmly packed brown sugar
- 1 cup boiling water

1. Preheat oven to 350°.
2. Melt 1 tablespoon butter in a small skillet over medium heat; add pecans. Cook 3 minutes or until toasted, stirring often. Set aside, and let cool.
3. Combine ¾ cup brown sugar and 2 tablespoons butter in a bowl; beat at medium speed of a mixer 3 minutes. Add milk and 1 tablespoon bourbon; beat well. Combine 1¼ cups flour, baking powder, cinnamon, and salt; gradually add to sugar mixture, beating well. Spoon batter into an 8-inch square baking pan coated with cooking spray.
4. Combine remaining ¼ cup flour, remaining 2 tablespoons bourbon, and ⅔ cup brown sugar in a small bowl; sprinkle over batter. Top with reserved toasted pecans. Pour boiling water over batter (do not stir). Bake at 350° for 35 to 40 minutes or until cake springs back when touched lightly in center. Let stand 10 minutes. Serve warm with ice cream. **YIELD:** 9 servings (serving size: 1 [3-inch] square cake).

POINTS: 6; **EXCHANGES:** 3½ Starch, 1 Fat;
PER SERVING: CAL 270 (22% from fat); PRO 2.9g; FAT 6.5g (sat 2.7g); CARB 51.4g; FIB 0.8g; CHOL 11mg; IRON 1.9mg; SOD 176mg; CALC 99mg

BLACK FOREST UPSIDE-DOWN CAKE

Substitute 1 tablespoon drained cherry juice for kirsch, if desired.

- Cooking spray
- 1 tablespoon butter or stick margarine, melted
- 1 tablespoon kirsch (cherry brandy)
- ¼ cup firmly packed brown sugar
- ⅛ teaspoon ground cinnamon
- 2 tablespoons sliced almonds, toasted
- 2 (16½-ounce) cans pitted dark sweet cherries in heavy syrup, drained
- 1 (1 lb., 4.5-ounce) package low-fat fudge brownie mix (such as Betty Crocker Sweet Rewards)
- ⅔ cup water
- 2 large egg whites, lightly beaten
- ¼ teaspoon ground cinnamon

1. Preheat oven to 350°.
2. Coat a 9-inch square baking pan with cooking spray. Place melted butter in pan; stir in kirsch. Combine brown sugar and ⅛ teaspoon cinnamon; sprinkle evenly over butter mixture. Sprinkle almonds over

(continued)

brown sugar; arrange cherries on top of almonds.

3. Combine brownie mix and remaining 3 ingredients in a large bowl; stir well. Spoon batter over cherries in prepared pan.

4. Bake at 350° for 45 minutes or until a wooden pick inserted in center comes out clean. Cool in pan 5 minutes on a wire rack. Using a thin spatula or a knife, loosen cake from edge of pan. Place a plate, upside down, on top of pan; invert cake onto plate. Let cool completely. **YIELD:** 12 servings.

POINTS: 6; **EXCHANGES:** 2½ Starch, 1 Fruit, 1 Fat; **PER SERVING:** CAL 278 (16% from fat); PRO 4g; FAT 5g (sat 2.1g); CARB 57g; FIB 2.0g; CHOL 2.6mg; IRON 1.9mg; SOD 198mg; CALC 7.9mg

PINEAPPLE-COCONUT UPSIDE DOWN CAKE

(pictured on page 4)

1 (20-ounce) can pineapple slices in juice, undrained
Butter-flavored cooking spray
1 tablespoon butter or margarine, melted
⅓ cup firmly packed brown sugar
12 maraschino cherry halves
¼ cup flaked sweetened coconut
¼ cup butter or stick margarine, softened
⅔ cup sugar
1 large egg
1¼ cups all-purpose flour
1½ teaspoons baking powder
⅛ teaspoon salt
½ cup mashed ripe banana
¼ cup 2% reduced-fat milk
1 teaspoon vanilla extract

1. Preheat oven to 350°.

2. Drain pineapple in a colander over a small saucepan, reserving juice. Cut 6 pineapple slices in half crosswise; reserve remaining pineapple slices for another use. Coat a 9-inch round cake pan with cooking spray. Coat bottom of pan with 1 tablespoon melted butter; sprinkle with brown sugar. Arrange pineapple, spokelike, on top of brown sugar, working from center of pan to edge. Arrange cherries between pineapple slices. Sprinkle evenly with coconut, and set aside.

3. Bring pineapple juice to a boil; cook 3 minutes or until reduced to ⅓ cup. Remove from heat; let cool.

4. Combine softened butter and sugar in a large bowl, beating at medium speed of a mixer until well blended. Add egg, beating well.

5. Combine flour, baking powder, and salt in a small bowl; stir well. Combine banana, milk, and vanilla in another bowl. Add dry ingredients to butter mixture, alternately with banana mixture, beginning and ending with dry ingredients. Pour batter into prepared pan.

6. Bake at 350° for 35 minutes or until a wooden pick inserted in center comes out clean. Cool in pan 5 minutes on a wire rack. Loosen cake from sides of pan, using a narrow metal spatula. Invert cake onto a serving plate. Poke holes in cake with a wooden pick; slowly drizzle with reduced pineapple juice. Cut into wedges, and serve warm. **YIELD:** 8 servings.

POINTS: 6; **EXCHANGES:** 3½ Starch, 2 Fat; **PER SERVING:** CAL 292 (29% from fat); PRO 3.5g; FAT 9.5g (sat 5.7g); CARB 49.5g; FIB 1.2g; CHOL 48mg; IRON 1.5g; SOD 226mg; CALC 79mg

CHOCOLATE CAKE WITH MOCHA GLAZE

(pictured on page 45)

This cake is a chocolate lover's dream. It earned our highest rating.

Cooking spray
1 teaspoon sifted cake flour
⅓ cup unsweetened cocoa
1 ounce sweet baking chocolate, chopped
½ cup boiling water
1¾ cups sugar
¼ cup butter or stick margarine, softened
2 tablespoons vegetable oil
2½ teaspoons vanilla extract
2 large eggs
2¼ cups sifted cake flour
2 teaspoons baking powder
½ teaspoon baking soda
¼ teaspoon salt
1¼ cups low-fat buttermilk
Mocha Glaze

1. Preheat oven to 350°.

2. Coat a 13- x 9-inch baking pan with cooking spray, and dust with 1 teaspoon cake flour; set aside.

3. Combine cocoa and chocolate in a small bowl; add boiling water, stirring until chocolate melts. Set aside.

4. Combine sugar, butter, and oil in a large bowl; beat at medium speed of a mixer about 2 minutes or until well blended. Add vanilla and eggs; beat well.

5. Combine 2¼ cups cake flour and next 3 ingredients. Add flour mixture to butter mixture alternately with buttermilk, beginning and ending with flour mixture. Beat in chocolate mixture.

6. Pour batter into prepared pan. Bake at 350° for 30 to 32 minutes or until a wooden pick inserted in center comes out clean.

7. Let cool completely in pan on a wire rack. Spread Mocha Glaze over cooled cake. **YIELD:** 15 servings.

POINTS: 7; **EXCHANGES:** 4 Starch, 1½ Fat;
PER SERVING: CAL 336 (21% from fat);
PRO 4.5g; FAT 7.8g (sat 3.6g); CARB 63.1g;
FIB 0.3g; CHOL 39mg; IRON 2.1mg;
SOD 245mg; CALC 90mg

MOCHA GLAZE

- 2 teaspoons instant coffee granules
- 5 tablespoons fat-free evaporated milk
- 2⅔ cups sifted powdered sugar
- 3 tablespoons unsweetened cocoa
- ¼ teaspoon salt
- 1 ounce sweet baking chocolate
- ½ teaspoon vanilla extract

1. Combine coffee granules and evaporated milk, stirring until coffee dissolves. Set aside.

2. Combine sugar, cocoa, and salt in a small bowl; stir well, and set aside.

3. Place chocolate in a large microwave-safe bowl. Microwave at HIGH 1 to 1½ minutes or until very soft, stirring until smooth. Immediately add milk mixture, stirring with a whisk until blended. Gradually add sugar mixture to chocolate mixture, beating at low speed of a mixer until blended and smooth. Stir in vanilla. Pour immediately over cooled cake, and spread to edges of pan. **YIELD:** 1 cup.

CREAM-FILLED HAZELNUT TEA CAKE

- Cooking spray
- ½ cup 1% low-fat milk
- 1 tablespoon butter or stick margarine
- 2 large eggs, separated
- ½ cup sugar
- 1 cup sifted cake flour
- 1 teaspoon baking powder
- 1 teaspoon vanilla extract
- ¼ cup finely chopped hazelnuts, divided
- Pastry Cream
- 1 teaspoon powdered sugar

1. Preheat oven to 350°.

2. Coat an 8-inch round cake pan with cooking spray. Line bottom of pan with a round of wax paper; coat wax paper and sides of pan with cooking spray.

3. Combine milk and butter in a small saucepan; place over medium heat 4 minutes until mixture almost comes to a simmer. Remove from heat, and set aside.

4. Beat egg whites in a large bowl until soft mounds form. Gradually add sugar, beating until stiff peaks form. Beat in egg yolks.

5. Combine flour and baking powder in a small bowl. Add half of flour mixture to egg mixture; beat briefly. Add hot milk mixture and vanilla to egg mixture; beat until thoroughly combined. Beat in remaining flour mixture and 3 tablespoons of hazelnuts. Batter will be thin. Pour into prepared pan, and sprinkle remaining 1 tablespoon hazelnuts over batter. Bake at 350° for 23 minutes until top springs back when lightly touched. Cool in pan on a wire rack 10 minutes. Run a knife around sides and unmold cake. Peel off wax paper, and place cake, right side up, on a rack. Let cool completely.

6. Split cake in half horizontally, using a serrated bread knife. Spread chilled Pastry Cream over bottom portion. Add top cake layer, and chill 1 hour. Remove from refrigerator 20 minutes before serving. Sift 1 teaspoon powdered sugar over top. **YIELD:** 8 servings (1 slice per serving).

POINTS: 5; **EXCHANGES:** 2½ Starch, 1½ Fat;
PER SERVING: CAL 227 (29% from fat);
PRO 5.5g; FAT 7.3g (sat 2.6g); CARB 34.8g;
FIB 0.4g; CHOL 91mg; IRON 1.5mg;
SOD 134mg; CALC 109mg

PASTRY CREAM

- ¼ cup sugar
- 2 tablespoons cornstarch
- 1 large egg
- 1 cup 1% low-fat milk
- 2 teaspoons butter or stick margarine
- 1 teaspoon vanilla extract
- ¼ teaspoon almond extract

1. Combine sugar and cornstarch in a small saucepan; stir well. Add egg; stir well with a whisk until smooth. Add milk, stirring until smooth.

2. Stir constantly over medium heat 8 minutes until mixture thickens and comes to a boil. Remove from heat, and stir in butter and flavorings. Spoon mixture into a bowl and chill. **YIELD:** about 1 cup.

CINNAMON-SWIRL ANGEL FOOD CAKE

A fragrant cinnamon swirl adds a delightful flavor to this classic cake.

- 1 cup sifted cake flour
- 1¼ cups sugar, divided
- 1 tablespoon sugar
- 1 tablespoon ground cinnamon
- 12 large egg whites
- 1 teaspoon cream of tartar
- ¼ teaspoon salt
- 1 teaspoon vanilla extract
- 1 teaspoon lemon juice

1. Preheat oven to 350°.
2. Sift together cake flour and ½ cup sugar; set aside. Sift together 1 tablespoon sugar and cinnamon; set aside. Beat egg whites until foamy. Add cream of tartar and salt; beat until soft peaks form. Add remaining sugar, 2 tablespoons at a time, beating until stiff peaks form. Sift flour mixture over egg white mixture, ¼ cup at a time, folding in flour mixture. Fold in vanilla and lemon juice.
3. Spoon one-third batter into an ungreased 10-inch tube pan. Run back of spoon around center of batter to indent. Sprinkle half of cinnamon mixture over batter. Repeat with remaining batter and cinnamon mixture, ending with batter.
4. Bake at 350° for 40 minutes or until cake springs back when lightly touched. Invert pan; cool 40 minutes. Loosen cake from sides of pan, using a narrow metal spatula; remove from pan. YIELD: 10 servings.

POINTS: 3; **EXCHANGES:** 2½ Starch;
PER SERVING: CAL 164 (0% from fat);
PRO 5.0g; FAT 0.1g (sat 0.0g); CARB 36.0g;
FIB 0.4g; CHOL 0mg; IRON 1.1mg;
SOD 122mg; CALC 13mg

LEMON-BUTTERMILK POUND CAKE

- Cooking spray
- 1 tablespoon all-purpose flour
- ¾ cup butter or stick margarine
- 2 cups sugar
- 4 large eggs
- ½ teaspoon baking soda
- 1 cup low-fat buttermilk
- 3 cups all-purpose flour
- ⅛ teaspoon salt
- 1 tablespoon plus 1 teaspoon grated lemon rind, divided
- ¼ cup plus 2 tablespoons fresh lemon juice, divided
- ¾ cup sifted powdered sugar

1. Preheat oven to 350°.
2. Coat a 10-inch tube pan with cooking spray. Dust with 1 tablespoon flour.
3. Beat butter at medium speed of a mixer until creamy. Gradually add sugar, beating well. Add eggs, one at a time, beating just until blended.
4. Combine baking soda and buttermilk; set aside.
5. Combine 3 cups flour, salt, and 1 tablespoon lemon rind; add to butter mixture alternately with buttermilk mixture, beginning and ending with flour mixture. Mix at low speed after each addition just until blended. Stir in ¼ cup lemon juice.
6. Pour batter into prepared pan. Bake at 350° for 1 hour or until a wooden pick inserted in center comes out clean. Let cool in pan 10 minutes; remove from pan, and place on a wire rack.
7. Poke holes in top of cake, using a wooden pick. Combine powdered sugar, 1 teaspoon lemon rind, and 2 tablespoons lemon juice. Beat at medium speed of a mixer until smooth. Drizzle glaze over warm cake. Let cool completely on a wire rack. YIELD: 18 servings (serving size: 1 slice).

POINTS: 6; **EXCHANGES:** 3 Starch, 2 Fat;
PER SERVING: CAL 276 (30% from fat);
PRO 4.2g; FAT 9.3g (sat 5.2g); CARB 44.7g;
FIB 0.6g; CHOL 70mg; IRON 1.2mg;
SOD 152mg; CALC 29mg

MEASURE RIGHT

Fat tenderizes a cake, and flour toughens it—so when we reduce fat in a recipe, it's important to measure the flour correctly for moist, tender cakes. Here's how to make sure you don't add more flour than you need.

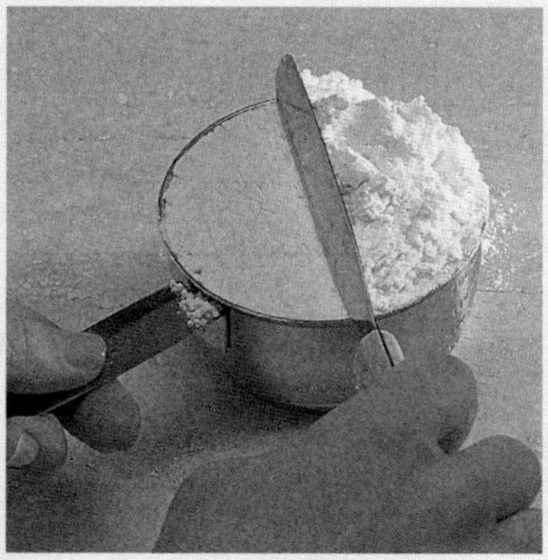

Stir the flour in the container to make sure it's not compact. Then lightly pile spoonfuls of flour into the correct size measuring cup. Don't pack it into the cup. Level the flour with a flat metal spatula.

LEMON DROP GINGERBREAD CUPCAKES

(pictured on page 42)

Line the muffin cups with paper liners; the cupcakes won't turn out well without them.

- 2½ cups all-purpose flour
- 1½ teaspoons baking soda
- 1¼ teaspoons ground ginger
- 1 teaspoon ground cinnamon
- ½ teaspoon salt
- ¼ teaspoon ground cloves
- ½ cup firmly packed brown sugar
- ⅓ cup butter or stick margarine, softened
- ¾ cup molasses
- 1 large egg, lightly beaten
- 1 cup very hot water
- 3 tablespoons frozen lemonade concentrate, thawed
- Lemonade Glaze

1. Preheat oven to 350°.

2. Combine first 6 ingredients in a medium bowl; stir well, and set aside. Beat brown sugar and butter in a large bowl at medium speed of a mixer until light and fluffy. Add molasses and egg, beating well. Add flour mixture to butter mixture alternately with very hot water, beginning and ending with flour mixture; beat well after each addition.

3. Place 18 paper muffin cup liners in muffin cups; divide batter evenly among cup liners. Bake at 350° for 20 minutes or until a wooden pick inserted in center of 1 cupcake comes out clean. Let cool in pans 10 minutes on a wire rack; remove cupcakes from pans, and place on wire rack. Poke several holes in the top of each warm cupcake with a wooden pick; brush lemonade concentrate evenly over cupcakes. Let cool completely.

4. Spoon about 1 teaspoon Lemonade Glaze on each cupcake, and spread gently. Let stand until glaze sets. **YIELD:** 18 servings (serving size: 1 cupcake).

POINTS: 4; **EXCHANGES:** 2½ Starch, 1 Fat; **PER SERVING:** CAL 187 (19% from fat); PRO 2g; FAT 4g (sat 2.2g); CARB 37g; FIB 0.5g; CHOL 21mg; IRON 1.7mg; SOD 180mg; CALC 40mg

LEMONADE GLAZE:

- 1 cup sifted powdered sugar
- 2 tablespoons frozen lemonade concentrate, thawed

1. Combine sugar and lemonade in a bowl; stir until smooth. **YIELD:** about 6 tablespoons.

BLACKBERRY-APPLE COBBLER

- 4 cups fresh blackberries
- 1¼ cups peeled and thinly sliced Rome apple (about 1 medium)
- 1 cup sugar
- 2 tablespoons all-purpose flour
- 1 tablespoon grated lemon rind
- ¼ teaspoon vanilla extract
- ¾ cup all-purpose flour
- 2 tablespoons sugar
- ½ teaspoon baking powder
- ¼ teaspoon salt
- 3 tablespoons chilled butter or stick margarine
- 1 large egg white, beaten
- 3 teaspoons ice water
- Cooking spray
- 2 tablespoons butter or stick margarine
- 1½ teaspoons sugar
- ¼ teaspoon ground cinnamon

1. Preheat oven to 375°.

2. Combine blackberries and apple. Combine 1 cup sugar, 2 tablespoons flour, and lemon rind; toss with fruit. Stir in vanilla; set aside.

3. Combine ¾ cup flour, 2 tablespoons sugar, baking powder, and salt in a large bowl. Cut in 3 tablespoons cold butter with a pastry blender or 2 knives until mixture resembles coarse meal. Add egg white; sprinkle ice water, 1 teaspoon at a time, over surface until mixture forms a loose ball. (Dough will be slightly crumbly.) Place mixture on heavy-duty plastic wrap; pat dough 3 or 4 times to form a disc. Cover with additional plastic wrap. Roll dough, still covered, into an 8-inch square. Chill 10 minutes.

4. Toss fruit mixture gently; spoon into an 8-inch square pan coated with cooking spray. Dot with 2 tablespoons butter.

5. Remove 1 sheet of plastic wrap from dough; invert dough over fruit mixture in pan. Remove top sheet of plastic wrap.

6. Combine 1½ teaspoons sugar and cinnamon; sprinkle over crust. Bake at 375° for 35 minutes or until crust is browned. Let stand 15 minutes before serving. **YIELD:** 8 servings (serving size: ⅛ of cobbler).

POINTS: 5; **EXCHANGES:** 2½ Starch, 1 Fruit, 1½ Fat; **PER SERVING:** CAL 277 (25% from fat); PRO 2.5g; FAT 7.8g (sat 4.5g); CARB 51.4g; FIB 4.5g; CHOL 19mg; IRON 1.1mg; SOD 184mg; CALC 47mg

CHERRY CLAFOUTI

Cooking spray
1 tablespoon all-purpose flour
1 (16-ounce) package pitted tart cherries, thawed and drained or 1 (16-ounce) can pitted dark sweet cherries in heavy syrup, drained
1 teaspoon cornstarch
2 teaspoons vanilla extract, divided
½ teaspoon almond extract
2 large eggs
2 large egg whites
½ cup sugar
⅓ cup all-purpose flour
¾ cup plain fat-free yogurt
¾ cup 1% low-fat milk
2 tablespoons sifted powder sugar

1. Preheat oven to 325°.
2. Coat an 8-inch square baking dish with cooking spray; dust with 1 tablespoon flour, tapping out excess. Set aside.
3. Blot cherries dry on paper towels. Combine cherries, cornstarch, 1 teaspoon vanilla, and almond extract in a small bowl; toss gently. Set aside.
4. Combine eggs, egg whites, and sugar in medium bowl, stirring with a whisk. Add ⅓ cup flour, yogurt, milk, and remaining teaspoon vanilla; stir with a wire whisk until smooth. Pour egg mixture slowly over cherries; do not stir. Bake at 325° for 50 minutes or until set and lightly browned. Sprinkle with sifted powdered sugar. Serve warm. **YIELD:** 6 servings (serving size: 1 cup).

POINTS: 4; **EXCHANGES:** 2 Starch, ½ Fruit, ½ Fat;
PER SERVING: CAL 191 (11% from fat);
PRO 7.4g; FAT 2.3g (sat 0.8g); CARB 34.4g;
FIB 0.9g; CHOL 75mg; IRON 0.8mg;
SOD 85mg; CALC 105mg

INDIVIDUAL LIME TARTS

(pictured on cover)

Don't worry about the color of the lime mixture when you first prepare the filling for these tarts. The mixture is almost clear when you first remove it from the cooktop; then the refreshing lime color develops as the tarts chill.

Cooking spray
1½ cups graham cracker crumbs
3 tablespoons sugar
3 tablespoons butter or stick margarine, melted
1 teaspoon vanilla extract
1 egg white, lightly beaten
⅔ cup sugar
¼ cup cornstarch
⅓ cup fresh lime or key lime juice
2 large egg yolks, lightly beaten
1½ cups cold water
2 teaspoons grated lime or key lime rind
6 tablespoons reduced-fat frozen whipped topping, thawed, optional
Lime slices, optional

1. Preheat oven to 350°.
2. Coat six 4½-inch individual tart pans with removable bottoms with cooking spray. Set aside.
3. Combine cracker crumbs and 3 tablespoons sugar in a medium bowl; stir well. Gradually add butter, stirring well. Stir in vanilla and egg white, stirring until well combined. Divide mixture evenly among tart pans; press mixture into bottom and up sides of pans. Place pans on a baking sheet. Bake at 350° for 13 minutes. Let cool completely on a wire rack.
4. Combine ⅔ cup sugar and cornstarch in a medium saucepan; stir well. Add lime juice and egg yolks, stirring with a whisk. Gradually add water, stirring well. Cook over medium heat, stirring constantly, 6 minutes or until mixture thickens. Remove from heat; stir in lime rind. Carefully pour into prepared crusts; let cool completely. Cover; chill at least 3 hours. Top each tart with 1 tablespoon whipped topping, and garnish with lime slices, if desired. **YIELD:** 6 servings (serving size: 1 tart).

VARIATION:
LIME TART

(pictured on page 43)

Prepare crust as directed for Individual Lime Tarts, using a 9-inch tart pan with removable bottom. Bake at 350° for 15 minutes. Proceed with tart filling as directed. **YIELD:** 6 servings (serving size: 1 slice tart).

POINTS: 7; **EXCHANGES:** 3½ Starch, 2 Fat;
PER SERVING: CAL 317 (29% from fat);
PRO 3.1g; FAT 10.1g (sat 4.7g); CARB 53.7g;
FIB 0.7g; CHOL 88mg; IRON 1.2mg;
SOD 229mg; CALC 21mg

LIME LINGO

To make a Key Lime Tart, start with fresh Key limes. (The two main varieties of limes are Persian and Key) Key limes are smaller and rounder than the Persian and are more yellow than green. They can be found in specialty markets and some larger grocery stores.

Face the Music

REUBEN JACKSON • **HEIGHT** 5'10" • **BEFORE** 265 LBS. • **AFTER** 167 LBS.

Tip: "At a social gathering where a meal is offered, I focus on why I'm there—to enjoy other people and draw comfort from the companionship."

Reuben Jackson is all smiles today. Not long ago, at age 39, he weighed 265 pounds. The next year, he suffered heart palpitations and learned his blood pressure was "sky high." A doctor told him to lose weight.

Reuben had struggled with pounds since junior high. "Like everyone at that age, I wondered, 'Where do I fit in?'" he recalls. "So I turned to food for comfort." Where he grew up, food was part of the social fabric—fellowship meant fried chicken, mashed potatoes, gravy, and the like. Reuben's attempts at dieting never worked, and he steadily gained weight in his twenties and thirties.

Soon after the doctor's warning, a friend asked Reuben to a Weight Watchers meeting. He felt awkward at first. "I didn't want to admit I had a problem," he explains. "Men are reluctant to say we need help or to talk about problems. We shouldn't be that way." Soon Reuben's discomfort turned to gratitude. "It was comforting to be with people who knew what my struggle was about," he says. That comfort led him to learn more about what he ate, and he became a vegetarian.

Today, when Reuben fills his plate, he turns on his imagination instead of his appetite. "I mentally draw a border on the plate. This imaginary line is a big help when it comes to portion control," he explains. "When I arrange my vegetables, I think of Miles Davis, the great jazz musician. Miles knew he needed a little electric piano, percussion, bass, and drum, but never too much of any one thing. I do the same with food."

"I turn to exercise, not food, for a release from stress."

Musical metaphors come easily to Reuben, who is an archivist in the National Museum of American History, where he handles collections of jazz greats such as Duke Ellington. Now, other things come easily, too, such as walking to work, and weight training. "I turn to exercise, not food, for a release from stress," says Reuben. "I go to a gym and work with a trainer twice a week. I like having a personal relationship with someone who is concerned about my weight and my health."

Since he improved his eating habits and started exercising, Reuben has had a positive change in his outlook. "I was 40 years old, and felt like the losing football team at halftime," he says. "Then I realized that the game may be half over, but I still have time to win."

Lemon Drop Gingerbread Cupcakes, page 39

Banana Split Pie, page 30

Lime Tart,
page 40

Turkish Rice
Pudding, page 50

Peanut Butter-Chocolate Cheesecake Squares, page 54

Chocolate Cake With Mocha Glaze, page 36

Crispy Peanut
Butterscotch Pie,
page 31

Strawberries 'n'
Cream Pie, page 30

Bread Pudding With Whiskey Sauce, page 50

In Balance

MICHELE KOSS • **HEIGHT** 5'4" • **BEFORE** 161 LBS. • **AFTER** 118 LBS.

Best Moment: Wearing a bikini again.

After two children, Michele Koss faced the dilemma that many new mothers face: balancing work, family, and taking care of herself—particularly regaining the shape she had before she became pregnant. Michele never lost the weight she gained with her first child, and gained even more with her second. Her weight fluctuated from 122 pounds to 200 and back down to 160, but even that was too much for her 5'4" frame. "I didn't realize how bad it was until I wore a size 14 instead of a 4," she says.

Michele knew what she was looking for in a weight-loss program. In fact, she didn't want a "program"—no prepackaged foods or supplements. She wanted to change her lifestyle. And she realized she had the opportunity to start good habits while undoing bad ones. "I wanted to teach my kids that it's better to have graham crackers and milk as a snack instead of a candy bar and soda."

"I like that my children are with me when I exercise."

When Michele joined Weight Watchers, in effect so did her family. She and her children went shopping for groceries, and her husband motivated her by posting bathing suit photos on the refrigerator. The rules Michele followed to get back in bikini shape were well defined, but not rigid. Balancing work and family, as all working mothers know, sometimes means eating "easier" meals. "My kids know that Mommy still goes to McDonald's or eats pizza," says Michele. "And that's okay to do once in awhile."

Like shopping, exercise also became a family activity. A pediatric nurse, Michele works long shifts, which means she's away from her family, so she was reluctant to spend more time at the gym. Instead, she walks her sons around the neighborhood in a double stroller. "The fresh air is as good for them as it is for me," she says. In a show of support, her husband bought her a bicycle, and his parents bought two kid's seats for the back of the bike. "I like that my children are with me when I exercise," she says.

Michele is not just a role model for her children. Inspired by Michele's success, several coworkers joined Weight Watchers. Now, instead of snacking on doughnuts, they have fruit.

While Michele worked toward her goal, she kept an eye on upcoming events. "From parties to christenings, I always wanted to look nice in that special dress," she says. As she reached for extra food, especially cake—her weakness—Michele reminded herself of the next special occasion. "At my baby shower three years ago, I ate about the entire cake." But now, she says, turning down sweets—or reaching for a more healthful alternative—gets easier each time. "I think of the incentives," she explains.

That kind of thinking is also helping Michele maintain her weight now that she's reached her goal. "I set a goal and I reached it," she says. "It's a choice. And I'm sticking to it, especially for my kids."

BROWN SUGAR PUDDING

⅔ cup firmly packed dark brown sugar
½ cup all-purpose flour
⅛ teaspoon salt
1 (12-ounce) can fat-free evaporated milk
1½ cups 1% low-fat milk
1 large egg yolk
2 tablespoons butter or stick margarine
1 teaspoon vanilla extract

1. Combine first 3 ingredients in a saucepan; stir with a wire whisk. Gradually add milks and egg yolk, stirring until blended.
2. Place over medium heat; cook, stirring constantly with a wooden spoon, 20 minutes or until thickened and mixture coats back of a spoon (do not boil). Remove from heat.
3. Add butter and vanilla, stirring until butter melts. Pour pudding evenly into 6 individual serving dishes. Cover surface of pudding with plastic wrap; chill. **YIELD:** 6 servings (serving size: ½ cup).

POINTS: 5; **EXCHANGES:** 2 Starch, 1 Low-Fat Milk;
PER SERVING: CAL 246 (% from fat);
PRO 8.0g; FAT 5.6g (sat 3.1g); CARB 41.2g;
FIB 0.3g; CHOL 51mg; IRON 1.2mg;
SOD 195mg; CALC 272mg

CARAMEL-BANANA CREAM PUDDING CUPS

1 (14-ounce) can fat-free sweetened condensed milk
1 cup graham cracker crumbs
1 tablespoon sugar
2 teaspoons all-purpose flour
3 tablespoons light butter, melted
Cooking spray
2¼ cups thinly sliced bananas (about 3 medium)
⅓ cup sugar
1½ tablespoons cornstarch
⅛ teaspoon salt
1 cup 1% low-fat milk
1 large egg yolk, lightly beaten
1 teaspoon light stick butter
½ teaspoon vanilla extract
2¼ cups frozen fat-free whipped topping, thawed

1. Preheat oven to 425°.
2. Pour condensed milk into an 11- x 7-inch baking dish. Cover with foil. Place covered dish in a 13- x 9-inch baking dish; add hot water to dish to a depth of 1 inch.
3. Bake at 425° for 45 to 55 minutes or until milk is caramel colored and about the consistency of unbeaten egg white (add hot water to 13-x 9-inch dish as needed). Remove 11-x 7-inch dish from hot water bath. Remove foil; set aside. Reduce oven temperature to 350°.
4. Combine graham cracker crumbs, 1 tablespoon sugar, flour, and 3 tablespoons melted butter; stir well. Divide graham cracker mixture evenly between 9 (6-ounce) custard cups coated with cooking spray; press crumb mixture firmly into bottoms of cups. Place custard cups on a baking sheet; bake at 350° for 8 to 10 minutes or until lightly browned. Set aside; let cool.
5. Layer banana slices evenly over graham cracker crust in custard cups. Spoon reserved caramel evenly over banana in each cup; set aside.
6. Combine ⅓ cup sugar, cornstarch, and salt in a medium saucepan; stir in milk. Bring to a boil over medium heat, stirring constantly. Cook, stirring constantly, 30 seconds or until thickened. Gradually add a small amount of hot milk mixture to egg yolk, stirring constantly with a whisk. Return egg mixture to pan; cook over medium-low heat, stirring constantly, 1 minute or until thick. Remove from heat; stir in 1 teaspoon butter and vanilla. Pour custard mixture evenly over caramel layer. Cover; chill 3 hours. Top each serving with ¼ cup whipped topping. **YIELD:** 9 servings.

POINTS: 6; **EXCHANGES:** 3½ Starch, ½ Fruit, 1 Fat;
PER SERVING: CAL 311 (13% from fat);
PRO 5.6g; FAT 4.6g (sat 2.2g); CARB 60.7g;
FIB 1.1g; CHOL 40mg; IRON 0.6mg;
SOD 199mg; CALC 154mg

TURKISH RICE PUDDING

(pictured on page 44)

1¼ cups water
3 tablespoons light stick butter
1 (3-inch) cinnamon stick
1 cup uncooked long-grain rice
3 cups fat-free milk, divided
⅔ cup sugar
¼ cup nonfat dry milk
1 teaspoon vanilla extract
4 teaspoons cinnamon-sugar
8 teaspoons chopped almonds
8 whole almonds (optional)
Cinnamon sticks (optional)

1. Bring first 3 ingredients to a boil in a medium saucepan. Stir in rice; cover, reduce heat to medium-low, and simmer 10 minutes or until liquid is absorbed.
2. Stir in 1 cup milk and sugar; cook, uncovered, 10 minutes or until liquid is nearly absorbed, stirring frequently. Add 1 cup milk and dry milk; cook, uncovered, 10 minutes or until liquid is nearly absorbed, stirring frequently. Add ½ cup milk; cook, uncovered, 15 minutes or until liquid is nearly absorbed, stirring constantly. Add remaining milk; cook until rice is tender and mixture is thick and creamy. Remove from heat; stir in vanilla.
3. Serve warm or chilled topped with cinnamon-sugar and chopped almonds. If desired, garnish with whole almonds and cinnamon sticks. **YIELD:** 8 servings (serving size: ½ cup pudding, ½ teaspoon cinnamon-sugar, and 1 teaspoon chopped almonds).

POINTS: 5; **EXCHANGES:** 2½ Starch, ½ Skim Milk, 1 Fat; **PER SERVING:** CAL 239 (21% from fat); PRO 6.9g; FAT 5.5g (sat 1.8g); CARB 44.3g; FIB 0.6g; CHOL 10mg; IRON 1.2mg; SOD 96mg; CALC 174mg

RICE PUDDING WITH DRIED CHERRIES AND CURRANTS

Cooking spray
1⅓ cups fat-free milk
⅛ teaspoon salt
½ cup firmly packed brown sugar
1 tablespoon butter or stick margarine, melted
1 teaspoon vanilla extract
1 teaspoon grated lemon rind
2 teaspoons thawed orange juice concentrate
2 large egg whites
2 cups cooked medium-grain rice
½ cup dried tart cherries
¼ cup currants

1. Preheat oven to 325°.
2. Coat a 1½-quart baking dish with cooking spray; set aside.
3. Combine milk and next 7 ingredients in a bowl; stir well with a whisk. Add rice, and stir well. Add cherries and currants; pour mixture into baking dish.
4. Place baking dish into a 13- x 9-inch baking pan. Pour hot water into baking pan to a depth of 1 inch. Bake at 325° for 55 to 57 minutes or until a knife inserted in center comes out clean. **YIELD:** 6 servings.

POINTS: 5; **EXCHANGES:** 2½ Starch, 1 Fruit, ½ Fat; **PER SERVING:** CAL 270 (9% from fat); PRO 5.4g; FAT 2.6g (sat 1.3g); CARB 56.0g; FIB 1.0g; CHOL 6mg; IRON 1.8mg; SOD 123mg; CALC 96mg

BREAD PUDDING WITH WHISKEY SAUCE

(pictured on page 47)

3 cups whole milk
½ cup raisins
½ cup fat-free sweetened condensed milk
¼ cup sugar
1 tablespoon vanilla extract
1 teaspoon ground cinnamon
3 large eggs, lightly beaten
2 tablespoons butter or stick margarine, melted
9 (1-ounce) slices French bread, cut into ¾-inch cubes
Cooking spray
Whiskey Sauce

1. Preheat oven to 350°.
2. Combine first 8 ingredients in a large bowl; stir well. Add bread cubes; toss gently. Let stand 30 minutes.
3. Spoon mixture into a 13- x 9-inch baking dish coated with cooking spray. Bake at 350° for 50 minutes or until pudding is set. Serve warm with Whiskey Sauce. **YIELD:** 12 servings (serving size: 1⁄12 of pudding and 2 tablespoons sauce).

WHISKEY SAUCE

1 cup whole milk
1 tablespoon butter
⅓ cup sugar
1 large egg, lightly beaten
¼ cup bourbon
2 tablespoons water
2 teaspoons cornstarch
⅛ teaspoon ground nutmeg
Additional nutmeg, optional

1. Combine first 3 ingredients in a saucepan; stir well. Cook over medium low heat 5 minutes, stirring often.

2. Gradually add half of milk mixture to egg, stirring constantly with a whisk. Return mixture to pan. Cook over medium-low heat 5 minutes or until slightly thick, stirring constantly. Remove from heat, and add bourbon.
3. Combine water and cornstarch; stir well. Add to milk mixture; bring almost to a boil; cook 1 minute. Stir in nutmeg. Serve warm with bread pudding. Sprinkle with additional nutmeg, if desired. **YIELD:** 1¾ cups (serving size: about 2 tablespoons).

POINTS: 6; **EXCHANGES:** 2½ Starch, 1½ Fat;
PER SERVING: CAL 256 (27% from fat);
PRO 8.3g; FAT 7.8g (sat 4.0g); CARB 38.5g;
FIB 0.7g; CHOL 95mg; IRON 1.2mg;
SOD 226mg; CALC 175mg

HONEY CUSTARD CUPS

Don't test this custard for doneness with a knife; the mixture will stick. The custard will jiggle slightly when removed from the oven and will set as it chills.

- 1 large egg
- 1 large egg white
- ¼ cup honey
- 2 teaspoons vanilla extract
- 1 cup 2% reduced-fat milk
- ½ cup low-fat evaporated milk

1. Preheat oven to 325°.
2. Combine first 4 ingredients in a medium bowl; stir well with a whisk.
3. Heat milks over medium heat in a small heavy saucepan to 180° or until tiny bubbles form around edge (do not boil). Gradually add hot milk to honey mixture, stirring constantly with a whisk.
4. Pour ½ cup custard mixture into each of 4 (6-ounce) custard cups. Place cups in an 8-inch square baking dish; add hot water to baking dish to a depth of 1 inch. Bake at 325° for 50 minutes or until almost set. Remove cups from baking dish; let cool completely on a wire rack. Cover and chill thoroughly. **YIELD:** 4 servings (serving size: ½ cup).

POINTS: 3; **EXCHANGES:** 1 Starch, ½ Low-Fat Milk;
PER SERVING: CAL 149 (18% from fat);
PRO 6.5g; FAT 3g (sat 1.1g); CARB 23.7g;
FIB 0g; CHOL 65mg; IRON 0.4mg;
SOD 91mg; CALC 155mg

LOW-FAT FLAN

- ⅔ cup sugar
- 1 (14-ounce) can fat-free sweetened condensed milk
- 1¼ cups 1% low-fat milk
- 1 cup fat-free egg substitute
- 1¼ teaspoons vanilla extract
- ⅛ teaspoon salt

1. Preheat oven to 325°.
2. Place sugar in a medium heavy skillet over medium-high heat; cook until sugar dissolves, stirring constantly. Cook 5 minutes or until golden, stirring constantly. Immediately pour into a 9-inch round cake pan, tipping quickly until caramelized sugar coats bottom of cake pan.
3. Combine sweetened condensed milk and remaining 4 ingredients, stirring until smooth. Pour milk mixture over syrup in cake pan.
4. Place cake pan in a large shallow baking pan; add hot water to a depth of 1 inch. Bake at 325° for 35 to 40 minutes or until almost set. Remove cake pan from water, and let cool completely on a wire rack. Cover and chill at least 3 hours. Loosen edges of custard with a knife. Place a plate, upside down, on top of pan; invert flan onto plate. Drizzle any remaining caramelized syrup over custard. **YIELD:** 8 servings.

POINTS: 5; **EXCHANGES:** 2½ Starch, 1 Skim Milk;
PER SERVING: CAL 237 (2% from fat);
PRO 8g; FAT 0.4g (sat 0.2g); CARB 49.6g;
FIB 0g; CHOL 8mg; IRON 0.6mg;
SOD 150mg; CALC 183mg

PUMPKIN CRÈME BRÛLÉE

- Cooking spray
- ½ cup sugar
- 1½ cups unsweetened canned pumpkin
- 1½ cups 2% reduced-fat milk
- ½ teaspoon pumpkin pie spice
- ½ teaspoon maple extract
- ½ teaspoon vanilla extract
- ⅛ teaspoon salt
- 4 large eggs, lightly beaten
- ¼ cup firmly packed brown sugar

1. Preheat oven to 350°.
2. Coat 8 ramekins with cooking spray; place on a baking sheet.
3. Combine sugar and next 7 ingredients; stir well with a whisk. Divide evenly among ramekins. Bake at 350° for 35 minutes or until almost set. Remove from baking sheet; let cool 30 minutes on a wire rack. Cover and chill at least 4 hours.
4. Uncover; press brown sugar through a wire sieve onto each custard. Place ramekins on baking sheet; broil 3 to 4 minutes or until sugar melts. Serve immediately. **YIELD:** 8 servings (serving size: 1 custard).

POINTS: 3; **EXCHANGES:** 1½ Starch, ½ Fat;
PER SERVING: CAL 154 (22% from fat);
PRO 5.2g; FAT 3.8g (sat 1.5g); CARB 25.1g;
FIB 1.9g; CHOL 114mg; IRON 1.2mg;
SOD 97mg; CALC 86mg

RUM AND COCONUT CRÈME BRÛLÉE

(pictured on page 1)

1 (12-ounce) package soft silken-style tofu (such as Mori-Nu), drained
½ cup coconut milk
½ cup maple syrup
2 tablespoons cornstarch
2 tablespoons rum
2 teaspoons coconut extract
⅛ teaspoon salt
1 tablespoon sugar
1 tablespoon brown sugar
4 teaspoons flaked sweetened coconut

1. Preheat oven to 325°.
2. Place first 7 ingredients in a food processor; process until smooth, scraping sides of processor bowl occasionally.
3. Spoon mixture evenly into 4 (4-ounce) ramekins or custard cups. Place ramekins in an 8-inch square baking dish; add hot water to baking dish to a depth of 1 inch. Cover and bake at 325° for 40 minutes or until a knife inserted near center comes out clean. Remove cups from baking dish; let cool on a wire rack. Cover and chill at least 2 hours.
4. Combine sugar, brown sugar, and coconut; sprinkle evenly over each serving. Place ramekins on a baking sheet; broil 2 minutes or until sugars melt and coconut is lightly browned. **YIELD:** 4 servings.

POINTS: 6; **EXCHANGES:** 3 Starch, 1 Fat;
PER SERVING: CAL 267 (30% from fat);
PRO 5g; FAT 9g (sat 6g); CARB 43g;
FIB 0.2g; CHOL 0mg; IRON 2.3mg;
SOD 88mg; CALC 54mg

CARAMEL APPLE CHEWS

Satisfy crispy cookie lovers with this tip: Roll tablespoonfuls of dough in ⅓ cup low-fat cinnamon graham cracker crumbs (about 1½ cracker sheets), and bake at 350° for 16 minutes.

1 (18.25-ounce) package caramel cake mix (such as Duncan Hines)
½ (8-ounce) container frozen reduced-calorie whipped topping, thawed (about 1½ cups)
1½ cups peeled diced Golden Delicious apple (about 8 ounces)
1 large egg, lightly beaten
Cooking spray

1. Combine first 4 ingredients in a large bowl; beat at medium speed of a heavy-duty stand mixer just until moistened. Chill batter 30 minutes, if necessary.
2. Drop by level tablespoons onto cookie sheets coated with cooking spray. Bake at 350° for 16 minutes or just until tops of cookies spring back when touched. (Do not over-bake.) Remove cookies from pan; let cool on wire racks. **YIELD:** 2½ dozen (serving size: 1 cookie).

POINTS: 2; **EXCHANGES:** 1 Starch, ½ Fat;
PER SERVING: CAL 87 (24% from fat);
PRO 1.1g; FAT 2.3g (sat 0.7g); CARB 16.4g;
FIB 0.1g; CHOL 7.4mg; IRON 0.5mg;
SOD 113mg; CALC 36mg

BRANDIED FRUITCAKE COOKIES

4 ounces red candied cherries, chopped
4 ounces green candied cherries, chopped
4 ounces candied pineapple, chopped
½ cup raisins
1½ cups all-purpose flour, divided
¼ teaspoon baking soda
1½ teaspoons apple pie spice
½ cup butter or stick margarine, softened
½ cup firmly packed brown sugar
1 large egg
2 teaspoons vanilla extract
⅓ cup brandy
Cooking spray

1. Preheat oven to 325°.
2. Combine first 4 ingredients in a bowl; toss with ½ cup flour.
3. Combine remaining 1 cup flour, baking soda, and apple pie spice.
4. Beat butter at medium speed of a mixer until creamy; gradually add sugar, beating well. Add egg, mixing well. Stir in vanilla and brandy. Add flour mixture, mixing just until blended; stir in fruit mixture.
5. Drop level tablespoonfuls onto baking sheets coated with cooking spray. Flatten cookies slightly with back of a spoon. Bake at 325° for 12 to 14 minutes or until golden. Remove from oven; let stand 2 to 3 minutes or until firm. Remove cookies from pan; let cool on wire racks. **YIELD:** 3 dozen (serving size: 1 cookie).

POINTS: 2; **EXCHANGES:** 1 Starch, ½ Fat;
PER SERVING: CAL 95 (27% from fat);
PRO 1.0g; FAT 2.8g (sat 1.7g); CARB 16.8g;
FIB 0.3g; CHOL 13mg; IRON 0.4mg;
SOD 49mg; CALC 11mg

ORANGE-POPPY SEED BISCOTTI

⅓ cup butter or stick margarine
⅔ cup sugar
1 large egg
1 tablespoon thawed orange juice concentrate
2 cups all-purpose flour, divided
2 tablespoons yellow cornmeal
1 teaspoon baking powder
½ teaspoon baking soda
3 tablespoons orange zest
1 tablespoon poppy seeds
Cooking spray

1. Preheat oven to 350°.
2. Beat butter; gradually add sugar, beating at medium speed of a mixer until well blended. Add egg and orange juice concentrate, beating until well blended.
3. Combine flour and next 5 ingredients; gradually add to butter mixture, beating until blended. Turn dough out onto a lightly floured surface, and knead lightly 2 to 3 times. Divide dough in half; shape dough into 15-inch-long rolls. Place on a baking sheet coated with cooking spray; flatten to 1¼-inch thickness. Bake at 350° for 21 minutes or until lightly browned. Remove rolls from baking sheet; let cool slightly on a wire rack.
4. Cut rolls diagonally into (½-inch) slices, using a serrated knife. Place slices, cut side down, on baking sheet. Bake at 350° for 6 minutes on each side or just until lightly browned. **YIELD:** 5 dozen (serving size: 1 piece).

POINTS: 1; **EXCHANGES:** ½ Starch;
PER SERVING: CAL 37 (29% from fat); PRO 0.7g; FAT 1.2g (sat 0.7g); CARB 5.9g; FIB 0.2g; CHOL 6mg; IRON 0.2mg; SOD 31mg; CALC 9mg

DATE SWIRL COOKIES

1 (8-ounce) package chopped dates
⅓ cup water
⅓ cup butter or stick margarine
¾ cup firmly packed brown sugar
¼ cup apricot-flavored baby food
1 large egg
2 cups all-purpose flour
1 teaspoon baking powder
¾ teaspoon pumpkin pie spice
¼ teaspoon salt
Date Filling
Cooking spray

1. Combine dates and water in a medium saucepan. Cook over medium heat, stirring constantly, 5 minutes or until thickened. Remove from heat, and cool.
2. Beat butter at medium speed of a mixer until light and fluffy; add sugar, and beat well. Add baby food and egg; beat well.
3. Combine flour and next 3 ingredients; gradually add to butter mixture. Shape dough into a ball. Place dough on a lightly floured surface, and roll into an 18- x 8-inch rectangle. Spread Date Filling over dough, leaving a ½-inch margin on sides. Beginning at 1 long edge, roll up dough tightly, jelly-roll fashion; pinch seam to seal. Cut roll in half, and wrap rolls in wax paper; freeze 3 hours or chill 8 hours.
4. Preheat oven to 350°.
5. Unwrap rolls; cut each roll into 30 (⅜-inch) slices. Place slices on baking sheets coated with cooking spray. Bake at 350° for 13 minutes or just until lightly browned. **YIELD:** 5 dozen (serving size: 1 cookie).

POINTS: 1; **EXCHANGES:** ½ Starch;
PER SERVING: CAL 47 (23% from fat); PRO 0.6g; FAT 1.2g (sat 0.7g); CARB 8.8g; FIB 0.4g; CHOL 6mg; IRON 0.3mg; SOD 31mg; CALC 10mg

BASIC BISCOTTI STEPS

Biscotti are Italian biscuits. Double-baking these cookies draws off moisture and gives them a hard, crisp texture. Try dipping them in coffee or tea.

1. Turn the dough out onto a lightly floured surface, and knead lightly 2 to 3 times.

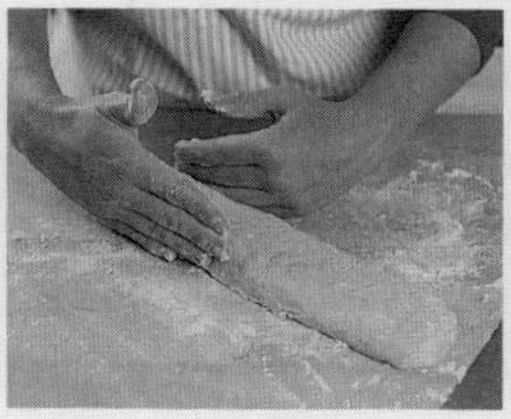

2. Shape dough into a 15-inch-long roll; place on a baking sheet, and flatten to 1¼-inch thickness. Bake 21 minutes. Remove from oven; let cool slightly on wire rack.

3. Slice the roll diagonally into ½-inch slices. Place on a baking sheet, and bake 6 minutes on each side or until lightly browned.

FUDGY PEANUT BUTTER TARTS

- ¾ cup all-purpose flour
- ⅓ cup sugar
- 3 tablespoons unsweetened cocoa
- ¼ cup chilled reduced-calorie stick margarine, cut into small pieces
- 3 teaspoons ice water
- ¼ cup reduced-fat semisweet chocolate chips
- ¼ cup peanut butter chips
- 1 tablespoon reduced-calorie stick margarine
- ⅓ cup sugar
- 1 tablespoon fat-free milk
- ¼ cup fat-free egg substitute
- ¾ teaspoon vanilla extract

1. Preheat oven to 350°.
2. Combine first 3 ingredients in a bowl; stir well. Cut in ¼ cup margarine with a pastry blender or 2 knives until mixture resembles coarse meal. Sprinkle ice water, 1 teaspoon at a time, over surface; toss with a fork until moist. Gently press dough into a ball. Divide dough into 20 equal portions, and press each portion into (1¾ inch) miniature muffin cups; set aside.
3. Place chocolate chips, peanut butter chips, and 1 tablespoon margarine in a small saucepan over low heat until mixture melts, stirring frequently. Remove from heat; add ⅓ cup sugar and milk, stirring with a whisk until well blended. Add egg substitute and vanilla; stir well.
4. Spoon about 2 teaspoons chocolate mixture into each prepared tart shell. Bake at 350° for 20 minutes. Let cool in pans 15 minutes on a wire rack. Loosen tarts from sides of pans, using a knife or narrow metal spatula. Remove from pans; let cool completely on wire racks. **YIELD:** 20 tarts (serving size: 1 tart).

POINTS: 2; **EXCHANGES:** 1 Starch, ½ Fat;
PER SERVING: CAL 90 (32% from fat); PRO 1.6g; FAT 3.2g (sat 1.3g); CARB 14g; FIB 0.1g; CHOL 0mg; IRON 0.4mg; SOD 40mg; CALC 7mg

PEANUT BUTTER-CHOCOLATE CHEESECAKE SQUARES

(pictured on page 45)

- ⅓ cup all-purpose flour
- 2 tablespoons brown sugar
- 2 tablespoons chilled light stick butter
- Cooking spray
- ½ cup fat-free hot fudge topping
- 1 (8-ounce) block-style fat-free cream cheese
- ½ cup sugar
- 1 large egg
- ½ cup reduced-fat creamy peanut butter
- 1 tablespoon fat-free milk
- 1 teaspoon vanilla extract

1. Preheat oven to 350°.
2. Combine flour and brown sugar; stir well. Cut in small pieces of butter with a pastry blender or 2 knives until mixture resembles coarse meal. Press mixture firmly into bottom of an 8-inch square pan coated with cooking spray. Bake at 350° for 8 minutes. Remove from oven.
3. Place fudge topping in a small microwave-safe bowl. Microwave at HIGH 1 minute or until thoroughly heated, stirring after 30 seconds.
4. Beat cream cheese at medium speed of a mixer until smooth. Gradually add sugar, beating well. Add egg and next 3 ingredients, beating well. Pour batter over prepared crust. Drizzle fudge topping over batter. Using the tip of a knife, swirl fudge into batter. Bake at 350° for 20 minutes or until set. Let cool completely in pan on wire rack. **YIELD:** 16 servings.

POINTS: 3; **EXCHANGES:** 1½ Starch, 1 Fat;
PER SERVING: CAL 135 (27% from fat); PRO 5.0g; FAT 4.1g (sat 1.2g); CARB 19.4g; FIB 0.8g; CHOL 19mg; IRON 0.4mg; SOD 195mg; CALC 49mg

CHEESECAKE BROWNIES

- 1 (1 lb., 4.5-ounce) package low-fat fudge brownie mix (such as Betty Crocker Sweet Rewards)
- Cooking spray
- ⅔ cup tub light cream cheese, softened (6 ounces)
- 3 tablespoons fat-free sour cream
- 2 teaspoons all-purpose flour
- 2 teaspoons vanilla extract

1. Preheat oven to 350°.
2. Prepare brownie mix according to package directions; spread into a 13- x 9-inch baking pan coated with cooking spray.
3. Combine cream cheese and remaining 3 ingredients, stirring until smooth. Dollop cream cheese mixture over brownie batter. Swirl batters together, using tip of a knife.
4. Bake at 350° for 30 minutes or until a wooden pick inserted 2 inches from center comes out clean. Let cool in pan on a wire rack. **YIELD:** 24 servings.

POINTS: 2; **EXCHANGES:** 1½ Starch, ½ Fat;
PER SERVING: CAL 116 (24% from fat); PRO 2.4g; FAT 3.1g (sat 1.1g); CARB 21g; FIB 0.8g; CHOL 4mg; IRON 0.8mg; SOD 131mg; CALC 13mg

LEMON SQUARES

Use a piece of plastic wrap or the bottom of a measuring cup to press the crust into the baking pan.

2¼ cups all-purpose flour, divided
½ cup sifted powdered sugar
½ cup butter or stick margarine
Cooking spray
½ teaspoon baking powder
3 large eggs
1½ cups sugar
½ teaspoon grated lemon rind
⅓ cup fresh lemon juice
2 teaspoons powdered sugar

1. Preheat oven to 350°.
2. Combine 1¾ cups flour and ½ cup powdered sugar; cut in butter with a pastry blender or 2 knives until mixture resembles coarse meal. Press mixture into bottom of a 13- x 9-inch baking pan coated with cooking spray. Bake at 350° for 20 minutes or until crust is lightly browned; cool on a wire rack.
3. Combine remaining ½ cup flour and baking powder; set aside. Combine eggs, 1½ cups sugar, lemon rind, and lemon juice; stir in flour mixture. Pour over prepared crust.
4. Bake at 350° for 25 minutes or until lightly browned and set. Cool on a wire rack. Dust lightly with powdered sugar; cut into bars. **YIELD:** 32 servings (serving size: 1 square).

POINTS: 2; **EXCHANGES:** 1 Starch, ½ Fat;
PER SERVING: CAL 110 (29% from fat); PRO 1.6g; FAT 3.5g (sat 2g); CARB 18.4g; FIB 0.2g; CHOL 28mg; IRON 0.5mg; SOD 43mg; CALC 9mg

CARAMEL APPLE PIE TARTLETS

These tartlets combine two American classics, apple pie and sugar cookies.

1¼ cups all-purpose flour
½ teaspoon baking powder
¼ teaspoon salt
½ cup sugar
¼ cup butter, softened
1 teaspoon vanilla extract
1 large egg
Cooking spray
1½ teaspoons butter or stick margarine
2 cups peeled diced cooking apple
3 tablespoons fat-free caramel ice cream topping
3 tablespoons sugar
2 tablespoons all-purpose flour
⅛ teaspoon salt
½ teaspoon lemon juice
½ teaspoon ground cinnamon

1. Preheat oven to 350°.
2. Combine flour, baking powder, and salt in a small bowl; set aside. Beat sugar and butter at medium speed of a mixer until light and fluffy. Add vanilla and egg; beat well. Add flour mixture; beat at low speed until well blended. Shape dough into a ball, and wrap in plastic wrap; freeze 15 minutes. Divide dough into 16 equal portions. Gently press each dough portion into bottom and up sides of 16 (1¾ inch) miniature muffin cups coated with cooking spray; set aside.
3. Melt butter in a large skillet over medium-high heat; add apple. Cook apple, stirring frequently, over medium-high heat 2 minutes. Add caramel and remaining 5 ingredients; mix well. Spoon filling evenly into shells. Bake at 350° for 22 minutes. Let cool in pans on wire racks. Loosen tartlets from sides of pans, using a knife or narrow metal spatula. Remove from pans; let cool completely on wire racks. **YIELD:** 16 servings (serving size: 1 tartlet).

POINTS: 3; **EXCHANGES:** 1½ Starch, ½ Fat;
PER SERVING: CAL 129 (27% from fat); PRO 1.6g; FAT 3.9g (sat 2.2g); CARB 21.9g; FIB 0.6g; CHOL 23mg; IRON 0.6mg; SOD 117mg; CALC 16mg

A IS FOR APPLE

Sinking your teeth into a crisp juicy apple is the most popular way to enjoy this tree-ripened fruit. But don't overlook the flavorful possibilities of cooking with apples. Each variety imparts its own characteristics.

• **Golden delicious:** Tender and mildly sweet makes it an excellent pick for pies and good for baking.

• **Granny Smith:** Tart, crisp, and juicy, making it an excellent choice for cooking or munching.

• **Idared:** Tart, firm, and juicy. Best in salads and fruit cups.

• **Red Delicious:** America's favorite apple. Excellent for snacking, but only fair for baking. Cooks up chunky in sauces.

• **Rome:** Crisp, firm, and slightly tart. Excellent for both pies and baking.

Fish & Shellfish

ENGLISH CODFISH PIE

This hearty one-dish meal is adapted from a traditional Shepherd's Pie.

- 2 pounds peeled baking potatoes, cut into 1-inch pieces (about 4 cups)
- 1 pound skinned cod fillets
- Cooking spray
- ½ cup 50%-less-fat sour cream
- ¼ cup 2% reduced-fat milk
- 1 teaspoon chopped fresh thyme
- 1 teaspoon butter or stick margarine
- ½ teaspoon salt
- ¼ teaspoon freshly ground black pepper
- 2 teaspoons butter or stick margarine
- ¾ cup diced carrot
- ¾ cup diced celery
- 1 cup diced leek
- 1 garlic clove, minced
- ¼ cup all-purpose flour
- ½ cup clam juice
- ½ cup dry white wine
- ½ cup 2% reduced-fat milk
- 1½ teaspoons chopped fresh thyme
- ¾ teaspoon salt
- ½ teaspoon fennel seeds
- ½ teaspoon freshly ground black pepper
- ½ teaspoon paprika

1. Place potatoes in a large saucepan; add water to cover. Bring to a boil; cover, reduce heat, and cook 15 minutes or until tender.
2. Place a large nonstick skillet over medium-high heat. Coat fish with cooking spray, and cook 2 minutes on each side or until done; set aside, and keep warm.
3. Drain potatoes, and place in a large bowl; add sour cream and next 5 ingredients, and beat at medium speed of a mixer until smooth. Set aside, and keep warm.
4. Preheat oven to 450°.
5. Heat 2 teaspoons butter in a large nonstick skillet over medium-high heat. Add carrot, celery, and leek; cook, stirring constantly, 7 minutes. Add garlic; cook 2 minutes. Sprinkle with flour; cook 2 minutes, stirring until well blended. Add clam juice and next 6 ingredients; bring to a boil. Reduce heat, and simmer until thickened, stirring constantly.
6. Spoon mixture into an 11- x 7-inch baking dish coated with cooking spray; top with fish. Spread potato topping over fish and vegetable mixture; coat potato topping with cooking spray, and sprinkle with paprika.
7. Bake at 450° for 18 minutes or until potato topping is lightly browned. **YIELD:** 4 servings.

POINTS: 9; **EXCHANGES:** 3½ Starch, 1½ Vegetable, 2 Lean Meat;
PER SERVING: CAL 459 (15% from fat); PRO 29.7g; FAT 7.7g (sat 4.6g); CARB 61.5g; FIB 5g; CHOL 71mg; IRON 3.0mg; SOD 985mg; CALC 179mg

GRILLED GROUPER WITH CILANTRO-LIME SAUCE

- 3 tablespoons low-sodium soy sauce
- 2 tablespoons fresh lime juice
- 2 tablespoons brown sugar
- 1 tablespoon dark sesame oil
- 1 garlic clove, crushed
- ½ teaspoon crushed red pepper
- ½ teaspoon ground ginger
- 4 (4-ounce) grouper fillets
- Cooking spray
- Cilantro-Lime Sauce

1. Combine first 7 ingredients in a large heavy-duty, zip-top plastic bag; add fish, and seal bag. Toss to coat well; marinate in refrigerator 1 hour.
2. Remove grouper from marinade; reserve marinade. Place marinade in a saucepan. Bring to a boil; remove from heat. Coat grill rack with cooking spray. Cover and grill grouper over medium-hot coals (350° to 400°) 5 minutes on each side or until fish flakes easily when tested with a fork, basting occasionally with reserved marinade. Serve grouper with Cilantro-Lime Sauce. **YIELD:** 4 servings (serving size: 1 fillet and 1½ tablespoons sauce).

POINTS: 4; **EXCHANGES:** ½ Starch, 3 Very Lean Meat, ½ Fat; **PER SERVING:** CAL 186 (33% from fat); PRO 22.8g; FAT 6.8g (sat 1.2g); CARB 7.7g; FIB 0.1g; CHOL 44mg; IRON 1.4mg; SOD 481mg; CALC 42mg

CILANTRO-LIME SAUCE

- 3 tablespoons low-fat sour cream
- 2 tablespoons reduced-fat mayonnaise
- 1 tablespoon chopped fresh cilantro
- 1 tablespoon fresh lime juice
- 1 garlic clove, minced

1. Combine all ingredients in a small bowl; stir well. **YIELD:** ¼ cup plus 2 tablespoons.

RED SNAPPER WITH FENNEL-POTATO RAGOÛT

A ragoût is a very thick, well-seasoned stew. It can be made with meat, poultry, or fish.

- 3 garlic cloves, minced
- 1/4 cup chopped fresh chives, divided
- 1/4 cup chopped fresh parsley, divided
- 1 teaspoon olive oil
- 1 teaspoon salt, divided
- 4 (6-ounce) red snapper fillets
- 1 tablespoon butter
- 2 large leeks, trimmed and chopped
- 2 medium baking potatoes, peeled and cut into 1½-inch pieces (about 1¼ pounds)
- 1 large fennel bulb, cored and cut into 2-inch pieces
- 3/4 cup dry white wine
- 1 cup fat-free, reduced-sodium chicken broth
- 2 tablespoons lemon juice
- Cooking spray
- Fennel leaves (optional)

1. Combine garlic, 2 tablespoons chives, 2 tablespoons parsley, olive oil, and 1/4 teaspoon salt. Rub on both sides of snapper fillets; cover and chill.
2. Heat butter in a large saucepan over medium heat; cook leeks in butter 5 minutes, stirring occasionally. Add potatoes, fennel, and wine. Increase heat to medium-high; cover and simmer 5 minutes. Add chicken broth and remaining 3/4 teaspoon salt. Bring to a boil; cover, reduce heat, and simmer 15 to 20 minutes or until potatoes are tender. Remove from heat, and gently stir in lemon juice and remaining 2 tablespoons each of chives and parsley. Set aside, and keep warm.
3. Coat a large nonstick skillet with cooking spray; place over medium-high heat until hot. Make 2 diagonal cuts through skin (but not flesh) of each fillet. Add fillets, skin side down, one at a time, to skillet. Cook 4 minutes; turn and cook an additional 4 minutes or until fish flakes easily when tested with a fork.
4. Divide each fillet into 3 portions. Spoon ragoût evenly among 4 bowls; top each bowl with a portion of fillet. Garnish with fennel leaves, if desired. **YIELD:** 4 servings (serving size: 1 fillet and 1 cup ragoût).

POINTS: 7; **EXCHANGES:** 1½ Starch, 2 Vegetable, 4½ Very Lean Meat, ½ Fat; **PER SERVING:** CAL 357 (17% from fat); PRO 40.4g; FAT 6.9g (sat 2.5g); CARB 33g; FIB 3g; CHOL 71mg; IRON 4.8mg; SOD 895mg; CALC 187mg

SOLE WITH TARRAGON CREAM SAUCE

Serve with angel hair pasta, steamed vegetables, and crusty French bread.

- 4 (6-ounce) sole fillets (about 1½ pounds)
- 1/2 teaspoon salt, divided
- 1/4 teaspoon pepper, divided
- 1/2 cup dry white wine
- 1/2 cup clam juice
- 1 diced carrot (about 2/3 cup)
- 1/3 cup chopped shallots
- 1 fresh thyme sprig
- 3/4 cup fat-free half-and-half
- 2½ teaspoons cornstarch
- 2 tablespoons 30%-less-fat sour cream (such as Breakstone)
- 1 teaspoon chopped fresh tarragon
- Tarragon leaves (optional)

1. Sprinkle sole fillets with 1/4 teaspoon salt and 1/8 teaspoon pepper. Roll up, starting with small end. Secure with wooden picks. Set aside.
2. Combine white wine and next 4 ingredients in a large skillet. Add rolled up fish; bring to a simmer over medium heat. Cover, reduce heat to low, and simmer 5 minutes. Remove fillets with a slotted spoon; set aside, and keep warm.
3. Increase heat to high, and cook wine mixture 5 minutes or until most of liquid is absorbed. Combine half-and-half and cornstarch, stirring well with a whisk. Add to mixture in skillet. Cook 2 minutes or until thickened, stirring constantly. Remove from heat; add sour cream, remaining 1/4 teaspoon salt, and 1/8 teaspoon pepper, stirring until thoroughly combined. Strain mixture through a sieve over a bowl; discard solids. Stir 1 teaspoon tarragon into sauce. Pour sauce over fish. Garnish with tarragon leaves, if desired. **YIELD:** 4 servings (serving size: 1 fillet and about 1/4 cup sauce).

POINTS: 4; **EXCHANGES:** ½ Starch, 4½ Very Lean Meat; **PER SERVING:** CAL 206 (13% from fat); PRO 32.5g; FAT 2.9g (sat 1.1g); CARB 7.1g; FIB 0.1g; CHOL 95mg; IRON 0.8mg; SOD 549mg; CALC 73mg

GREEK-STYLE ORANGE ROUGHY

(pictured on page 67)

The black-purple, almond-shaped kalamata olive is also known as a Greek-style olive.

- 1 tablespoon olive oil
- 1 onion, halved and thinly sliced (about 2 cups)
- 1 green bell pepper, thinly sliced (about 1½ cups)
- 1 red bell pepper, thinly sliced
- 5 garlic cloves, coarsely chopped
- 1 medium tomato, chopped (about 1¼ cups)
- ¾ teaspoon salt
- 6 (6-ounce) orange roughy fillets
- Cooking spray
- ¼ cup pitted and chopped kalamata olives

1. Preheat oven to 425°.

2. Place oil in a large nonstick skillet over medium-high heat until hot. Add onion and next 3 ingredients; cook 10 minutes or until vegetables are crisp-tender, stirring frequently. Add tomato and salt; cook 2 minutes, stirring frequently.

3. Place fillets in a 13- x 9-inch baking dish coated with cooking spray. Place onion mixture on top of fillets. Sprinkle with olives. Bake, uncovered, at 425° for 20 minutes or until fish flakes easily when tested with a fork. **YIELD:** 6 servings (serving size: 1 fillet and about ⅔ cup onion mixture).

POINTS: 4; **EXCHANGES:** 1½ Vegetable, 3½ Very Lean Meat; **PER SERVING:** CAL 180 (25% from fat); PRO 26.1g; FAT 4.9g (sat 0.4g); CARB 7.0g; FIB 1.5g; CHOL 34mg; IRON 0.9mg; SOD 445mg; CALC 67mg

COLD POACHED SALMON WITH SUMMER TOMATO DRESSING

(pictured on page 68)

- 1 cup water
- 1 cup dry white wine
- 6 (6-ounce) salmon fillets
- ¼ cup minced shallots
- 2 tablespoons white wine vinegar
- 1 tablespoon extra-virgin olive oil
- 1 tablespoon Dijon mustard
- 2 garlic cloves, minced
- ½ teaspoon salt
- ¼ teaspoon freshly ground black pepper
- 1 large tomato, finely chopped
- ⅓ cup packed fresh basil leaves, finely chopped

1. Combine water and wine in a large skillet. Bring to a boil. Add fillets, skin side up; cover, reduce heat, and simmer 5 minutes. Remove from heat, and let stand, covered, 20 minutes or until fish flakes easily when tested with a fork. Remove salmon from poaching liquid, reserving ½ cup liquid. Cover salmon, and chill.

2. Combine reserved ½ cup poaching liquid, shallot, and next 6 ingredients in a bowl; cover and chill. Combine tomato and basil; cover and chill. Stir tomato and basil into shallot dressing just before serving. Remove and discard skin from salmon. Serve pink side up. Spoon tomato dressing over salmon. **YIELD:** 6 servings (serving size: 1 salmon fillet and ⅓ cup dressing.

POINTS: 7; **EXCHANGES:** 1 Vegetable, 4½ Lean Meat; **PER SERVING:** CAL 282 (43% from fat); PRO 34.4g; FAT 13.4g (sat 2.0g); CARB 4.1g; FIB 0.6g; CHOL 94mg; IRON 1.9mg; SOD 353mg; CALC 34mg

GLAZED SALMON STEAKS

Serve with couscous, a mixed greens salad, and for dessert, fresh fruit.

- ½ cup low-sodium soy sauce
- ⅓ cup dry sherry
- 1 garlic clove, crushed
- 8 (4-ounce) salmon steaks (½ inch thick)
- ⅓ cup firmly packed brown sugar
- 2 tablespoons honey
- 2 teaspoons vegetable oil
- Cooking spray
- Flowering chives (optional)

1. Combine first 3 ingredients in a large heavy-duty, zip-top plastic bag. Add fish; seal bag, and shake until fish is well coated. Marinate in refrigerator 1 hour, turning bag occasionally.

2. Remove fish from marinade, reserving 3 tablespoons marinade. Discard remaining marinade. Combine reserved marinade, brown sugar, honey, and oil in a small saucepan. Cook over medium heat until mixture comes to a boil and sugar dissolves.

3. Coat grill rack with cooking spray; place on grill over medium-hot coals (350° to 400°). Place fish on rack. Cover and grill 4 to 5 minutes on each side or until fish flakes easily when tested with a fork, basting occasionally with brown sugar mixture. Garnish with flowering chives, if desired. **YIELD:** 8 servings.

POINTS: 6; **EXCHANGES:** 1 Starch, 3 Lean Meat; **PER SERVING:** CAL 261 (38% from fat); PRO 25.0g; FAT 10.9g (sat 1.9g); CARB 14.7g; FIB 0g; CHOL 77mg; IRON 1mg; SOD 546mg; CALC 18mg

NUTRITION

The Fats You Need

Omega-3 fatty acids are essential to good health. Fitting them into your diet can be a delicious proposition.

Omega-3 and alpha-linolenic acid may sound like words from science fiction. But they're not part of an alien language; instead, they're important fats to incorporate in your diet.

Omega-6 fatty acids, found in sunflower seeds and peanut, corn, and safflower oils, are plentiful in most American diets. Omega-3 fatty acids aren't as widely consumed, even though research suggests that they may have more positive health benefits than omega-6s.

OMEGA-3 SOURCES. There are three omega-3 fatty acids. Eicosapentaenoic acid (EPA) and docosahexaenoic acid (DHA) are typically found in cold water fish such as salmon, albacore tuna, lake trout, and sardines; alpha-linolenic acid is found in canola oil, walnuts, flaxseed, and leafy vegetables.

Although there are no official recommended dietary allowances for omega-3s, some experts suggest an intake of 0.7 grams of EPA/DHA per day for adults. Pregnant and nursing women should follow the general recommendations and ensure a DHA intake of 0.3 grams per day.

Omega-3s are part of the structure of our cells, particularly those of the central nervous system. This cell development occurs primarily in the last trimester of pregnancy and the first year of life. The beneficial role of omega-3s for pregnant women and infants is clear, but recent research indicates that we should consume omega-3s throughout life.

EXAGGERATED CLAIMS?

Claims extolling the power of omega-3 fatty acids are plentiful. But many of the claims lack sound scientific evidence. Research does show that omega-3 fatty acid intake may reduce the risk of heart attacks, improve joint tenderness in arthritis, lessen the danger associated with cardiac arrhythmia, and improve immune function. A long-term study of 76,000 nurses found that those consuming the equivalent of a daily tablespoon of canola oil or half an ounce of walnuts lowered their risk of fatal heart attack by one-third to one-half, compared to those who consumed little alpha-linolenic acid.

DOSAGE CONCERNS. Avoid taking fish oil supplements, which contain concentrated forms of omega-3s, unless your doctor prescribes them for you. Larger-than-recommended doses can lead to upset stomach, nausea, and diarrhea.

Fish-oil supplements and cod-liver oil also contain large amounts of vitamins A and D, both of which can be toxic. Vitamin A toxicity can cause liver damage and may contribute to birth defects. Vitamin D toxicity can cause kidney damage.

Remember that many of the food sources rich in omega-3s are also high in calories. When you watch your weight, be sure to balance your intake of fatty acid foods with your daily calorie count.

GOOD CATCH

Studies show that people who ate at least one serving of fatty fish a week reduced their risk for heart attacks than those who didn't eat EPA/DHA-rich fish. Fish is also an excellent source of protein and is recommended by the American Heart Association as a part of a healthful diet. Use this chart to identify your favorites.

Fish/Shellfish (4 ounces, cooked)	**Fatty Acids** (grams)
Sardines	5.8
Pink salmon	2.5
Albacore tuna	2.4
Atlantic mackerel	2.2
Lake trout	1.6
Atlantic halibut	1.5
Swordfish	1.0
Striped sea bass	0.8
Red snapper	0.7
Oysters	0.6
Mussels	0.5
Clams	0.3
Flounder	0.3
Bay scallops	0.2
Cod	0.2
Haddock	0.2
Perch	0.2
Sea scallops	0.2
Shrimp	0.2
Lobster	0.1
Sole	0.1

ORANGE AND MIRIN SEA BASS

Tamari is similar to soy sauce, but it's slightly thicker. Mirin is a sweet rice wine. Look for both in the Oriental foods section of your supermarket.

2 teaspoons vegetable oil
1 large leek, trimmed and cut into thin strips
1 small red bell pepper, thinly sliced
½ pound fresh snow peas, trimmed
½ teaspoon salt, divided
Cooking spray
4 sea bass or halibut fillets (about 2 pounds)
2 teaspoons grated orange rind
¼ cup fresh orange juice
⅓ cup mirin
1½ teaspoons dark sesame oil
1 teaspoon tamari
1 tablespoon grated fresh ginger

1. Preheat oven to 425°.
2. Heat oil in a large skillet over medium-high heat. Add leek and red pepper; cook, stirring constantly, 2 minutes. Add snow peas and ¼ teaspoon salt; cook over medium heat 1 minute. Remove from heat. Transfer vegetables to an 11- x 7-inch baking dish coated with cooking spray. Top with fish.
3. Combine remaining salt, orange rind, and remaining 5 ingredients. Pour orange mixture over fish.
4. Bake at 425° for 25 minutes or until fish flakes easily when tested with a fork. **YIELD:** 4 servings (serving size: 1 fillet and ½ cup vegetables).

POINTS: 8; **EXCHANGES:** 2½ Vegetable, 5½ Lean Meat ; **PER SERVING:** CAL 361 (34% from fat); PRO 44.5g; FAT 13.6g (sat 2.7g); CARB 13.4g; FIB 2.6g; CHOL 93mg; IRON 3.2mg; SOD 527mg; CALC 74mg

TUNA WITH TAPENADE

(pictured on page 67)

A tapenade is a thick, flavorful paste made from capers and olives. It's ideal as a spread or condiment with meat or fish, or for dipping raw vegetables.

1 (4-ounce) jar capers, drained
1 (4-ounce) jar diced pimiento, drained
1 tablespoon sun-dried tomato paste (such as Amore)
15 kalamata olives, pitted
3 garlic cloves, halved
6 (6-ounce) tuna steaks
¼ teaspoon salt
¼ teaspoon pepper
Cooking spray
Lemon wedges (optional)
Fresh rosemary sprigs (optional)

1. Combine first 5 ingredients in a food processor. Pulse 5 times or until finely chopped, scraping down sides of bowl, if necessary. Transfer to a small bowl, and set aside.
2. Sprinkle tuna evenly with salt and pepper.
3. Coat grill rack with cooking spray; place on grill over medium-hot coals (350° to 400°). Place fish on rack; grill, covered, 4 to 6 minutes on each side or until fish flakes easily when tested with a fork. Serve with tapenade. Garnish with lemon wedges and rosemary sprigs, if desired.
YIELD: 6 servings (serving size: 1 tuna steak and 2 tablespoons tapenade).

POINTS: 6; **EXCHANGES:** 5½ Very Lean Meat, 1 Fat; **PER SERVING:** CAL 271 (33% from fat); PRO 40.5g; FAT 9.8g (sat 2.3g); CARB 2.4g; FIB 0.3g; CHOL 65mg; IRON 2.5mg; SOD 1062mg; CALC 10mg

TUNA STEAKS WITH PASTA AND BEANS

1 tablespoon olive oil, divided
1 medium onion, chopped
4 garlic cloves, minced and divided
1 (14½-ounce) can chicken broth
1 (19-ounce) can cannellini beans, rinsed and drained
1 small ripe tomato, chopped
¼ cup fresh basil, chopped
4 teaspoons balsamic vinegar, divided
3½ cups hot cooked orecchiette pasta (about 7 ounces uncooked pasta)
3 (6-ounce) tuna steaks, cut into 2-inch pieces
¼ teaspoon salt
¼ teaspoon freshly ground pepper
⅓ cup freshly grated Romano cheese

1. Heat 2 teaspoons olive oil in a large nonstick skillet over medium-high heat. Add onion and 3 minced garlic cloves; cook, stirring constantly, 4 minutes. Add chicken broth and beans; cook, uncovered, over medium-high heat 8 minutes. Add tomato; cook 2 minutes. Stir in basil and 2 teaspoons vinegar. Spoon over pasta in a large bowl; set aside, and keep warm.
2. Combine tuna, 1 teaspoon oil, remaining garlic clove, 2 teaspoons vinegar, salt, and pepper.
3. Heat skillet over medium-high heat. Add tuna mixture; cook, stirring constantly, 2 to 4 minutes or to desired degree of doneness. Spoon over pasta and bean mixture. Sprinkle with cheese; toss gently. Serve warm. **YIELD:** 6 servings.

POINTS: 8; **EXCHANGES:** 2½ Starch, 3½ Lean Meat; **PER SERVING:** CAL 404 (25% from fat); PRO 34g; FAT 11g (sat 3.7g); CARB 40.3g; FIB 4.5g; CHOL 41mg; IRON 3.6mg; SOD 686mg; CALC 195mg

PANFRIED TROUT WITH WILD RICE

4 teaspoons vegetable oil, divided
½ cup thinly sliced leeks
2 cups sliced fresh mushrooms
2 garlic cloves, crushed
5 cups water
1 cup uncooked wild rice
½ teaspoon salt
¼ teaspoon black pepper
¼ cup all-purpose flour
½ teaspoon salt
½ teaspoon ground red pepper
1 tablespoon chopped fresh thyme
4 (4-ounce) trout fillets
4 lemon wedges

1. Heat 2 teaspoons oil in a medium saucepan over medium-high heat. Add leeks, mushrooms, and garlic; cook, stirring constantly, 3 minutes. Add water and rice; bring to a boil. Cover, reduce heat, and simmer 50 minutes or until rice is tender; drain. Stir in ½ teaspoon salt and black pepper. Set aside, and keep warm.
2. Combine flour and next 3 ingredients in a shallow dish; stir well. Dredge trout fillets in flour mixture.
3. Heat a large cast-iron skillet over medium-high heat until hot; add remaining 2 teaspoons oil. Add fillets to skillet; cook in batches 2 minutes on each side or until fish flakes easily when tested with a fork.
4. Divide rice mixture evenly among 4 serving plates, and top each with 1 fillet. Serve with lemon wedges. YIELD: 4 servings (serving size: 1 fillet and about ¾ cup rice).

POINTS: 7; EXCHANGES: 2½ Starch, 3 Lean Meat; PER SERVING: CAL 364 (23% from fat); PRO 31.0g; FAT 9.1g (sat 1.3g); CARB 39.7g; FIB 3.1g; CHOL 65mg; IRON 4.1mg; SOD 623mg; CALC 98mg

CATFISH FILLETS WITH THAI CUCUMBER RELISH

If seedless English cucumbers aren't available in your supermarket, substitute regular cucumbers. Just remove the seeds before slicing.

¼ cup white vinegar
¼ cup firmly packed brown sugar
1 (¾-pound) English cucumber, peeled, halved, and sliced
½ teaspoon salt
½ cup very thinly sliced red onion
2 jalapeño peppers, seeded and very thinly sliced
½ teaspoon crushed red pepper
¼ cup packed fresh cilantro leaves, finely chopped
4 (8-ounce) farm-raised catfish fillets
¼ teaspoon salt
Cooking spray

1. Combine vinegar and sugar in a small saucepan; cook over medium heat 5 minutes or until sugar dissolves, stirring occasionally. Remove from heat; let cool.
2. Combine cooled vinegar mixture, cucumber, and next 5 ingredients; toss well. Let stand 30 minutes.
3. Heat a large nonstick skillet over medium-high heat. Sprinkle fillets with salt; coat fillets with cooking spray. Cook fillets in batches 4 minutes on each side or until fish flakes easily when tested with a fork. Spoon cucumber relish over catfish; serve immediately. YIELD: 4 servings (serving size: 1 catfish fillet and ½ cup relish).

POINTS: 7; EXCHANGES: 1 Starch, 5 Lean Meat; PER SERVING: CAL 336 (27% from fat); PRO 42g; FAT 10g (sat 2.3g); CARB 18g; FIB 1.1g; CHOL 132mg; IRON 2.9mg; SOD 592mg; CALC 121mg

GRILLED SWORDFISH TACOS WITH TOMATILLO-AVOCADO SALSA

Tomatillos are the base for salsa verde. The tomatillo is a fruit that looks like a small green tomato but is encased in a thin, parchmentlike husk.

½ cup boiling water
1 chipotle chile
¼ cup chopped onion
1 garlic clove, halved
1 teaspoon ground cumin
1 teaspoon chili powder
½ teaspoon salt
2 tablespoons lemon juice
2 teaspoons olive oil
1½ pounds swordfish steaks
1 (7-ounce) can salsa verde (such as Herdez)
⅔ cup coarsely mashed avocado (about 1 medium avocado)
6 (6-inch) corn tortillas

1. Combine boiling water and chipotle chile in a small bowl; cover and let stand 30 minutes or until soft. Drain; discard stems, seeds, and membranes. Combine chile, onion, and next 6 ingredients in bowl of food processor. Process until puréed, scraping down sides of bowl occasionally. Spread 1 teaspoon chipotle mixture on each side of swordfish steaks. Set aside remaining chipotle mixture.
2. Heat a grill pan over medium-high heat until hot. Add fish, and grill 6 minutes on each side. Cut fish into 1-inch cubes; combine fish with remaining chipotle mixture. Set aside.
3. Combine salsa verde and avocado. Heat tortillas according to package directions. Spoon ⅔ cup fish mixture and 2 tablespoons salsa verde mixture into center of each tortilla.

Fold tortilla in half. Serve immediately. **YIELD:** 6 servings (serving size: 1 tortilla).

POINTS: 5; **EXCHANGES:** 1 Starch, 3 Lean Meat; **PER SERVING:** CAL 255 (33% from fat); PRO 24.6g; FAT 9.4g (sat 2.0g); CARB 16.4g; FIB 2.6g; CHOL 44mg; IRON 2.7mg; SOD 707mg; CALC 59mg

CLAM FETTUCCINE WITH MUSHROOMS

- 2 (6½-ounce) cans chopped clams, undrained
- 1 (1.6-ounce) envelope Alfredo pasta sauce mix
- ½ cup fat-free milk
- 1 (6-ounce) can sliced mushrooms, drained
- ½ cup nonfat sour cream
- 4 cups hot cooked fettuccine (about 8 ounces uncooked pasta)
- ¼ cup chopped fresh parsley

1. Drain clams, reserving ½ cup clam juice. Set clams aside.
2. Place pasta sauce mix in a small saucepan. Gradually add clam juice and milk, stirring with a whisk until blended. Bring to a boil, and cook 1 minute or until slightly thickened, stirring constantly with whisk. Stir in mushrooms and clams; cook until thoroughly heated, stirring constantly. Remove from heat; stir in sour cream.
3. Combine sauce and fettuccine in a bowl; toss well. Sprinkle with parsley. Serve immediately. **YIELD:** 4 servings (serving size: 1¼ cups).

POINTS: 7; **EXCHANGES:** 3½ Starch, 1½ Very Lean Meat; **PER SERVING:** CAL 336 (8% from fat); PRO 21.0g; FAT 2.9g (sat 1.3g); CARB 55.4g; FIB 2.0g; CHOL 27mg; IRON 4.9mg; SOD 1,127mg; CALC 137mg

MUSSELS À LA RAVIGOTE

This tangy sauce is a variation on the classic French ravigote vinaigrette, which typically includes various herbs, capers, and onion.

- 8 ounces gemelli pasta, uncooked
- 3 tablespoons white wine vinegar
- 3 tablespoons lemon juice
- 2½ tablespoons extra-virgin olive oil
- ¼ teaspoon salt
- ¼ teaspoon dry mustard
- ¼ teaspoon freshly ground pepper
- 1 teaspoon capers
- 1 tablespoon finely chopped shallots
- 1 teaspoon chopped fresh parsley
- 1 teaspoon chopped fresh chives
- 1 teaspoon chopped fresh tarragon
- 1½ cups water
- 48 mussels (about 2 pounds), scrubbed and debearded

1. Cook pasta according to package directions, omitting salt and fat; drain. Set aside, and keep warm. Combine vinegar and next 10 ingredients in a bowl, stirring well with a whisk. Cover and chill.
2. Bring water to a boil in a large Dutch oven. Add mussels; cover and cook 3 minutes or until shells open. Remove from heat, and discard any unopened shells. Drain mussels, reserving 2 tablespoons cooking liquid. Cool mussels. Divide mussels into 4 individual shallow bowls.
3. Add reserved liquid to vinaigrette; stir well. Spoon evenly over mussels. Serve over pasta. **YIELD:** 4 servings (serving size: 12 mussels, 2 tablespoons sauce, and 1 cup pasta).

POINTS: 8; **EXCHANGES:** 3 Starch, 1 Very Lean Meat, 2 Fat; **PER SERVING:** CAL 351 (28% from fat); PRO 15.6g; FAT 10.9g (sat 1.6g); CARB 46.5g; FIB 1.5g; CHOL 19mg; IRON 5mg; SOD 403mg; CALC 33mg

DEBEARDING MUSSELS

Mussels are a member of the mollusk family, which includes oysters, clams, and scallops. Mollusks have soft bodies with no spinal column and are covered by a shell of one or more pieces. Like all shellfish, freshness is critical for mollusks.

1. Thump an opened mussel shell; if it closes, the mussel is still alive and fine to use. Discard any mussels that refuse to close.

2. Grasp the hairlike beard with your thumb and forefinger; pull it away from the shell. Follow recipe instructions to prepare mussels.

LEMON-PEPPER SEA SCALLOPS

The larger sea scallops and the smaller, more delicate bay scallops can be used interchangeably in recipes, but cooking times will vary.

- 1 pound sea scallops (about 25)
- 1 tablespoon vegetable oil
- 1 medium onion, halved and thinly sliced
- 2 garlic cloves, minced
- ¼ cup clam juice
- 2 tablespoons mirin
- 1½ teaspoons lemon-pepper seasoning
- 1 tablespoon lemon juice
- 2 tablespoons minced fresh chives

1. Place scallops on paper towels to remove excess moisture.
2. Place a large nonstick skillet over high heat until hot. Add half of scallops; cook 2 minutes on each side or until browned. Remove scallops from skillet; scrape off any residue in pan with a wooden spoon. Repeat procedure with remaining scallops.
3. Heat oil in skillet over medium-high heat until hot. Add onion and garlic; cook, stirring constantly, 3 minutes or until tender.
4. Return scallops to skillet; add clam juice and next 3 ingredients. Simmer 1 minute or until thoroughly heated. Sprinkle with chives before serving. **YIELD:** 2 servings (serving size: 1¼ cups scallop mixture).

POINTS: 6; **EXCHANGES:** ½ Starch, 1 Vegetable, 5 Very Lean Meat, ½ Fat;
PER SERVING: CAL 293 (27% from fat); PRO 39.3g; FAT 8.7g (sat 1.5g); CARB 12.9g; FIB 1.6g; CHOL 76mg; IRON 1.5mg; SOD 434mg; CALC 86mg

SCALLOPS WITH SAFFRON PASTA

(pictured on page 68)

- 1½ cups finely chopped onion
- 6 garlic cloves, minced
- 4 teaspoons butter, divided
- 2 (8-ounce) bottles clam juice
- 1½ cups dry white wine
- ¾ teaspoon salt
- ¾ teaspoon saffron threads, crushed
- 7 cups hot cooked angel hair pasta (about 12 ounces uncooked pasta)
- ⅔ cup chopped green onions
- ½ teaspoon freshly ground pepper
- Cooking spray
- 1½ pounds bay scallops, rinsed and drained

1. Cook onion and garlic in 2 teaspoons butter in a large nonstick skillet over medium-high heat 3 minutes or until tender, stirring constantly. Add clam juice and next 3 ingredients. Bring to a boil; cook 15 minutes or until reduced to 2 cups. Add remaining butter; stir until melted. Pour over cooked pasta. Add green onions and pepper to pasta mixture; stir well.
2. Place a large nonstick skillet coated with cooking spray over medium-high heat. Add scallops; cook, stirring often, 5 minutes or until done. Drain well. To serve, divide pasta evenly among 4 bowls; top with scallops. **YIELD:** 6 servings.

POINTS: 7; **EXCHANGES:** 3½ Starch, 2½ Very Lean Meat, ½ Fat;
PER SERVING: CAL 364 (11% from fat); PRO 27.7g; FAT 4.6g (sat 1.9g); CARB 51.6g; FIB 2.5g; CHOL 47mg; IRON 3.4mg; SOD 684mg; CALC 76mg

CRAB LOUIS

Crab Louis is a classic cold entrée. Lump crabmeat is placed on a bed of lettuce and topped with a creamy dressing of mayonnaise, chili sauce, and seasonings.

- 1 pound fresh lump crabmeat
- ½ cup finely diced celery
- ⅔ cup chili sauce
- ½ cup nonfat mayonnaise
- ¼ cup finely diced red bell pepper
- ¼ cup sliced green onions
- ¼ cup minced fresh parsley
- ¼ cup lemon juice
- 1 tablespoon prepared horseradish
- ¼ teaspoon pepper
- 8 cups sliced romaine lettuce
- 3 tomatoes, each cut into 6 wedges
- 6 lemon wedges (optional)
- 4 large eggs, hard-cooked and chopped

1. Combine crab and celery in a medium bowl; toss well.
2. Combine chili sauce and next 7 ingredients in a medium bowl; stir well.
3. Place 1⅓ cups lettuce on each of 6 serving plates. Top each with ½ cup crab mixture. Arrange 3 tomato wedges and 1 lemon wedge, if desired, around each salad; sprinkle with chopped egg. Serve with dressing. **YIELD:** 6 servings.

POINTS: 4; **EXCHANGES:** 1 Starch, 1 Vegetable, 2 Lean Meat; **PER SERVING:** CAL 211 (22% from fat); PRO 22.4g; FAT 5.2g (sat 1.3g); CARB 19.5g; FIB 2.9g; CHOL 217mg; IRON 3mg; SOD 938mg; CALC 145mg

Young at Heart

SUSAN LOPEZ • **HEIGHT** 5'7" • **BEFORE** 185 LBS. • **AFTER** 139 LBS.

Happiest Moment: When her daughter's friends say "That can't be your mom. She has to be your sister."

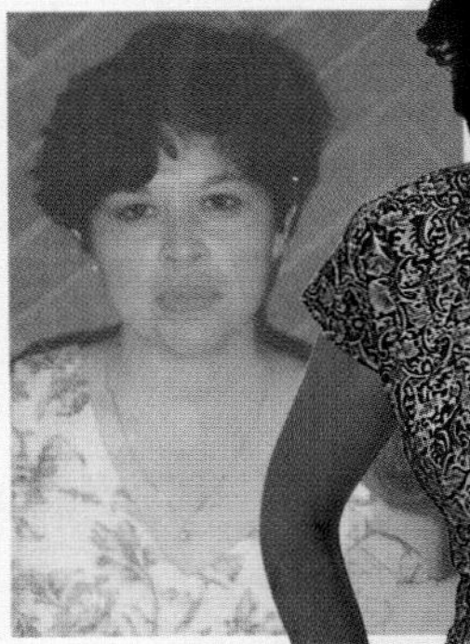

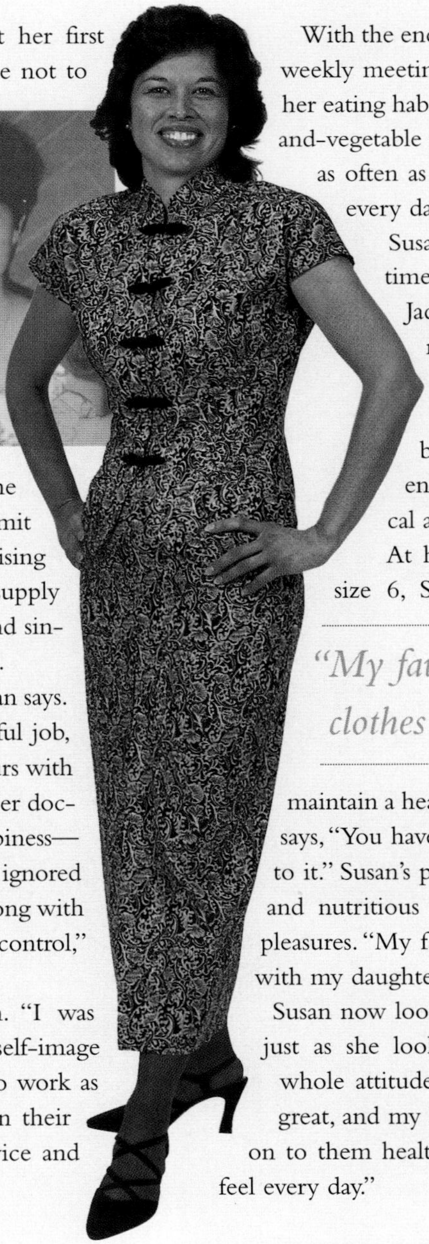

Susan Lopez slouched in the back row at her first Weight Watchers meeting, willing everyone not to look at her. "I felt I had 'size 16' printed on my forehead," she remembers. "Being there mortified me." She didn't know then that within a few weeks those people would smile as she sailed in, flush with stories about her weight-loss success.

Susan comes from a family of independent—and overweight—women. "My grandmother and mother always carried too many pounds," she says. "I became just like them: I refused to admit anything was wrong." She devoted herself to raising her children and running a business—a party-supply store and bakery—until the stress of her job and single parenting caused exhaustion and migraines.

"I was working so hard that I overdid it," Susan says. When she closed the store to take a less stressful job, Susan had more free time, and she filled the hours with eating until she weighed nearly 200 pounds. Her doctor noted the weight gain—and Susan's unhappiness—and recommended a weight-loss program. "I ignored him; I wanted to think there was something wrong with my health—that it was something I couldn't control," she says. "But deep down I felt I had failed."

She also felt she had failed her children. "I was ashamed of how I looked and how my low self-image was affecting them," she says. "I knew I had to work as hard on my weight as I expected them to on their schoolwork." Susan accepted her doctor's advice and joined Weight Watchers.

With the encouragement of everyone at her weekly meetings, Susan made big changes in her eating habits. She had never been a "fruit-and-vegetable person," but now she eats both as often as possible. She says that walking every day is key to her success, too.

Susan now has the energy to spend time with her children, Sara and Jacob. No longer burdened by migraines, she's able to ferry them to after-school sports activities, music lessons, and baby-sitting jobs. And she has the energy to join them in fun physical activities such as swimming.

At her goal weight and wearing a size 6, Susan attributes her ability to maintain a healthy weight to consistency. She says, "You have to get into a pattern and stick to it." Susan's patterns, including daily exercise and nutritious meals, have brought her new pleasures. "My favorite thing is to trade clothes with my daughter," she says.

"My favorite thing is to trade clothes with my daughter."

Susan now looks forward to weekly meetings, just as she looks forward to every day. "My whole attitude has changed," she says. "I feel great, and my kids see that in me. I'm passing on to them healthful habits and the happiness I feel every day."

Shrimp With Feta, page 74

Greek-Style Orange Roughy, page 59

Tuna With Tapenade, page 61

Scallops With Saffron Pasta, page 64

Cold Poached Salmon With Summer Tomato Dressing, page 59

Tofu Calzones,
page 81

Four-Cheese Eggplant
Casserole, page 83, and Salad
of Vegetables, page 123

Pesto, Bean, and Vegetable Pizza, page 83

Tofu Tamale Pie, page 80

A Call to Action

TINA RABINOWITZ • **HEIGHT** 5'3" • **BEFORE** 156 LBS. • **AFTER** 115 LBS.

Biggest Surprise: "I turned out to be more motivated than I knew I was. I didn't really know I could do it."

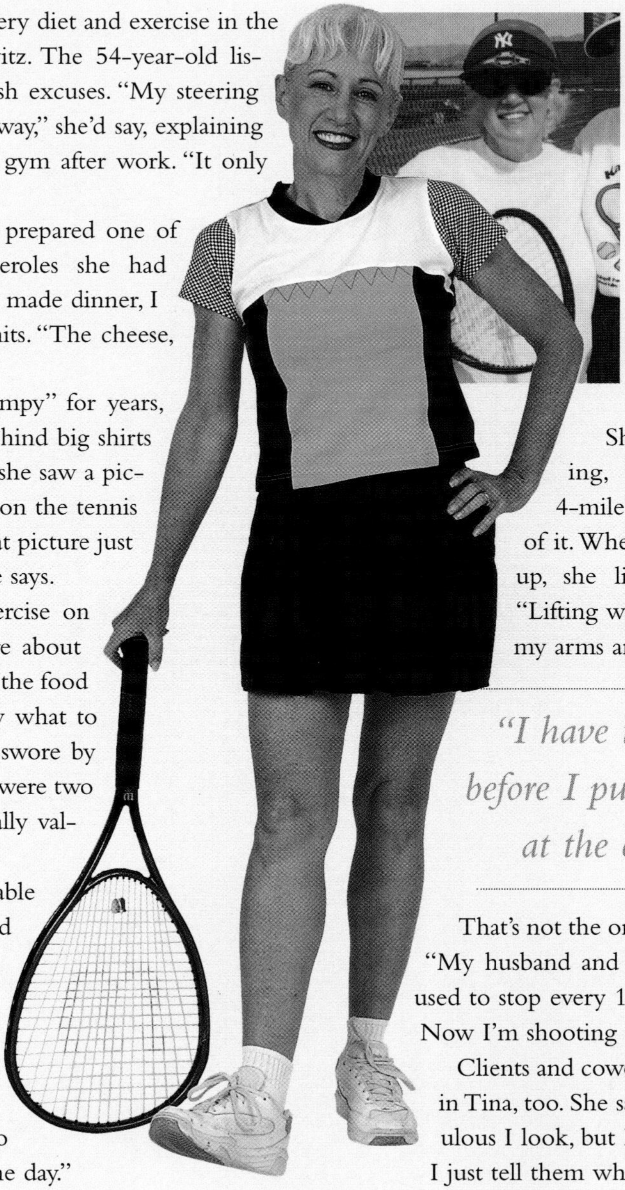

Friends recommended every diet and exercise in the book to Tina Rabinowitz. The 54-year-old listened but invented outlandish excuses. "My steering wheel won't turn the right way," she'd say, explaining why she couldn't go to the gym after work. "It only takes me home."

Once home, Tina usually prepared one of the easy, cheese-filled casseroles she had always cooked. "And while I made dinner, I ate another dinner," she admits. "The cheese, the chips, the dip, whatever."

Though she had felt "frumpy" for years, Tina was content to hide behind big shirts until December 1997 when she saw a picture of herself with a friend on the tennis courts. "Something about that picture just pushed me over the top," she says.

Tina knew she could exercise on her own, but she was unsure about her diet. "I needed help with the food thing, because I didn't know what to do," she recalls. Two friends swore by Weight Watchers. "And they were two women whose opinion I really valued and trusted."

Dinner is now a reasonable portion of fish or chicken and vegetables. Tina's favorite is pasta, which she eats in moderation. She drinks up to 2 liters of water a day. "I tell myself I have to finish my water before I pull into my driveway at the end of the day."

Tina finds ways to work fitness into her life. She changes into exercise clothes before leaving work to walk on an outdoor trail nearby. She says, "The trick for me is, 'Don't go home.' " If she went home first, Tina knows she might never leave the house for exercise, so she brings clothes to work to avoid the temptation of the couch.

She started exercising by walking, but Tina now finishes her 4-mile workout faster by jogging half of it. When she gets home, still warmed up, she lifts weights for 10 minutes. "Lifting weights has created definition in my arms and shoulders," she says.

"I have to finish my water before I pull into my driveway at the end of the day."

That's not the only difference Tina has noticed. "My husband and I go hiking in the summer. I used to stop every 15 minutes to catch my breath. Now I'm shooting up the trail."

Clients and coworkers have noticed the change in Tina, too. She says, "They all tell me how fabulous I look, but I shy away from giving advice. I just tell them what worked for me."

OYSTERS BIENVILLE CASSEROLE

We've updated this "on-the-half-shell" appetizer and made it a casserole ideal for spooning over toast points.

1 (16-ounce) container Standard oysters, undrained
2 slices lower sodium bacon
1 large shallot, minced
1 cup sliced fresh mushrooms
¼ cup all-purpose flour
1½ cups fat-free milk, divided
¼ cup dry sherry
½ pound small shrimp, peeled
¾ teaspoon salt
¼ teaspoon freshly ground pepper
4 (1-ounce) slices white bread, toasted
1 tablespoon chopped fresh chives

1. Drain oysters, reserving ¼ cup liquid; set oysters and liquid aside.
2. Cook bacon in a large nonstick skillet over medium heat until crisp; drain, reserving 1 teaspoon drippings in pan. Crumble bacon; set aside.
3. Add shallots and mushrooms to pan; cook, stirring constantly, over medium-high heat 3 minutes. Add reserved oyster liquid; cook 1 minute, stirring well. Reduce heat to medium.
4. Combine flour and ¼ cup milk, stirring with a whisk until smooth; stir in remaining milk. Add milk mixture to mushroom mixture; bring to a simmer over medium heat. Cook 3 minutes or until mixture thickens, stirring frequently. Stir in sherry, oysters, shrimp, salt, and pepper; bring mixture to a simmer. Cook 2 minutes or until shrimp turn pink.
5. Cut toasted bread in half diagonally; place 2 toast points on each of 4 individual serving plates. Spoon mixture evenly over toast points. Sprinkle with crumbled bacon and chives. **YIELD:** 4 (¾-cup) servings.

POINTS: 6; **EXCHANGES:** 2 Starch, 3 Very Lean Meat, ½ Fat; **PER SERVING:** CAL 292 (20% from fat); PRO 26.4g; FAT 6.4g (sat 1.8g); CARB 30.9g; FIB 1.2g; CHOL 144mg; IRON 9.4mg; SOD 890mg; CALC 223mg

CAJUN BARBECUED SHRIMP

2 teaspoons garlic powder
2 teaspoons paprika
1 teaspoon onion powder
1 teaspoon dried thyme
½ teaspoon dried oregano
½ teaspoon ground red pepper
¼ teaspoon salt
¼ teaspoon ground black pepper
1½ pounds large shrimp, peeled and deveined
Cooking spray

1. Combine first 8 ingredients in a large heavy-duty, zip-top plastic bag. Add shrimp. Seal bag; shake to coat. Let stand 5 minutes.
2. Remove shrimp from bag, discard seasoning mixture. Thread shrimp onto 4 skewers. Place skewers on grill rack coated with cooking spray; grill over medium-hot coals (350° to 400°) 3 minutes on each side or until done. **YIELD:** 4 servings.

POINTS: 4; **EXCHANGES:** 4½ Very Lean Meat; **PER SERVING:** CAL 178 (15% from fat); PRO 32.2g; FAT 3.0g (sat 0.6g); CARB 4.1g; FIB 0.5g; CHOL 237mg; IRON 4.7mg; SOD 379mg; CALC 97mg

PEELING SHRIMP

If you're short on time, have someone in your grocer's seafood department peel the shrimp while you shop. If you choose to peel your own, here's a step-by-step guide.

1. To peel shrimp, grasp the tail in one hand and the legs in the other.

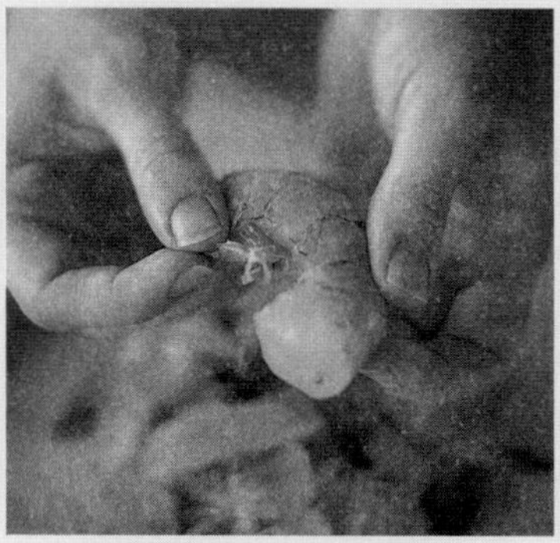

2. In one motion, pull off the legs.

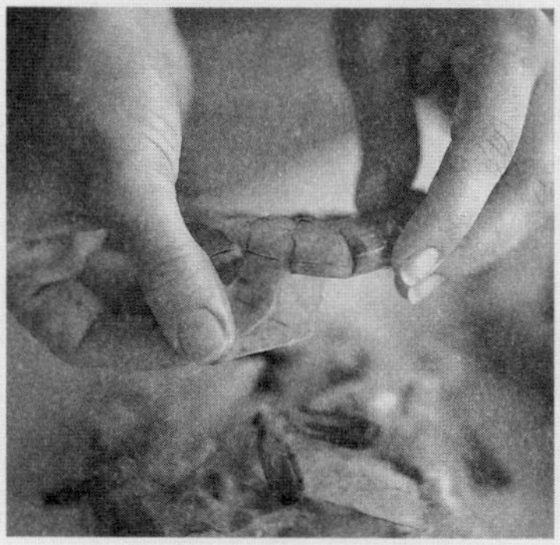

3. Peel back the shell, and remove it. The tail may be left on the shrimp for presentation, if desired.

SHRIMP WITH FETA

(pictured on page 66)

This dish can be ready to serve in about 30 minutes. Simply buy peeled and deveined shrimp from your supermarket's seafood department.

- 1 teaspoon olive oil
- 1½ pounds large shrimp, peeled and deveined
- 1 cup sliced green onions
- 4 garlic cloves, minced
- 1 (14.5-ounce) can diced tomatoes, undrained
- 1 teaspoon dried oregano
- 1 teaspoon dried basil
- ¼ teaspoon sugar
- ¼ teaspoon ground red pepper
- ¾ cup (3 ounces) crumbled feta cheese

1. Preheat broiler.
2. Heat oil in a large nonstick skillet over medium-high heat until hot. Add shrimp; cook, stirring constantly, 3 minutes or until done. Divide shrimp evenly among 4 individual gratin dishes; set aside.
3. Return skillet to medium-high heat. Add green onions and garlic; cook, stirring constantly, 1 minute. Add tomatoes, oregano, basil, sugar, and red pepper; cook 3 minutes or until liquid almost evaporates. Spoon tomato mixture evenly over shrimp, and sprinkle with cheese.
4. Broil 5 minutes or until cheese softens. (Cheese will not melt.) **YIELD:** 4 servings.

POINTS: 5; **EXCHANGES:** 1 Vegetable, 4 Very Lean Meat, ½ Fat; **PER SERVING:** CAL 237 (29% from fat); PRO 32.9g; FAT 7.6g (sat 3.8g); CARB 8.8g; FIB 1.5g; CHOL 282mg; IRON 5.6mg; SOD 711mg; CALC 219mg

QUICK SHRIMP CURRY

This mildly spiced curry is a complete meal. Serve it with Indian flatbreads, warm fresh pita bread, or flour tortillas to soak up the curry sauce.

- 1 tablespoon vegetable oil
- 1 medium onion, cut into thin wedges (about 1¼ cups)
- 3 garlic cloves, minced
- 1 tablespoon minced fresh ginger
- 2 teaspoons curry powder
- 1 cup fat-free, reduced-sodium chicken broth
- ½ cup canned diced tomatoes, undrained
- 1 pound red potatoes, cut into ¼-inch pieces (about 2⅓ cups)
- ¼ teaspoon salt
- 1 (12-ounce) package frozen peeled and cooked shrimp, thawed
- 1 (10-ounce) package frozen green peas, thawed (about 2⅓ cups)
- 2 tablespoons minced fresh cilantro

1. Heat oil in a large nonstick skillet. Add onion, and cook, stirring constantly, over medium heat until tender and golden, about 7 minutes. Add garlic, ginger, and curry powder; cook, stirring constantly, about 1 minute.
2. Add broth and next 3 ingredients. Bring to a boil. Cover, reduce heat, and cook, stirring once, about 15 minutes or until potato is tender.
3. Stir in shrimp and peas; cook, uncovered, about 4 minutes or until shrimp and peas are thoroughly heated. Stir in cilantro. Serve immediately in individual serving bowls. **YIELD:** 4 servings (serving size: 1½ cups).

POINTS: 5; **EXCHANGES:** 2½ Starch, 3 Very Lean Meat; **PER SERVING:** CAL 289 (13% from fat); PRO 29.5g; FAT 4.1g (sat 0.7g); CARB 36.5g; FIB 6.8g; CHOL 130mg; IRON 5.9mg; SOD 767mg; CALC 83mg

DO I NEED TO DEVEIN?

Is deveining shrimp really necessary? Deveining shrimp is more of an aesthetic choice than a necessity.

The black line that runs down the back of a shrimp (the sand vein) is its intestinal tract. In small shrimp, it's not really noticeable. But in larger shrimp, the vein is unsightly and can add a slightly gritty, muddy taste to the shrimp.

There's no harm in eating cooked shrimp that aren't deveined, but most people prefer the look and taste of cleaned shrimp. Deveining is easy to do and worth the effort.

Remove the shell. Slit shrimp lengthwise down its back, using a small paring knife or a deveiner (available at most supermarket seafood departments). Pull away the vein with tip of knife.

Meatless Main Dishes

BOW TIE PASTA WITH CHICKPEAS AND SPINACH IN A CREAMY FETA-TOMATO VINAIGRETTE

Pasta is done when it's al dente ("to the tooth" in Italian)—firm but tender, chewy not soggy.

- 5 cups torn fresh spinach
- 3½ cups hot cooked farfalle pasta (about 2¾ cups uncooked bow tie pasta)
- 2 cups halved cherry tomatoes
- 1 (19-ounce) can chickpeas (garbanzo beans), drained
- ½ cup chopped onion
- 1 cup (4 ounces) crumbled feta cheese, divided
- ¼ cup thinly sliced fresh basil
- ½ cup tomato juice
- 2 tablespoons red wine vinegar
- 2 teaspoons olive oil

1. Combine first 5 ingredients in a large bowl; add ½ cup feta cheese. Toss gently.
2. Combine remaining ½ cup feta cheese, basil, and remaining 3 ingredients; stir well. Pour over pasta mixture; toss gently to coat. **YIELD:** 5 servings (serving size: 2 cups).

POINTS: *7*; **EXCHANGES:** 3½ Starch, 1 Vegetable, 1½ Fat; **PER SERVING:** CAL 360 (21% from fat); PRO 14.8g; FAT 8.5g (sat 3.9g); CARB 57.4g; FIB 8.7g; CHOL 20mg; IRON 4.8mg; SOD 591mg; CALC 208mg

CREAMY LINGUINE PRIMAVERA

- Cooking spray
- 1 teaspoon olive oil
- 1 cup (1-inch) sliced asparagus
- 1 cup packaged preshredded carrot
- 1 cup sliced fresh mushrooms
- ½ cup sliced green onions
- 1 medium yellow squash, halved lengthwise and thinly sliced (about 1 cup)
- 3 tablespoons all-purpose flour
- 1½ teaspoons dried Italian seasoning
- ½ teaspoon salt
- ½ teaspoon freshly ground pepper
- 2 cups fat-free milk
- 1 tablespoon butter or stick margarine
- 3 garlic cloves, minced
- ¾ cup (3 ounces) freshly grated Parmesan cheese, divided
- 3 cups hot cooked linguine (8 ounces uncooked pasta)
- Freshly ground pepper (optional)

1. Coat a large nonstick skillet with cooking spray; add oil, and place over medium-high heat until hot. Add asparagus and carrot; cook 2 minutes, stirring constantly. Add mushrooms, green onions, and squash; cook 3 minutes or until crisp-tender. Remove from heat; set aside, and keep warm.
2. Combine flour and next 3 ingredients in a small bowl; gradually add milk, stirring with a whisk until completely blended. Melt butter in a medium saucepan over medium heat. Add garlic, and cook 30 seconds. Add milk mixture to saucepan; cook until thick and bubbly, stirring constantly. Remove saucepan from heat; stir in ½ cup Parmesan cheese.
3. Combine sauce, reserved vegetables, and pasta in a large bowl; toss gently to coat. Sprinkle with remaining ¼ cup cheese. Sprinkle with additional pepper, if desired. **YIELD:** 4 servings (serving size: 1½ cups pasta mixture).

POINTS: *7*; **EXCHANGES:** 2½ Starch, 1 Vegetable, 1 High-Fat Meat, ½ Fat; **PER SERVING:** CAL 353 (28% from fat); PRO 19g; FAT 11g (sat 5.8g); CARB 45g; FIB 3.9g; CHOL 25mg; IRON 3.3mg; SOD 738mg; CALC 455mg

FETTUCCINE WITH VEGETABLES AND BLACK BEANS

- 8 ounces fettuccine, uncooked
- 1 pound fresh asparagus
- ¼ cup water
- 2 teaspoons margarine
- ½ teaspoon minced garlic (about 1 clove)
- 1 tablespoon all-purpose flour
- 1¼ cups fat-free milk
- 3 tablespoons light process cream cheese
- ¾ cup (3 ounces) freshly grated Parmesan cheese
- 1 (15-ounce) can black beans, rinsed and drained
- Freshly ground pepper (optional)

1. Cook pasta according to package directions, omitting salt and fat; drain. Set aside, and keep warm.
2. Snap off tough ends of asparagus. Remove scales from stalks with a vegetable peeler or knife, if desired. Cut asparagus into 1-inch pieces; place in a microwave-safe dish. Add ¼ cup water and cover. Microwave at HIGH 2 minutes; drain.

3. Melt margarine in a medium saucepan over medium heat; add garlic. Cook, stirring constantly, 1 minute. Add flour; cook, stirring constantly, 1 minute. Gradually add milk, and cook, stirring constantly, 8 minutes or until thickened and bubbly. Stir in cream cheese; cook, stirring constantly, 2 minutes. Stir in Parmesan cheese.
4. Combine asparagus, cheese sauce, pasta, and beans in a large bowl; toss well. Sprinkle with freshly ground pepper, if desired. **YIELD:** 6 servings (serving size: 1⅓ cups).

POINTS: 6; **EXCHANGES:** 1 High-Fat Meat, 2 Starch, 2 Vegetable; **PER SERVING:** CAL 298 (22% from fat); PRO 16.6g; FAT 7.2g (sat 3.5g); CARB 42.3g; FIB 4.1g; CHOL 15mg; IRON 3.4mg; SOD 419mg; CALC 227mg

TORTELLINI WITH PESTO SAUCE

1 (9-ounce) package refrigerated cheese tortellini, uncooked
1 (16-ounce) package frozen broccoli stir-fry vegetables
1 (8-ounce) carton fat-free sour cream
2 tablespoons pesto
¼ teaspoon salt
¼ cup (1 ounce) freshly grated Parmesan cheese
⅛ teaspoon freshly ground pepper

1. Cook tortellini and vegetables in 3 quarts boiling water 5 to 7 minutes or until vegetables and pasta are tender. Drain and return to pan.
2. Combine sour cream, pesto, and salt, stirring well. Gently stir sour cream mixture into pasta mixture. Sprinkle with Parmesan cheese and pepper. Serve immediately. **YIELD:** 4 servings (serving size: 1¼ cups).

POINTS: 7; **EXCHANGES:** 2 Starch, 2 Vegetable, 1 High-Fat Meat, 1 Fat; **PER SERVING:** CAL 331 (33% from fat); PRO 18.7g; FAT 12.2g (sat 4.5g); CARB 38.1g; FIB 3g; CHOL 32mg; IRON 1.5mg; SOD 659mg; CALC 264mg

SPINACH AND BARLEY-STUFFED PORTOBELLOS

6 medium portobello mushroom caps (about 1½ pounds)
⅔ cup 2% reduced-fat milk
2 tablespoons all-purpose flour
Cooking spray
½ cup coarsely chopped carrot
½ cup coarsely chopped onion
5 garlic cloves, minced
¾ teaspoon salt
1 (10-ounce) bag fresh spinach leaves (about 10 cups)
1 cup cooked quick-cooking pearl barley
1 cup (4 ounces) grated Gruyère cheese, divided
½ teaspoon freshly ground pepper
⅛ teaspoon ground nutmeg
½ cup fresh whole-wheat breadcrumbs

1. Preheat broiler.
2. Remove brown gills from the undersides of mushrooms, using a spoon; discard gills. Set aside.
3. Combine milk and flour, stirring with a whisk until blended; set aside.
4. Place a large nonstick skillet coated with cooking spray over medium-high heat until hot. Add carrots and next 3 ingredients; cook, stirring constantly, 5 minutes. Add spinach; cook, stirring constantly, 4 minutes or until spinach wilts.
5. Stir in flour mixture; bring to a boil. Reduce heat; simmer 1 to 2 minutes or until thick. Stir in cooked barley, ½ cup cheese, pepper, and nutmeg; cook 1 minute or until cheese melts.
6. Coat reserved mushroom caps with cooking spray; place on a broiler pan. Broil 5 minutes or until tender. Fill each cap with about ½ cup spinach-barley mixture, pressing firmly to pack. Broil 3½ minutes.
7. Combine breadcrumbs and remaining ½ cup cheese; sprinkle evenly on top of each mushroom. Broil 1½ minutes or until cheese melts. **YIELD:** 6 servings (serving size: 1 mushroom and ½ cup spinach-barley mixture).

POINTS: 4; **EXCHANGES:** 1 Starch, 2 Vegetable, 1 High-Fat Meat; **PER SERVING:** CAL 209 (35% from fat); PRO 12.2g; FAT 8.1g (sat 4.2g); CARB 24.4g; FIB 5.4g; CHOL 23mg; IRON 3.6mg; SOD 461mg; CALC 299mg

A CAP FULL

To remove mushroom gills, hold cap in one hand, and gently scrape out with a spoon.

PORTOBELLO MUSHROOM STEW WITH RED WINE AND ROSEMARY

Substitute crimini mushrooms for the portobellos, and spoon the stew over mashed potatoes for another hearty vegetarian entrée.

1 (6.6-ounce) package polenta (such as Contadina)
1 teaspoon salt, divided
6 medium portobello mushroom caps (about 1½ pounds)
1½ tablespoons olive oil
1 medium onion, chopped
½ teaspoon pepper
1½ tablespoons all-purpose flour
⅔ cup dry red wine
¾ cup vegetable broth
2 tablespoons chopped fresh parsley
1 tablespoon minced fresh rosemary
¼ cup grated Parmesan cheese

1. Prepare polenta according to package directions, using ½ teaspoon salt. Set aside, and keep warm.
2. Remove brown gills from the undersides of mushrooms, using a spoon; discard gills. Slice mushroom caps; set aside.
3. Heat oil in a large Dutch oven. Add onion; cook over medium heat, stirring constantly, 3 minutes or until softened. Add remaining ½ teaspoon salt, sliced mushrooms, and pepper. Cook 5 minutes or until mushrooms are tender, stirring frequently.
4. Sprinkle flour over mushrooms, and cook 30 seconds, stirring constantly. Add wine and broth; bring to a boil. Reduce heat, and simmer, uncovered, 2 minutes or until thickened, stirring constantly. Stir in parsley and rosemary. Serve immediately over prepared polenta. Sprinkle 1 tablespoon cheese over each serving. **YIELD:** 4 servings (serving size: about ¾ cup polenta, about ½ cup stew, and 1 tablespoon cheese).

POINTS: 6; **EXCHANGES:** 3½ Starch, 1 Vegetable, 1½ Fat; **PER SERVING:** CAL 327 (23% from fat); PRO 10g; FAT 8.5g (sat 1.9g); CARB 58.1g; FIB 4.2g; CHOL 4mg; IRON 3mg; SOD 880mg; CALC 110mg

MEDITERRANEAN BULGUR PILAF

1 teaspoon olive oil
1 cup sliced green onions
½ cup sliced celery
2 garlic cloves, minced
1¼ cups water
1¼ cups vegetable broth
1½ teaspoons curry powder
1 teaspoon ground cumin
½ teaspoon salt
¼ teaspoon ground red pepper
1⅓ cups uncooked bulgur wheat with soy grits (such as Hodgson Mill) or bulgur
¼ cup dried currants
¼ cup pine nuts, toasted
1 tablespoon chopped fresh parsley
1 (15-ounce) can chickpeas (garbanzo beans), drained

1. Heat oil in a large saucepan over medium-high heat until hot. Add green onions, celery, and garlic; cook, stirring constantly, 3 minutes. Add water and next 5 ingredients; bring to a boil. Stir in bulgur; remove from heat. Cover and let stand 30 minutes or until liquid is absorbed.
2. Add currants and remaining ingredients to bulgur mixture; toss well. Serve at room temperature. **YIELD:** 6 servings (serving size: 1 cup).

POINTS: 5; **EXCHANGES:** 3 Starch, ½ Very Lean Meat, 1 Fat; **PER SERVING:** CAL 254 (25% from fat); PRO 12g; FAT 7g (sat 0.8g); CARB 42g; FIB 3.5g; CHOL 0mg; IRON 4.2mg; SOD 551mg; CALC 62mg

RISOTTO WITH PEAS AND PEPPERS

Risotto is an Italian rice dish made with short-grain Arborio rice. As you cook the rice, keep adding simmering liquid so that it will be thick and creamy.

1 (14½-ounce) can vegetable broth
2¾ cups water
Cooking spray
1 cup plus 2 tablespoons Arborio rice, uncooked
¼ cup diced dried tomato (packed without oil)
⅔ cup frozen English peas, thawed
⅔ cup (2⅔ ounces) freshly grated Parmesan cheese
⅓ cup roasted red peppers, drained and chopped
1 teaspoon dried Italian seasoning
½ teaspoon pepper

1. Combine broth and water in a medium saucepan; place over medium heat. Cover and bring to a simmer; reduce heat to low, and keep warm. (Do not boil.)
2. Coat a large saucepan with cooking spray; place over medium-low heat until hot. Add rice and 1 cup simmering broth mixture. Cook, stirring constantly, until most of liquid is absorbed. Add 1½ cups broth mixture, ½ cup at a time, cooking and stirring constantly until

each ½ cup addition is absorbed. Stir in tomato. Add remaining 2 cups broth mixture, ½ cup at a time, cooking and stirring constantly until each ½ cup addition is absorbed. (Rice will be tender and will have a creamy consistency.) Add peas and remaining ingredients, stirring until cheese melts; serve immediately. **YIELD:** 4 servings (serving size: 1 cup).

POINTS: 6; **EXCHANGES:** 3½ Starch, ½ Vegetable, 1 Fat; **PER SERVING:** CAL 303 (14% from fat); PRO 10.6g; FAT 4.7g (sat 2.3g); CARB 54g; FIB 3.0g; CHOL 9mg; IRON 3.4mg; SOD 857mg; CALC 186mg

TACO SALAD

Cooking spray
¼ cup chopped onion
2 to 3 garlic cloves, minced
1½ cups cooked long-grain brown rice
1 teaspoon chili powder, divided
1 teaspoon ground cumin, divided
¼ teaspoon ground red pepper, divided
¼ teaspoon ground coriander, divided
1 (16-ounce) can red kidney beans, rinsed and drained
⅓ cup reduced-calorie ranch dressing
4 cups torn iceberg lettuce
1½ cups chopped tomato
½ cup (2 ounces) shredded reduced-fat Cheddar cheese
⅓ cup chopped green onions
1 (4.5-ounce) can chopped green chiles, drained
2 (2.25-ounce) cans sliced ripe olives, drained
3 ounces baked salsa and cream cheese tortilla chips (about 60 chips)

1. Coat a medium skillet with cooking spray; place over medium-high heat until hot. Add onion and garlic; cook 5 minutes, stirring constantly. Add cooked rice, ½ teaspoon chili powder, ½ teaspoon cumin, ⅛ teaspoon red pepper, ⅛ teaspoon coriander, and beans; cook until thoroughly heated, stirring occasionally. Remove from heat, and cool. Cover and chill.

2. Combine ranch dressing, remaining chili powder, cumin, red pepper, and coriander; set aside.

3. Combine lettuce and next 5 ingredients in a large bowl, tossing well. Add reserved rice mixture and salad dressing; toss gently to coat. Cover and chill. Just before serving, place tortilla chips on a serving platter; spoon salad over chips. **YIELD:** 6 servings (serving size: about 2 cups salad and 10 chips).

POINTS: 6; **EXCHANGES:** 3 Starch, 1 Vegetable, 2 Fat; **PER SERVING:** CAL 317 (27% from fat); PRO 12.1g; FAT 9.6g (sat 2.2g); CARB 48.9g; FIB 6g; CHOL 6mg; IRON 3.6mg; SOD 801mg; CALC 174mg

TAKE A SPIN

Use a salad spinner to make sure you don't end up with a soggy Taco Salad. Just a few turns of this handy tool, and you'll remove excess water from freshly washed lettuce.

ZUCCHINI-SALSA FRITTATA

1½ cups fat-free egg substitute
½ cup salsa
1 teaspoon chili powder
¼ teaspoon pepper
⅛ teaspoon salt
Cooking spray
1 cup diced zucchini
½ cup chopped red bell pepper
¼ cup sliced green onions
½ cup frozen whole-kernel corn, thawed
¼ cup plus 2 tablespoons (1½ ounces) shredded Monterey Jack cheese with jalapeño peppers

1. Combine first 5 ingredients in a bowl; stir well, and set aside.

2. Coat a large nonstick skillet with cooking spray; place over medium-high heat until hot. Add zucchini, bell pepper, and green onions; cook, stirring constantly, 5 minutes or until tender. Stir in corn. Pour egg mixture over vegetables; cover, reduce heat to medium-low, and cook 15 minutes or until set.

3. Sprinkle cheese over frittata. Wrap handle of skillet with foil; broil 2 minutes or until cheese melts. Serve immediately. **YIELD:** 4 servings (serving size: 1 wedge).

POINTS: 2; **EXCHANGES:** ½ Starch, 1 Vegetable, 1 Lean Meat; **PER SERVING:** CAL 121 (27% from fat); PRO 13.3g; FAT 3.6g (sat 2.1g); CARB 10.1g; FIB 1.9g; CHOL 8mg; IRON 2.6mg; SOD 350mg; CALC 136mg

KOREAN BRAISED TOFU

- 1 (12.3-ounce) package extra-firm tofu, drained
- ½ cup vegetable broth, divided
- 4 teaspoons peanut or vegetable oil, divided
- ⅓ cup low-sodium soy sauce
- ¼ cup grated fresh onion
- 2 tablespoons Dijon mustard
- 2 garlic cloves, minced
- 1 tablespoon sugar
- 1 tablespoon molasses
- 2 tablespoons chopped fresh cilantro
- 2 cups thin strips carrot
- 1 cup thin strips red bell pepper
- 1 cup slivered red onion
- 1 cup snow peas, trimmed
- ¼ teaspoon salt
- 4 cups hot cooked long-grain rice

1. Place tofu on several layers of heavy-duty paper towels; cover with additional paper towels, and place on a plate. Place a saucepan filled with potatoes on top of paper towels; let stand 20 minutes to remove excess water. Cut tofu crosswise into 12 slices; set aside.
2. Combine ¼ cup vegetable broth, 2 teaspoons oil, soy sauce, and next 5 ingredients in an 11- x 7-inch baking dish. Place tofu slices in baking dish, turning to coat. Cover and marinate in refrigerator 1 hour.
3. Preheat oven to 350°.
4. Uncover tofu, and bake at 350° for 45 minutes or until marinade is almost absorbed. Remove tofu from baking dish; set aside, and keep warm. Add remaining ¼ cup vegetable broth to baking dish; stir, scraping dish to loosen browned bits. Pour over tofu, and sprinkle with cilantro.
5. Heat remaining 2 teaspoons oil in a large nonstick skillet over medium-high heat. Add carrot, red pepper, and onion; cook, stirring constantly, 4 minutes. Add snow peas and salt; cook, stirring constantly, 1 minute or until vegetables are crisp-tender. Serve tofu and vegetables over rice. **YIELD:** 4 servings (serving size: 1 cup rice, 3 tofu slices, and 1 cup vegetables).

POINTS: 8; **EXCHANGES:** 2½ Vegetable, 3½ Starch, 1 Fat; **PER SERVING:** CAL 399 (16% from fat); PRO 13.5g; FAT 7.5g (sat 0.9g); CARB 68g; FIB 4.2g; CHOL 0mg; IRON 4.7mg; SOD 1,366mg; CALC 90mg

TOFU TAMALE PIE

(pictured on page 71)

- 1 (12.3-ounce) package firm tofu, drained
- 2 teaspoons olive oil
- 1 cup finely chopped onion
- 2 garlic cloves, minced
- 1 tablespoon ground cumin
- 1 tablespoon hot chili powder
- 1 teaspoon salt, divided
- 1 (1.25-ounce) package 40%-less-sodium taco seasoning mix
- 3 cups water, divided
- 1 (16-ounce) can pinto beans, rinsed and drained
- 1 (10-ounce) can diced tomatoes and green chiles, undrained
- 1 (8¾-ounce) can whole-kernel corn, drained
- Cooking spray
- 1 tablespoon butter or stick margarine
- 1 tablespoon sugar
- 1 cup yellow cornmeal
- 1 teaspoon baking powder
- 2 large eggs, lightly beaten

1. Place tofu on several layers of heavy-duty paper towels; cover with additional paper towels, and place on a plate. Place a saucepan filled with potatoes on top of paper towels; let stand 20 minutes to remove excess water. Crumble tofu into small pieces.
2. Heat oil in a large skillet over medium-high heat until hot. Add onion and garlic; cook 3 minutes, stirring constantly. Add tofu, cumin, chili powder, ½ teaspoon salt, and seasoning mix; cook 3 minutes, stirring constantly. Add ½ cup water, pinto beans, tomatoes, and corn; bring to a boil. Reduce heat; simmer 15 minutes or until thickened. Spoon into an 11- x 7-inch baking dish coated with cooking spray.
3. Preheat oven to 375°.
4. Combine remaining 2½ cups water, ½ teaspoon salt, butter, and sugar in a medium saucepan; bring to a boil. Slowly add cornmeal, stirring constantly with a whisk. Reduce heat, and simmer 2 minutes, stirring constantly. Add baking powder and eggs; stir well. Pour cornmeal mixture over tofu mixture. Bake at 375° for 40 minutes or until lightly browned and bubbly. Let stand 10 minutes before serving. **YIELD:** 6 servings.

POINTS: 5; **EXCHANGES:** 2 Starch, 2 Vegetable, 1 Fat; **PER SERVING:** CAL 270 (27% from fat); PRO 11g; FAT 8g (sat 2.1g); CARB 40g; FIB 6.5g; CHOL 76mg; IRON 3.4mg; SOD 1,272mg; CALC 125mg

CURRIED TOFU WITH COUSCOUS

1¼ cups coarsely chopped onion (about 1 small)
1 (2-inch) piece peeled fresh ginger, coarsely chopped
3 garlic cloves, chopped
Cooking spray
2 tablespoons curry powder
¼ cup unsalted cashews
1 (14½-ounce) can vegetable broth, divided
¾ cup diagonally sliced carrot (about 2 medium)
1 pound firm tofu, drained and cubed
3 cups coarsely chopped fresh spinach
½ teaspoon salt
1¼ cups coarsely chopped tomato (about 1 medium)
1 (10-ounce) package couscous
2 tablespoons unsalted cashews, toasted and chopped

1. Place first 3 ingredients in a food processor; process until finely minced. Coat a large nonstick skillet with cooking spray; place over medium heat. Add onion mixture. Cook 3 minutes, stirring often. Add curry powder; cook an additional 2 minutes or until onion is tender. Remove from heat.
2. Place ¼ cup cashews and 1 cup broth in food processor; process 1 minute. Add cashew mixture to onion mixture in skillet; stir in carrot, tofu, and remaining broth. Bring to a simmer; cover and cook 8 minutes or until carrot is tender. Add spinach and salt; cover and simmer 2 minutes. Stir in tomato.
3. Cook couscous according to package directions.
4. Spoon couscous evenly onto 4 plates; top with tofu mixture. Sprinkle with toasted cashews. **YIELD:** 5 servings (serving size: 1 cup couscous, 1¼ cups tofu mixture, and about 2 teaspoons cashews).

POINTS: 8; **EXCHANGES:** 1½ Vegetable, 3 Starch, 1 Very Lean Meat, 2 Fat; **PER SERVING:** CAL 412 (24% from fat); PRO 17g; FAT 11g (sat 2.3g); CARB 55g; FIB 6.1g; CHOL 0mg; IRON 5.4mg; SOD 511mg; CALC 57mg

TOFU CALZONES

(pictured on page 69)

1 (12.3-ounce) package firm tofu, drained
½ teaspoon olive oil
1 garlic clove, minced
4 teaspoons lemon juice
2½ tablespoons minced fresh basil or 2¼ teaspoons dried
1 tablespoon pine nuts, toasted
1 (2-ounce) jar diced pimiento, drained
4 marinated artichoke heart quarters, drained and finely chopped (about ⅔ cup)
½ teaspoon salt
Dash of pepper
1 (10-ounce) can refrigerated pizza crust dough
Cooking spray
1 cup sliced crimini mushrooms
1 cup pasta sauce with mushrooms and olives (such as Classico)
Fresh basil sprigs (optional)

1. Place tofu on several layers of heavy-duty paper towels; cover with additional paper towels, and place on a plate. Place a saucepan filled with potatoes on top of paper towels; let tofu stand 20 minutes to remove excess water. Crumble tofu in a medium bowl.
2. Preheat oven to 450°.
3. Heat oil in a small nonstick skillet over medium heat until hot; add garlic. Cook 30 seconds or until garlic is lightly browned. Add garlic, lemon juice, and next 6 ingredients to crumbled tofu; stir well.
4. Unroll pizza dough onto a baking sheet coated with cooking spray; cut into 4 squares. Spoon ½ cup tofu mixture into center of each square; top with ¼ cup mushrooms. Fold each corner to center of the square, pinching points to seal; pinch edges to seal. Coat tops of each square with cooking spray.
5. Bake at 450° for 10 minutes or until lightly browned. Serve with pasta sauce. Garnish with fresh basil sprigs, if desired. **YIELD:** 4 servings (serving size: 1 calzone and ¼ cup pasta sauce).

POINTS: 7; **EXCHANGES:** 2 Vegetable, 2½ Starch, ½ Very Lean Meat, 1½ Fat; **PER SERVING:** CAL 342 (29% from fat); PRO 15g; FAT 11g (sat 1g); CARB 45g; FIB 2.4g; CHOL 0mg; IRON 4.5mg; SOD 1,071mg; CALC 98mg

TOFU TIP

Tofu comes in a variety of textures including soft, firm, and extra firm. Soft tofu can be puréed and added to soups, dips, and spreads. Firm and extra-firm tofu can be marinated, stir-fried, or panfried. Tofu in aseptic packages tends to be more delicate, regardless of whether it's labeled firm or extra firm, while water-packed tofu tends to be sturdier.

SPAGHETTI SQUASH WITH WHITE BEAN PROVENÇAL

- 1 (2½-pound) spaghetti squash
- Cooking spray
- 1 teaspoon roasted garlic-flavored vegetable oil
- 2 cups thinly sliced leek (about 1 leek)
- 2 (16-ounce) cans navy beans, drained
- 1 (14½-ounce) can no-salt-added stewed tomatoes, undrained
- 2 tablespoons chopped ripe olives
- 1 tablespoon balsamic vinegar
- ¼ teaspoon salt
- ¼ teaspoon pepper
- Fresh celery leaves (optional)

1. Preheat oven to 350°.
2. Wash squash; cut in half lengthwise. Remove and discard seeds. Place squash, cut sides down, in a 13- x 9-inch baking dish coated with cooking spray. Add water to depth of ½ inch. Bake at 350° for 45 minutes or until tender when pierced with a fork; let cool slightly. Using a fork, scrape spaghetti-like strands onto a platter; set aside, and keep warm.
3. Coat a saucepan with cooking spray; add oil. Place over medium-high heat until hot. Add leek; cook, stirring constantly, 3 minutes or until tender. Add beans and tomatoes; cook over medium heat 5 minutes. Stir in olives and next 3 ingredients; cook until thoroughly heated. Spoon bean mixture over squash. Garnish with celery leaves, if desired. **YIELD:** 4 servings.

POINTS: 4; **EXCHANGES:** 1½ Starch, 4 Vegetable, ½ Fat; **PER SERVING:** CAL 226 (11% from fat); PRO 10.5g; FAT 2.9g (sat 0.6g); CARB 43.0g; FIB 6.8g; CHOL 0mg; IRON 4.3mg; SOD 508mg; CALC 157mg

HOW TO COOK SPAGHETTI SQUASH

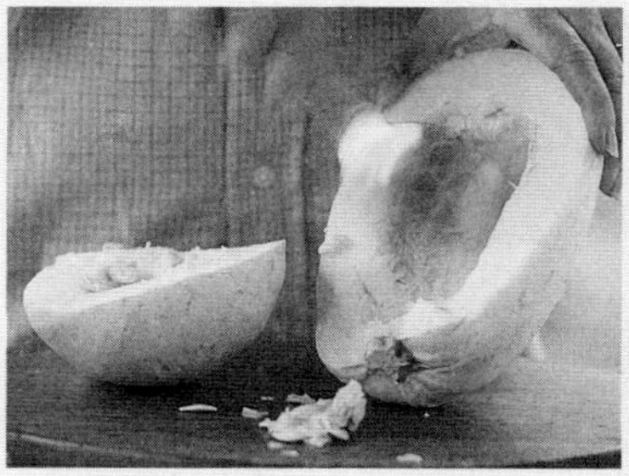

1. Wash squash. Cut squash in half lengthwise with a heavy knife, and scrape out the seeds.

2. Place cut sides down in baking dish coated with cooking spray. Add water to depth of ½ inch.

3. Bake at 350° for 45 minutes or until squash is tender when pierced with a fork.

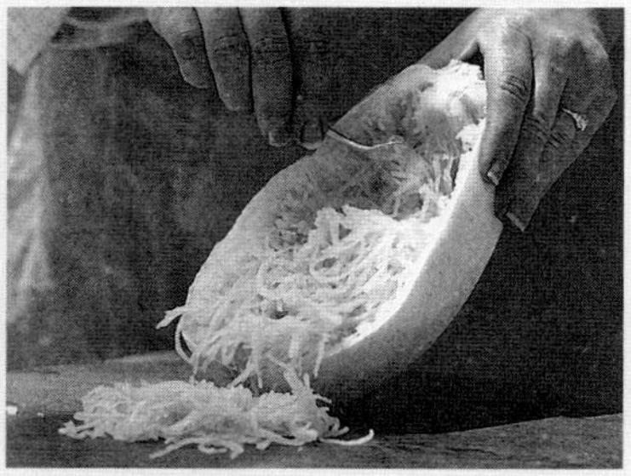

4. Use a fork to scrape out strands of squash.

SPAGHETTI SQUASH, LEEK, AND POTATO FRITTATA

- ⅓ cup 1% low-fat milk
- 2 tablespoons finely chopped fresh or 2 teaspoons dried basil
- ¼ teaspoon salt
- ¼ teaspoon black pepper
- 5 large egg whites, lightly beaten
- 2 large eggs, lightly beaten
- 2 cups cooked spaghetti squash
- 1 teaspoon stick margarine
- Cooking spray
- 2 cups frozen Southern-style hash brown potatoes, thawed
- 1 cup thinly sliced leek (about 1 large)
- ¼ cup (1 ounce) shredded Gruyère or Swiss cheese

1. Combine first 6 ingredients in a large bowl; stir in squash.
2. Melt margarine in a large nonstick skillet coated with cooking spray over medium-high heat. Add potatoes and leek; cook, stirring constantly, 7 minutes or until lightly browned. Add egg mixture to skillet. Cover, reduce heat to low; cook 10 minutes or until center is almost set. Uncover and sprinkle with cheese.
3. Preheat broiler. Wrap handle of skillet with foil; broil 5 minutes or until cheese melts. **YIELD:** 4 servings.

POINTS: 4; **EXCHANGES:** 1 Starch, 1½ Vegetable, 1 Medium-Fat Meat; **PER SERVING:** CAL 202 (29% from fat); PRO 12.1g; FAT 6.5g (sat 2.5g); CARB 23.7g; FIB 1.7g; CHOL 119mg; IRON 1.7mg; SOD 315mg; CALC 154mg

PESTO, BEAN, AND VEGETABLE PIZZA

(pictured on page 71)

1 cup cannellini beans, undrained
3 tablespoons pesto
1 garlic clove, peeled
Cooking spray
1 cup thinly sliced onion
1 cup sliced fresh mushrooms
1 cup red bell pepper strips
1 (16-ounce) Italian cheese-flavored pizza crust
⅓ cup drained canned coarsely chopped artichoke hearts
3 tablespoons sliced ripe olives
1 cup (4 ounces) shredded part-skim mozzarella cheese
¼ cup (1 ounce) freshly grated Parmesan cheese

1. Preheat oven to 425°.
2. Drain beans in a colander over a bowl, reserving 2 tablespoons liquid. Place beans, reserved bean liquid, pesto, and garlic in a food processor; process until smooth. Set aside.
3. Coat a large nonstick skillet with cooking spray; place over medium-high heat until hot. Add onion, mushrooms, and bell pepper; cook, stirring constantly, 5 minutes.
4. Place pizza crust on a baking sheet; spread bean mixture over crust, leaving a ½-inch border. Top with onion mixture, artichokes, and olives. Bake at 425° for 5 minutes. Sprinkle with cheeses; bake an additional 6 minutes or until cheese melts. **YIELD:** 8 servings (serving size: 1 slice).

POINTS: 6; **EXCHANGES:** 2 Starch, 1 Vegetable, 1 High-Fat Meat; **PER SERVING:** CAL 274 (32% from fat); PRO 13.2g; FAT 9.8g (sat 3.5g); CARB 34.2g; FIB 3.5g; CHOL 11mg; IRON 3.3mg; SOD 619mg; CALC 333mg

FOUR-CHEESE EGGPLANT CASSEROLE

(pictured on page 70)

5 small eggplants (about 4¾ pounds)
⅔ cup grated Parmesan cheese, divided
1½ cups (6 ounces) crumbled feta cheese
1 cup fat-free ricotta cheese
½ cup fat-free cottage cheese
¼ cup fat-free egg substitute
1 teaspoon freshly ground pepper
½ teaspoon salt
8 saltine crackers, crushed
Cooking spray

1. Preheat oven to 400°.
2. Pierce eggplants several times with a fork; place on a foil-lined baking sheet. Bake at 400° for 25 minutes or until very tender but not mushy. Remove from oven, and let cool slightly.
3. Reduce oven temperature to 350°.
4. Cut each eggplant in half lengthwise; scoop out pulp, and drain pulp well in a colander. Finely chop pulp.
5. Combine eggplant pulp, ½ cup Parmesan cheese, feta cheese, and next 6 ingredients in a large bowl; stir well. Spoon mixture into an 11- x 7-inch baking dish coated with cooking spray. Sprinkle remaining Parmesan cheese evenly over casserole. Bake at 350° for 1 hour and 15 minutes or until top is golden brown. Let stand 15 minutes before serving. **YIELD:** 8 servings.

POINTS: 4; **EXCHANGES:** 1½ Vegetable, 1 Low-Fat Milk, ½ Medium-Fat Meat; **PER SERVING:** CAL 189 (35% from fat); PRO 14.9g; FAT 7.4g (sat 4.6g); CARB 19g; FIB 5.5g; CHOL 28mg; IRON 1.2mg; SOD 632mg; CALC 274mg

NUTRITION

Calcium Counts

Do you consume enough calcium to build and maintain healthy bones? Learn how to be sure you're getting enough.

After the bran flakes, do you leave the cereal bowl half-full of milk? It can be difficult to convince the average American that a good bet for a lifetime of health is in the bottom of that bowl.

Most people are mindful of the calcium connection in children. But many don't realize that the building period for peak bone mass continues up to age 35. In fact, bones change continually throughout our lives.

BONING UP. The body requires a certain level of circulating calcium to perform vital functions such as helping muscles, including the heart, to contract; aiding nerve function; and helping blood to clot. Calcium is deposited and withdrawn daily from the bones, which store 99% of the mineral. When calcium levels drop, our bones release more into the bloodstream to fuel these activities. If your diet continually comes up short on calcium, the bones deplete their store of calcium. The end result is a calcium deficiency, which can lead to osteoporosis, the thinning of bones.

Fewer than 50% of adults consume enough calcium to maintain bone health and minimize bone loss typical of the aging process. An

(continued)

estimated 52% of women ages 30 and older mistakenly perceive their calcium intake as adequate.

Bones aren't the only thing that benefit from a calcium-rich diet. Calcium also reduces the risk of diseases such as high blood pressure, heart disease, kidney stones, and colon cancer. So calcium is more than just a skeleton-saver—it could be a lifesaver.

SUPPLEMENT SENSE. A supplement is an addition to a healthful diet, not the primary source of any mineral. There are clear advantages to obtaining dietary calcium through food instead of pills (see Calcium Countdown). Calcium-rich foods also supply vitamin D, which is necessary for optimum calcium absorption. But some situations call for a calcium supplement. Knowing the risks and benefits of each supplement type is important in deciding which is best for you.

- Calcium carbonate has the most calcium (40%) but is not easily absorbed by individuals lacking sufficient stomach acid (common in people over 60). It may irritate the stomach and cause bloating, gas, and constipation. It also can reduce absorption of some medications such as aspirin and tetracycline.
- Calcium citrate has only 24% calcium, but is more efficiently absorbed by the body. It may have the fewest side effects, including a lesser contribution to kidney stone formation.
- Calcium chloride can irritate the stomach, causing gas.
- Calcium lactate and calcium gluconate may cause diarrhea.

Antacids are advertised as calcium supplements, but those with both calcium and aluminum are not good choices because aluminum actually causes a loss of calcium. Avoid supplements with dolomite or bone meal—these may contain trace amounts of metal contaminants such as lead, mercury, arsenic, and cadmium, all of which can be toxic.

If you do take a calcium supplement, there are steps you can take to make sure you're getting the most from it.

- Space supplements throughout the day to optimize absorption. The body can only absorb a certain amount of calcium at a time.
- Drink plenty of fluids with calcium supplements to avoid constipation.
- Take a supplement with milk. Lactose (milk sugar) and vitamin D in the milk enhance absorption.
- When iron supplements are necessary, avoid taking them with a calcium supplement. These two minerals compete for absorption.

SIDE EFFECTS. Excessive supplemental calcium has been linked to loss of appetite, nausea, vomiting, weakness, dizziness, lethargy, and in some cases, kidney stones and poor kidney function. Large amounts of calcium are also associated with adverse effects on iron, magnesium, copper, and zinc absorption. It's important to note that this occurs when excess calcium is taken through supplements rather than food.

CAFFEINE CONNECTION. Caffeine may reduce the absorption of calcium, but the effect is quite small. A cup of regular coffee prevents the body from absorbing the amount of calcium in 1 teaspoon of milk. But if your caffeine intake is high, the effect adds up. Remember, when you choose a caffeinated beverage, you're choosing not to drink a calcium-rich beverage.

CALCIUM COUNTDOWN

Food (Serving)	Calcium Content (mg)
Yogurt	
plain fat-free (1 cup)	450
fruit (1 cup)	315
Goat milk (1 cup)	325
Fat-free milk (1 cup)	300
Orange juice, calcium fortified (1 cup)	300
Soy milk, calcium fortified (8 ounces)	250-300
Swiss cheese (1 ounce)	270
Cheddar cheese (1 ounce)	205
Blackstrap molasses (1 tablespoon)	170
Yogurt, frozen (½ cup)	105
Turnip greens (½ cup)	100
Sardines with edible bones (1 ounce)	90
Ice cream (½ cup)	85
Dried figs (3)	80
Parmesan cheese (1 tablespoon)	70

Meats

NUTRITION

Pumping Iron

Spinach isn't the only way to incorporate iron into your diet. Discover why iron is important and what's the best way to get it.

You eat spinach salad every day for lunch, you've given up steak, and you've made bran cereal your new best friend. But you find yourself longing for an afternoon nap. So you wonder, "Why am I so tired?" It could be a lack of iron.

A mineral essential to good health, iron carries oxygen throughout the body. It's also needed for proper immune function. The Recommended Dietary Allowance (RDA) for women up to age 50 is 15 milligrams daily; for women over 50 and adult men, it's 10 milligrams.

FAMILIAR SYMPTOMS. Iron deficiency often results in anemia, which is characterized by fatigue, pale skin, headache, weakness, lack of concentration, and irritability. A lack of iron commonly affects women of childbearing age, children, and teens.

Iron deficiency is not always the result of a poor diet. Periods of growth, blood loss through menstruation, and food restriction related to dieting contribute to deficiency. As with any condition, a physician should make the diagnosis. Treatment may include a change in diet.

IRONING OUT THE FACTS

These are the best bets for foods rich in the two kinds of iron and vitamin C.

SOURCE	PORTION	AMOUNT
HEME IRON		
Oysters, steamed	3 ounces	7.8 mg
Beef liver, braised	3 ounces	5.8 mg
Lean sirloin, broiled	3 ounces	2.9 mg
Lean ground beef, broiled	3 ounces	1.8 mg
Skinned chicken breast, broiled	3 ounces	1.1 mg
Lean pork, roasted	3 ounces	1 mg
NONHEME IRON		
Fortified breakfast cereals	1 cup	4.5 mg–18mg
Pumpkin seeds	1 ounce	4.3 mg
Bran	½ cup	3.5 mg
VITAMIN C		
Strawberries	1 cup	84 mg
Kiwifruit	1 medium	74 mg
Cantaloupe	1 cup	68 mg
Orange	1 medium	59 mg
Broccoli, cooked	½ cup	58 mg
Bell peppers, chopped, cooked	½ cup	45 mg
Soybeans	½ cup	4 mg
Spinach, cooked	½ cup	3.2 mg
Red kidney beans, cooked	½ cup	2.6 mg

Most people assume that if they eat iron-rich foods, they won't be at risk. But prevention takes more than just eating lots of spinach. Spinach is rich in iron, but the iron is bound by a compound called oxalic acid, which inhibits absorption. Likewise, phytic acid in wheat bran and legumes, tannins in tea, polyphenols in coffee, and antacids, calcium, and soy protein all inhibit iron absorption. Other factors, including combination of foods, the amount of iron already stored in the body, and the form of iron present in food, influence your ability to absorb iron.

IRON PARTNERS. Heme iron, from animal sources, is absorbed more readily than plant-based nonheme iron. Depending on how much iron your body has stored, 15% to 35% of heme iron is absorbed. Only 2% to 20% of nonheme iron can be absorbed. RDAs take these variances into consideration.

Creating partnerships between foods enhances absorption of vitamins and minerals. Vitamin C–rich foods and foods containing heme iron, such as meat, poultry, and fish, aid in the absorption of nonheme iron. For example, iron from whole-grain pasta is better absorbed when topped with red bell pepper strips, a source of vitamin C.

So while spinach and bran are great, certain partnerships make them even better. Have a glass of orange juice with your cereal. Enjoy steak again, as long as the meat is lean, the serving size modest, and you include a side of broccoli. Maybe now, you'll have the energy to enjoy it.

SKILLET BEEF AND MACARONI

This hearty family favorite is a cinch to make on busy weeknights. Round out the meal with a tossed salad and reduced-fat chocolate chip cookies.

- 1 (14-ounce) package light deluxe macaroni and cheese dinner mix with cheese sauce packet (such as Kraft)
- 1 pound ground round
- 1 cup chopped onion
- 1 teaspoon dried Italian seasoning
- 1 (14.5-ounce) can no-salt-added diced tomatoes, undrained

1. Cook macaroni according to package directions. Drain; rinse under hot water, and drain. Set aside, and keep warm. Set cheese sauce packet aside.
2. Cook beef and onion in a large nonstick skillet over medium-high heat until beef is browned, stirring to crumble. Add Italian seasoning, cooked macaroni, reserved cheese sauce packet, and tomatoes; cook over medium heat until thoroughly heated, stirring occasionally. **YIELD:** 8 servings (serving size: 1 cup).

POINTS: 5; **EXCHANGES:** 2 Starch, 2 Lean Meat; **PER SERVING:** CAL 244 (19% from fat); PRO 20.2g; FAT 5.1g (sat 2.3g); CARB 28.6g; FIB 1.8g; CHOL 40mg; IRON 3mg; SOD 459mg; CALC 119mg

ARABIC BEEF AND RICE

- 1 pound ground round or lean ground lamb
- 1 cup chopped onion
- 2 cups water
- 1 cup uncooked basmati or long-grain rice
- 2 teaspoons beef-flavored bouillon granules
- 1½ teaspoons garlic powder
- 1½ teaspoons ground cinnamon
- ½ teaspoon ground allspice
- Cooking spray
- ½ cup golden raisins
- ¼ cup pine nuts, toasted
- 5 tablespoons seasoned rice vinegar

1. Preheat oven to 350°.
2. Cook beef and onion in a large nonstick skillet over medium-high heat until beef is browned, stirring to crumble. Drain in a colander; return to skillet. Add water and next 5 ingredients; stir well.
3. Spoon mixture into an 11- x 7-inch baking dish coated with cooking spray. Cover and bake at 350° for 45 minutes or until liquid is absorbed. Stir in raisins and pine nuts. Serve with seasoned rice vinegar. **YIELD:** 5 servings (serving size: 1 cup beef mixture and 1 tablespoon vinegar).

POINTS: 9; **EXCHANGES:** 2½ Starch, 1 Fruit, 2½ Lean Meat, 1 Fat; **PER SERVING:** CAL 417 (26% from fat); PRO 25.1g; FAT 12.1g (sat 2.9g); CARB 52.1g; FIB 2.5g; CHOL 53mg; IRON 4.5mg; SOD 723mg; CALC 41mg

ITALIAN STUFFED ZUCCHINI

- 4 medium zucchini (about 1½ pounds)
- 1 teaspoon olive oil
- ¾ cup chopped onion
- ½ cup chopped celery
- 4 garlic cloves, minced
- ½ pound ground round
- 3 large plum tomatoes, chopped (about 1⅓ cups)
- ¼ teaspoon salt
- ¼ cup chopped fresh basil
- 2 tablespoons chopped fresh oregano
- ½ cup fine, dry breadcrumbs
- 1 large egg white
- Cooking spray
- 1 (26-ounce) jar fire-roasted tomato and garlic pasta sauce (such as Classico)
- ¼ cup (1 ounce) freshly grated Parmesan cheese

1. Cut each zucchini in half lengthwise; scoop out pulp, leaving a ¼-inch-thick shell. Finely chop pulp; set pulp aside.
2. Steam zucchini shells, covered, 4 to 5 minutes or until crisp-tender. Place on paper towels to drain.
3. Heat olive oil in a large nonstick skillet over medium-high heat. Add onion, celery, and garlic; cook 3 minutes, stirring constantly, until tender. Add beef, and cook 5 minutes, stirring to crumble. Drain; set aside, and keep warm.
4. Add reserved zucchini pulp, tomato, and salt to skillet; cook over medium heat 15 minutes, stirring frequently. (Mixture will be dry.) Remove from heat; stir in beef mixture, basil, and oregano. Let cool slightly.

(continued)

5. Add breadcrumbs and egg white to beef mixture; stir well.
6. Preheat oven to 375°.
7. Divide beef mixture evenly among shells (about ⅓ cup per shell). Place stuffed shells in an 11- x 7-inch baking dish coated with cooking spray. Pour pasta sauce over shells. Bake at 375° for 20 minutes or until bubbly. Remove from oven; sprinkle with cheese. **YIELD:** 4 servings (serving size: 2 shells).

POINTS: 6; **EXCHANGES:** 1½ Starch, 3 Vegetable, 2 Lean Meat; **PER SERVING:** CAL 312 (24% from fat); PRO 23.0g; FAT 8.2g (sat 2.3g); CARB 36.9g; FIB 5.8g; CHOL 36mg; IRON 4.6mg; SOD 998mg; CALC 303mg

BEEF, PINEAPPLE, AND RED ONION STIR-FRY WITH GINGER SAUCE

- ¾ pound lean beef flank steak
- 1 tablespoon dry sherry
- ¼ teaspoon pepper
- 1 (20-ounce) can unsweetened pineapple chunks, undrained
- 2 tablespoons low-sodium soy sauce
- 1 tablespoon rice vinegar
- 2 teaspoons peanut oil or vegetable oil
- 1 medium-size red onion, cut into thin wedges
- 2 tablespoons minced fresh ginger or bottled chopped fresh ginger
- 2 garlic cloves, minced
- 1 cup finely chopped green onions
- 4 cups hot cooked rice, cooked without salt or fat
- ¼ cup diagonally sliced green onions

1. Cut steak in half lengthwise (with the grain). Cut steak across grain into ⅛-inch-thick slices. Combine steak, sherry, and pepper in a bowl; toss well.
2. Drain pineapple chunks, reserving pineapple and ½ cup juice. Combine juice, soy sauce, and vinegar.
3. Heat oil in a large nonstick skillet or wok over high heat. Add steak; stir-fry 3 minutes or until browned. Remove steak from wok; drain well.
4. Add onion, ginger, garlic, and 1 cup green onions to skillet; stir-fry 3 minutes or until lightly browned. Add pineapple; stir-fry 1 minute or until lightly browned. Return steak to skillet; add juice mixture. Stir-fry 2 minutes or until thoroughly heated. Serve over rice. Top with green onions. **YIELD:** 4 servings (serving size: 1 cup stir-fry and 1 cup rice).

POINTS: 8; **EXCHANGES:** 2 Starch, 1½ Fruit, 2 Lean Meat, ½ Fat; **PER SERVING:** CAL 388 (25% from fat); PRO 20.9g; FAT 10.6g (sat 3.9g); CARB 53g; FIB 3.4g; CHOL 43mg; IRON 3.8mg; SOD 267mg; CALC 76mg

MANDARIN BEEF

- 2 (3.5-ounce) bags quick-cooking boil-in-bag rice or 4 cups hot cooked rice, cooked without salt or fat
- ¾ pound lean beef flank steak
- Cooking spray
- 2 teaspoons grated fresh ginger
- 1 (16-ounce) package fresh broccoli florets (about 6½ cups)
- 1 (10½-ounce) can beef consommé, divided
- 1 (11-ounce) can mandarin oranges in light syrup, undrained
- 1 teaspoon garlic paste
- 2 tablespoons cornstarch
- 3 green onions, sliced diagonally into 1-inch pieces

1. Cook rice according to package directions, omitting salt and fat.
2. Cut steak diagonally across grain into ⅛-inch-thick slices. Coat a large skillet or wok with cooking spray; heat over medium-high heat until hot. Add steak and ginger; cook 3 minutes or until steak is done. Remove steak from skillet; set aside, and keep warm.
3. Place broccoli in skillet; add ¼ cup beef consommé. Bring to a boil; cover, reduce heat, and cook 2 to 3 minutes or until broccoli is crisp-tender.
4. Drain oranges, reserving liquid. Set oranges aside. Combine reserved orange liquid, remaining beef consommé, garlic paste, and cornstarch, stirring well. Pour over broccoli; stir in onions and steak. Cook over medium heat, stirring constantly, until slightly thickened. Gently stir in oranges. Serve over rice. **YIELD:** 4 servings (1 cup rice and about 1½ cups beef mixture per serving).

POINTS: 8; **EXCHANGES:** 2 Starch, 1 Vegetable, 1 Fruit, 2½ Lean Meat; **PER SERVING:** CAL 372 (20% from fat); PRO 26g; FAT 8.4g (sat 3.4g); CARB 48g; FIB 2g; CHOL 43mg; IRON 4mg; SOD 475mg; CALC 94mg

Running for His Life

KEN KRIEG • **HEIGHT** 5'6" • **BEFORE** 230 LBS. • **AFTER** 150 LBS.

Strategy: Ken runs 10 miles with friends every Saturday morning. "I have peace of mind and more patience . . . . I come home calmer."

Ken Krieg played football and lifted weights in high school. He played baseball in college. But he never won a trophy. He had always carried extra pounds, but he became heavier as an adult, carrying 230 pounds on his 5'6" frame.

But when Ken turned 40 he began to win trophies and ribbons. "Knowing that you earned it, especially when you never got one as a kid, means a lot," says Ken. "I've worked hard at it."

Ken earned his first awards for losing pounds through the Weight Watchers At Work program, which he began in September 1996. He joined after he noticed that short walks with his dog were wearing him out. "I was the heaviest I'd ever been," recalls Ken. "They say things go downhill once you turn 40, and I thought, 'I'm already at the bottom.' "

"Knowing that you earned it . . . means a lot. I've worked hard at it."

The weekly meetings motivated Ken. He stopped eating when he wasn't hungry and turned down seconds. A snack was a handful of chips instead of a whole bag. And Ken decided to try running with his dog, Hank. "I thought I'd made a major accomplishment when I could run ⅛ mile," remembers Ken. And he had: The distance wasn't the accomplishment though, the commitment to exercise was.

In eight weeks, Ken and Hank were running 1½ miles. Ken had lost more than 25 pounds, and Hank had lost nearly 15. Ken added sit-ups, push-ups, cycling, and strength training to his routine to keep it interesting. He saw results that kept him going. "I went hunting in Wisconsin; I was tromping around in the snow for nine days and didn't get tired," says Ken. "I knew things were going right, but that week told me how right they were."

Six months after joining Weight Watchers, Ken reached his goal weight of 170 pounds. Then, two of Ken's coworkers asked him to run a 4-mile race with them. "I don't think those guys thought I had a prayer," recalls Ken. "I had never run a road race. But I set a goal to finish the race, and also to beat them. By the first mile, I had already passed them." With his first race under his belt, Ken signed up for a 5K, an 8K, and a triathlon. Two years later, he had run four 26.2-mile races, including the Boston Marathon.

Finisher's medals are great, but Ken says the change in his teenage son is the best reward of all. "My oldest son had put on weight," Ken says. "But I couldn't say anything. I was a terrible example. I was afraid he was going to end up like me." Now that son and three of his siblings are running with Ken. The entry fees add up, but Ken says it's a small price to pay for a healthy family.

Corn Bread-Crusted Pork Cutlets, page 101

Glazed Herbed Pork Tenderloin, page 102

Lamb Shish Kebabs,
page 99

Spanish-Style Chicken and Rice With Peppers, page 107

Lemon and Rosemary Roasted Chicken With Potatoes, page 110

Tortilla-and-Chicken Casserole, page 106, With Refried Black Beans, page 132, and Cone of Paradise, page 131

Chicken With Cornmeal Dumplings, page 106

Stuffed Shells, page 111

Mustard-Crusted
Steak With Orange-Balsamic
Sauce, opposite page

MUSTARD-CRUSTED STEAK WITH ORANGE-BALSAMIC SAUCE

(pictured on opposite page)

This recipe generates plenty of pepper-scented smoke, so you may want to cook outdoors. We seared the steaks in a cast-iron skillet over hot coals. You can also prepare the steaks on your cooktop—just make sure the fan is on and the kitchen is well-ventilated.

Orange-Balsamic Sauce
- 2 teaspoons paprika
- 1 teaspoon dried thyme
- ½ teaspoon dried oregano
- ¼ teaspoon cracked black pepper
- ⅛ teaspoon salt
- ⅛ teaspoon ground red pepper
- 1 teaspoon Dijon mustard
- 4 (4-ounce) beef tenderloin steaks (1 inch thick)
- 4 teaspoons minced fresh parsley

1. Place a 10-inch cast-iron skillet on grill rack over hot coals (400° to 500°); let skillet heat at least 10 minutes or until very hot.
2. Prepare Orange-Balsamic Sauce; set aside, and keep warm.
3. Combine paprika and next 5 ingredients in a shallow dish; stir well. Spread mustard evenly over both sides of each steak. Dredge each steak in spice mixture.
4. Place steaks in preheated skillet; cook 3 minutes on each side or until desired degree of doneness (outside of steaks should be charred but not burned).
5. Place steaks on each of 4 plates; spoon Orange-Balsamic Sauce evenly over each steak, and sprinkle with parsley. YIELD: 4 servings (serving size: 1 steak and 3 tablespoons sauce).

NOTE: You can substitute four 4-ounce fresh tuna steaks for the beef tenderloin. Cook 2 to 3 minutes on each side or until desired degree of doneness. One tuna steak and 3 tablespoons sauce has 4 ***POINTS***.

ORANGE-BALSAMIC SAUCE

- ½ cup minced shallots (about 3)
- 1 garlic clove, halved
- ⅔ cup orange juice
- ⅓ cup balsamic vinegar
- 1 teaspoon sugar
- ½ teaspoon cracked black pepper
- ⅛ teaspoon salt

1. Combine all ingredients in a small saucepan; bring to a boil. Reduce heat to medium; cook, uncovered, 10 minutes. Strain mixture through a fine sieve into a bowl; discard solids. YIELD: ¾ cup.

POINTS: 5; **EXCHANGES:** ½ Starch, 3 Lean Meat;
PER SERVING: CAL 199 (35% from fat);
PRO 24.2g; FAT 7.7g (sat 3g); CARB 7.2g;
FIB 0.6g; CHOL 70mg; IRON 4.3mg;
SOD 247mg; CALC 26mg

ALL-AMERICAN GRILLED STEAK

- 1 cup dry red wine
- ¼ cup ketchup
- 3 tablespoons Dijon mustard
- 2 tablespoons red wine vinegar
- ½ teaspoon salt
- ½ teaspoon dried thyme
- ½ teaspoon pepper
- 2 garlic cloves, minced
- 1 bay leaf
- 1 (1½-pound) lean boneless top round steak (about 1½ inches thick)

Cooking spray

1. Combine first 9 ingredients in a large heavy-duty, zip-top plastic bag; add steak, and seal bag. Marinate in refrigerator 8 hours or overnight, turning occasionally.
2. Remove steak from bag, reserving marinade; discard bay leaf. Place marinade in a saucepan. Bring to a boil; remove from heat. Coat grill rack with cooking spray. Place steak on rack over hot coals (400° to 500°); grill 5 minutes on each side or until desired degree of doneness, basting with reserved marinade.
3. Slice steak diagonally across grain into thin slices. YIELD: 6 servings.

POINTS: 4; **EXCHANGES:** 3½ Lean Meat;
PER SERVING: CAL 177 (26% from fat);
PRO 26.2g; FAT 5.2g (sat 1.7g); CARB 4.5g;
FIB 0.2g; CHOL 65mg; IRON 2.8mg;
SOD 599mg; CALC 13mg

STEAK FAJITAS WITH CILANTRO AND OLIVE SALSA

1 pound top sirloin, thinly sliced
1 tablespoon chili powder
1 teaspoon ground cumin
½ teaspoon salt, divided
1¼ cups finely chopped tomato (about 1 medium)
1 (2.5-ounce) can sliced ripe olives, drained
1 green onion, finely chopped (about 2 tablespoons)
3 tablespoons chopped fresh cilantro
3 tablespoons lime juice, divided
Cooking spray
1 (16-ounce) bag frozen pepper stir-fry, thawed
4 (10-inch) flour tortillas, warmed
1 cup nonfat sour cream

1. Combine steak, chili powder, cumin, and ¼ teaspoon salt; toss well. Set aside.
2. Combine tomato, olives, green onion, cilantro, 2 tablespoons lime juice, and remaining ¼ teaspoon salt; set aside.
3. Heat a large nonstick skillet over medium-high heat until hot. Coat beef mixture lightly with cooking spray; toss well. Add beef mixture to skillet; cook, stirring constantly, 3 minutes or until browned. Remove beef mixture from skillet. Set aside; keep warm.
4. Pat pepper stir-fry dry with paper towels; add to skillet. Cook over high heat 4 minutes or until lightly browned. Return beef mixture to skillet. Add remaining 1 tablespoon lime juice; stir well. Serve with tortillas, reserved cilantro and olive salsa, and sour cream.

YIELD: 4 servings (serving size: 1 tortilla, ½ cup beef mixture, about ½ cup salsa, and ¼ cup sour cream).

POINTS: 9; **EXCHANGES:** 2½ Starch, 1 Vegetable, 3½ Lean Meat, ½ Fat; **PER SERVING:** CAL 423 (26% from fat); PRO 34.7g; FAT 12.1g (sat 3.1g); CARB 43g; FIB 4.8g; CHOL 69mg; IRON 7mg; SOD 816mg; CALC 195mg

VEAL STROGANOFF

¼ cup all-purpose flour
½ teaspoon dried thyme
¼ teaspoon salt, divided
½ teaspoon pepper, divided
1 pound veal scaloppine or very thin veal cutlets
Cooking spray
1 tablespoon butter or margarine, divided
1 (8-ounce) package presliced fresh mushrooms
½ cup finely chopped onion
½ cup dry white wine
1 (15½-ounce) can beef broth
⅓ cup 30%-less-fat sour cream (such as Breakstone)
1 (10.5-ounce) package spaetzle (such as Maggi), uncooked

1. Combine flour, thyme, ⅛ teaspoon salt, and ¼ teaspoon pepper; set aside 2 tablespoons flour mixture.
2. Place each piece of veal between 2 sheets of plastic wrap; flatten to ¼-inch thickness, using a meat mallet or rolling pin.
3. Combine veal and flour mixture in a large zip-top plastic bag; seal bag, and shake to coat veal.
4. Heat a large nonstick skillet over medium heat. Coat half of veal pieces with cooking spray; add to skillet. Cook 1 minute on each side or until browned. Remove veal from skillet. Set aside, and keep warm. Repeat procedure with remaining veal.
5. Add 2 teaspoons butter to skillet; cook mushrooms and onion 2 minutes, stirring constantly. Add wine, scraping skillet to loosen browned bits; simmer 2 minutes.
6. Whisk together beef broth and reserved 2 tablespoons flour mixture; stir into mushroom mixture. Simmer 5 minutes, stirring constantly. Remove from heat; stir in sour cream.
7. Cook spaetzle according to package directions, omitting salt and fat; drain well. Melt remaining 1 teaspoon butter in a large nonstick skillet over medium-high heat; add spaetzle. Sprinkle with remaining ⅛ teaspoon salt and ¼ teaspoon pepper; cook, stirring constantly 3 minutes or until lightly browned. Place spaetzle in a serving dish; top with veal and sauce.

YIELD: 6 servings (serving size: ½ cup spaetzle, about 2½ ounces veal, and about ½ cup sauce).

POINTS: 7; **EXCHANGES:** 3 Starch, 2½ Lean Meat; **PER SERVING:** CAL 357 (19% from fat); PRO 27.6g; FAT 7.5g (sat 3g); CARB 42.4g; FIB 3g; CHOL 109mg; IRON 37mg; SOD 1,052mg; CALC 64mg

LAMB CHOPS WITH SWEET POTATO SAUCE

Serve with glazed baby carrots, a salad of mixed greens, and sourdough rolls.

4 (4-ounce) lean lamb loin chops (about 1½ inches thick)
½ teaspoon salt, divided
½ teaspoon pepper, divided
Cooking spray
1 tablespoon butter, divided
¾ cup diced sweet potato
¼ cup minced shallots
4 garlic cloves, minced
½ cup balsamic vinegar
1 cup fat-free, reduced-sodium chicken broth
1 tablespoon plus 1 teaspoon sugar
1 tablespoon Dijon mustard
2 teaspoons chopped fresh or ¼ teaspoon dried thyme
1 tablespoon thinly sliced fresh tarragon leaves

1. Sprinkle both sides of lamb with ¼ teaspoon each salt and pepper. Coat a large nonstick skillet with cooking spray; place over medium-high heat until hot. Add chops; cook 3 minutes on each side. Reduce heat to medium; cook 4 minutes on each side or until desired degree of doneness. Set aside; keep warm.
2. Add half of butter to skillet; cook over medium-high heat until butter melts. Add sweet potato, and cook 3 minutes or until tender, stirring often. Set aside, and keep warm.
3. Add remaining butter, shallots, and garlic; cook, stirring constantly, 2 minutes. Increase heat to high, and add balsamic vinegar. Simmer until liquid is almost evaporated. Add chicken broth and sugar; simmer 3 minutes. Add reserved sweet potato, Dijon mustard, thyme, tarragon, and remaining ¼ teaspoon each salt and pepper; stir well. Spoon sauce over chops. **YIELD:** 4 servings (serving size: 1 lamb chop and ¼ cup sauce).

POINTS: 7; **EXCHANGES:** 1½ Starch, 3 Lean Meat, ½ Fat; **PER SERVING:** CAL 305 (35% from fat); PRO 27.2g; FAT 11.8g (sat 4.8g); CARB 21g; FIB 1.8g; CHOL 89mg; IRON 2.9mg; SOD 655mg; CALC 54mg

LAMB SHISH KEBABS

(pictured on page 91)

¼ cup dry red wine
1½ tablespoons dried oregano
1½ tablespoons dried mint flakes
2 tablespoons lemon juice
2 teaspoons olive oil
4 garlic cloves, minced
1½ pounds lean cubed boned leg of lamb
18 (1-inch) squares green bell pepper
18 cherry tomatoes
1 large onion, cut into 6 wedges
Cooking spray

1. Combine first 6 ingredients in a large heavy-duty, zip-top plastic bag; add lamb, and seal bag. Marinate in refrigerator 12 to 24 hours.
2. Remove lamb from bag, reserving marinade. Place marinade in a saucepan. Bring to a boil; remove from heat. Thread lamb, pepper, tomatoes, and onion alternately onto 12 (10-inch) skewers. Coat grill rack with cooking spray; place on grill over medium-hot coals (350° to 400°). Place kebabs on rack; grill, covered, 5 minutes on each side or until lamb is desired degree of doneness, turning and basting kebabs frequently with marinade. **YIELD:** 6 servings (serving size: 2 kebabs).

POINTS: 4; **EXCHANGES:** 1½ Vegetable, 3 Lean Meat; **PER SERVING:** CAL 195 (33% from fat); PRO 24.6g; FAT 7.1g (sat 2.1g); CARB 8.3g; FIB 1.8g; CHOL 73mg; IRON 3.3mg; SOD 78mg; CALC 39mg

SKEWERING TIPS

If you haven't skewered in a while, remember that in terms of taste, efficiency, and appearance, there is no difference between metal and wooden skewers. Metal is good if you skewer often, but avoid round skewers (the meat will turn and twist). Wooden skewers are inexpensive and disposable, but they must be soaked in water for 10 minutes before using.

Alternately thread lamb cubes and vegetable chunks onto skewers. To be sure kebabs cook evenly, don't crowd pieces on the skewers.

STUFFED ARTICHOKES WITH SHIITAKE MUSHROOMS

Shiitake mushrooms are prized for their rich, meaty taste. Buy fresh mushrooms that are plump, firm, and unblemished, with edges that curl under. Shiitake stems are extremely tough, so remove them and use only the caps in this recipe.

4 medium artichokes
2 tablespoons lemon juice
Cooking spray
½ pound fresh ground pork
1 shallot, minced
¼ cup diced carrot
1½ cups sliced shiitake or button mushrooms
1 clove garlic, minced
¾ cup beef broth
½ teaspoon dried thyme
¼ teaspoon salt
⅛ teaspoon pepper
2 tablespoons all-purpose flour
1¼ cups 1% low-fat milk
1 cup cooked basmati rice
¼ cup minced fresh parsley
2 tablespoons freshly grated Parmesan cheese
2 tablespoons fine, dry breadcrumbs

1. Preheat oven to 350°.
2. Wash artichokes by plunging up and down in cold water. Cut off stem ends; trim about ½ inch from top of each artichoke. Remove any loose bottom leaves. With scissors, trim one-fourth off top of each outer leaf.
3. Place artichokes in a Dutch oven; add water to depth of 1 inch. Add lemon juice. Bring to a boil; cover, reduce heat, and simmer 25 minutes or until almost tender. Drain; cool. Spread leaves apart; discard inner leaves. Scrape out fuzzy choke with a spoon. Set artichokes aside.
4. Coat a large nonstick skillet with cooking spray; place over medium-high heat until hot. Add pork, shallot, and carrot. Cook 5 minutes, stirring to crumble pork. Add mushrooms and garlic; cook, stirring often, 2 minutes. Add beef broth and next 3 ingredients. Simmer 4 to 5 minutes or until liquid is absorbed and mushrooms are tender. Combine flour and milk, stirring to dissolve flour. Add to mushroom mixture. Simmer 3 minutes or until thickened. Stir in rice and parsley.
5. Spoon about ½ cup mixture into center of each reserved artichoke. Combine Parmesan cheese and breadcrumbs. Sprinkle 1 tablespoon Parmesan cheese mixture on top of mushroom mixture in each artichoke. Coat Parmesan cheese mixture with cooking spray.
6. Bake at 350° for 25 minutes or until tops are lightly browned.
YIELD: 4 servings (serving size: 1 artichoke).

POINTS: 7; **EXCHANGES:** 2 Starch, 2 Vegetable, 2 Medium-Fat Meat; **PER SERVING:** CAL 331 (24% from fat); PRO 23.3g; FAT 9g (sat 3.3g); CARB 41.4g; FIB 7.9g; CHOL 45mg; IRON 4.4mg; SOD 624mg; CALC 217mg

ONION-SMOTHERED PORK CHOPS

Cooking spray
1 pound Vidalia or other sweet onions, thinly sliced
1 teaspoon Creole seasoning, divided
4 (4-ounce) boneless center-cut pork loin chops (½ inch thick)
½ teaspoon dried thyme
¼ cup water
1 tablespoon Worcestershire sauce

1. Coat a large nonstick skillet with cooking spray, and place skillet over high heat until hot. Add onion slices and ¼ teaspoon Creole seasoning. Cook 7 minutes or until onions are tender and browned, stirring frequently. Set aside, and keep warm.
2. Trim fat from chops. Combine remaining ¾ teaspoon Creole seasoning and thyme. Sprinkle evenly over both sides of chops. Recoat skillet with cooking spray, and place over medium-high heat until hot. Add chops to skillet; cook 1 minute on each side. Reduce heat to medium; cook 4 to 6 additional minutes on each side or until done. Transfer chops to a serving platter. Place reserved onions on top of chops; keep warm.
3. Add water and Worcestershire sauce to skillet, stirring well. Cook over high heat, stirring constantly to deglaze skillet. Cook 1 minute. Pour sauce over chops. **YIELD:** 4 servings (serving size: 1 chop, about ⅓ cup onions, and 1 tablespoon sauce).

POINTS: 5; **EXCHANGES:** 2 Vegetable, 3 Lean Meat; **PER SERVING:** CAL 230 (34% from fat); PRO 26.4g; FAT 8.6g (sat 2.9g); CARB 10.7g; FIB 2.2g; CHOL 71mg; IRON 1.4mg; SOD 115mg; CALC 36mg

CORN BREAD-CRUSTED PORK CUTLETS

(pictured on page 90)
Serve with a garden salad and Creamy Scalloped Potatoes With Bacon (page 136).

¾ cup low-fat buttermilk
1 tablespoon Dijon mustard
1 tablespoon grated onion
½ teaspoon poultry seasoning
4 (4-ounce) pork cutlets (about ½ inch thick)
2⅓ cups seasoned corn bread stuffing mix (such as Stove Top)
Cooking spray
Fresh thyme sprigs (optional)

1. Preheat oven to 425°.
2. Combine first 4 ingredients in a large baking dish. Add pork, turning to coat. Marinate in refrigerator 30 minutes, turning pork occasionally.
3. Place stuffing mix in a food processor, and process until finely crushed. Pour stuffing mix into a shallow dish or pie plate. Remove pork from baking dish, and discard marinade. Dredge both sides of pork cutlets in stuffing mix, pressing to coat thoroughly. Place pork cutlets on a baking sheet coated with cooking spray, and bake at 425° for 12 minutes or until done. Garnish with thyme sprigs, if desired. **YIELD:** 4 servings (serving size: 1 cutlet).

POINTS: 9; **EXCHANGES:** 1½ Starch, 3½ Medium-Fat Meat; **PER SERVING:** CAL 374 (39% from fat); PRO 28g; FAT 16.4g (sat 4.3g); CARB 25g; FIB 0.7g; CHOL 78mg; IRON 1.5mg; SOD 811mg; CALC 66mg

PECAN-CORN BREAD-STUFFED PORK WITH APPLE-BOURBON GRAVY

Because the roast is boned and rolled, it cooks in less time than a bone-in roast. Be sure to check it after 4 hours so it doesn't overcook.

1 cup corn bread stuffing mix (such as Pepperidge Farm)
3 tablespoons bourbon, divided
2 tablespoons maple syrup, divided
½ cup finely chopped Vidalia or other sweet onion
½ cup finely chopped peeled Granny Smith apple
3 tablespoons chopped pecans
1½ tablespoons water
¼ teaspoon rubbed sage
⅛ teaspoon dried thyme
⅛ teaspoon pepper
1 (2-pound) lean rolled boned pork loin roast
¼ teaspoon salt
Cooking spray
4 (¼-inch-thick) slices Vidalia or other sweet onion
4 (¼-inch-thick) rings Granny Smith apple
1 cup unsweetened apple juice
⅛ teaspoon salt
3 tablespoons all-purpose flour
¼ cup water

1. Combine stuffing mix, 1½ tablespoons bourbon, 1 tablespoon syrup, chopped onion, and next 6 ingredients in a bowl; toss until well blended.
2. Unroll roast, and trim fat. Spread stuffing mixture over inside surface of roast. Reroll roast, and secure at 1-inch intervals with heavy string; sprinkle with ¼ teaspoon salt.
3. Coat a large nonstick skillet with cooking spray; place over medium-high heat until hot. Add stuffed roast, browning on all sides. Place browned roast in a 4-quart electric slow cooker. Arrange onion slices and apple rings on top of roast. Combine 1½ teaspoons bourbon, remaining 1 tablespoon syrup, and 1 cup apple juice; stir well, and pour over roast. Cover and cook on low-heat setting for 4 hours or until pork is done. Place roast, onion slices, and apple rings on a platter. Cut roast into 8 slices; cut onion slices and apple rings in half crosswise. Set aside, and keep warm.
4. Pour cooking liquid into a medium saucepan; stir in remaining 1 tablespoon bourbon and ⅛ teaspoon salt. Place flour in a small bowl; gradually add ¼ cup water, stirring with a whisk until well blended. Add flour mixture to pan; cook over medium heat until thick and bubbly, stirring constantly. Serve gravy with roast, onion slices, and apple rings. **YIELD:** 8 servings (serving size: 1 slice roast, ½ onion slice, ½ apple ring, and gravy).

POINTS: 6; **EXCHANGES:** 1 Starch, 3 Lean Meat; **PER SERVING:** CAL 270 (33% from fat); PRO 24.8g; FAT 10g (sat 2.8g); CARB 18.9g; FIB 1.4g; CHOL 67mg; IRON 1.6mg; SOD 262mg; CALC 23mg

GLAZED HERBED PORK TENDERLOIN

(pictured on page 90)

2 (¾-pound) pork tenderloins
⅓ cup reduced-sodium soy sauce
2 tablespoons brown sugar
2 tablespoons Dijon mustard
2 tablespoons chopped green onions
2 garlic cloves, crushed
1 tablespoon chopped fresh thyme
1 tablespoon chopped fresh oregano
½ teaspoon pepper
Cooking spray

1. Trim fat from pork. Place tenderloins in a large heavy-duty, zip-top plastic bag. Combine soy sauce and next 7 ingredients in a small bowl; stir well with a whisk. Pour soy sauce mixture over tenderloins. Seal bag, and marinate in refrigerator 8 hours, turning occasionally.
2. Remove tenderloins from bag, reserving marinade. Place marinade in a saucepan; bring to a boil. Remove from heat. Coat grill rack with cooking spray; place on grill over medium-hot coals (350° to 400°). Place tenderloins on rack; grill, covered, 7 minutes. Turn pork, and baste with reserved marinade. Grill, covered, 7 additional minutes or until a meat thermometer inserted into thickest part of tenderloin registers 160°. YIELD: 6 servings.

POINTS: 3; EXCHANGES: 3½ Very Lean Meat; PER SERVING: CAL 158 (18% from fat); PRO 24.7g; FAT 3.4g (sat 1g); CARB 5.6g; FIB 0.3g; CHOL 74mg; IRON 2.3mg; SOD 645mg; CALC 30mg

CIDER-GLAZED PORK WITH ONIONS AND CARROTS

2⅔ cups frozen mashed potatoes
1⅓ cups fat-free milk
¼ cup minced fresh parsley
1½ teaspoons rubbed sage
½ teaspoon salt
½ teaspoon pepper
1 tablespoon water
¾ teaspoon cornstarch
1 (1-pound) pork tenderloin
1 tablespoon olive oil, divided
3 medium onions, slivered (about 4 cups)
1 (16-ounce) package carrots, scraped and diagonally sliced (about 3 cups)
1¼ cups apple cider

1. Prepare mashed potatoes according to package directions, using 1⅓ cups milk.
2. Combine parsley, sage, salt, and pepper in a small bowl; set aside. Combine water and cornstarch in a bowl; stir well, and set aside.
3. Trim fat from pork. Slice tenderloin crosswise into ½-inch slices, and flatten to ¼-inch thickness. Rub 2 tablespoons parsley mixture evenly over pork.
4. Heat 1½ teaspoons oil in a large nonstick skillet over medium-high heat. Add half of pork slices, and cook 2 minutes on each side or until browned. Transfer pork slices to a plate; cover tightly with foil. Repeat with remaining oil and pork slices.
5. Add onion and carrot to skillet; cook 6 minutes, stirring often. Add cider and remaining parsley mixture. Cover, reduce heat, and simmer 5 minutes or until vegetables are tender. Return pork to skillet. Cook, uncovered, over medium-high heat 4 minutes or until liquid reduces to a light syrup. Add reserved cornstarch mixture to pan. Bring to a boil; cook 1 minute, stirring constantly, until thick and bubbly. Serve over mashed potatoes. YIELD: 4 servings (serving size: 3 ounces pork, ⅔ cup cooked mashed potatoes, and about 1 cup vegetables and sauce).

POINTS: 8; EXCHANGES: 2½ Starch, 2 Vegetable, 2½ Lean Meat, ½ Fat; PER SERVING: CAL 392 (21% from fat); PRO 28.7g; FAT 9.3g (sat 2.6g); CARB 47.5g; FIB 6.1g; CHOL 78mg; IRON 2.7mg; SOD 540mg; CALC 162mg

SAUSAGE-BEEF ENCHILADAS

(pictured on page 2)

1 pound ground round
½ pound lean turkey breakfast sausage
½ cup chopped onion
1 tablespoon ground cumin
1 tablespoon chili powder
1 teaspoon pepper
2 (10-ounce) cans enchilada sauce
1 (11-ounce) can whole-kernel corn, drained
12 (6-inch) corn tortillas
Cooking spray
¾ cup (3 ounces) shredded reduced-fat sharp Cheddar cheese
½ cup thinly sliced green onions

1. Place a large nonstick skillet over medium-high heat until hot. Add first 6 ingredients. Cook 5 minutes, stirring until meat is browned, stirring to crumble. Drain meat mixture well, and wipe skillet with paper towels. Return meat mixture to skillet; stir in 1 can enchilada sauce and corn. Heat until hot.

2. Stack tortillas between 2 damp paper towels. Microwave at HIGH 1 minute. Spoon meat mixture down center of each tortilla; roll up tortillas; arrange in a 13- x 9-inch baking dish coated with cooking spray.

3. Pour remaining can of enchilada sauce over tortillas. Cover and bake at 350° for 25 minutes. Uncover, sprinkle with cheese and green onions, and bake an additional 5 minutes. Serve immediately. **YIELD:** 6 servings (serving size: 2 enchiladas).

POINTS: 9; **EXCHANGES:** 2½ Starch, 3½ Lean Meat, 1 Fat; **PER SERVING:** CAL 408 (32% from fat); PRO 31.9g; FAT 14.5g (sat 4.7g); CARB 40.5g; FIB 4g; CHOL 88mg; IRON 4.2mg; SOD 737mg; CALC 248mg

SPINACH FETTUCCINE WITH BACON-CHEESE SAUCE

- 1 tablespoon margarine
- 2 teaspoons minced garlic
- 4 slices Canadian bacon, diced
- 1 tablespoon plus 2 teaspoons all-purpose flour
- 1½ cups 1% low-fat milk
- 3 tablespoons light process cream cheese
- ½ teaspoon freshly ground pepper
- ¾ cup grated Parmesan cheese
- 6 cups cooked spinach fettuccine, cooked without salt or fat

1. Melt margarine in a large nonstick skillet over medium-high heat. Add garlic and bacon; cook until bacon begins to brown. Reduce heat to medium; stir in flour. Gradually add milk, stirring with a whisk until blended; cook, stirring constantly, until thickened and bubbly. Stir in cream cheese and pepper; cook, stirring constantly, until blended. Add Parmesan cheese; cook, stirring often, until cheese melts.

2. Add hot fettuccine to ham mixture; toss well. Serve immediately. **YIELD:** 6 servings (serving size: 1 cup).

POINTS: 7; **EXCHANGES:** 3 Starch, 1½ Lean Meat, 1 Fat; **PER SERVING:** CAL 355 (25% from fat); PRO 19.2g; FAT 10g (sat 4.6g); CARB 45.9g; FIB 2.4g; CHOL 27mg; IRON 2.4mg; SOD 610mg; CALC 282mg

RIGATONI WITH PESTO AND PROSCIUTTO

- 3 cups fresh basil leaves
- ¼ cup fat-free, reduced-sodium chicken broth
- 1 tablespoon slivered almonds
- 1 tablespoon freshly grated Parmesan cheese
- 2 teaspoons olive oil
- ½ teaspoon salt
- 3 garlic cloves, peeled
- 6 cups hot cooked rigatoni (about 8 ounces uncooked pasta)
- 1 (14-ounce) can quartered artichoke hearts, drained
- 4 ounces very thinly sliced prosciutto, cut into strips

1. Place first 7 ingredients in a food processor; process until smooth, scraping sides of processor bowl occasionally. Combine basil mixture, pasta, artichokes, and prosciutto in a bowl; toss well. **YIELD:** 4 servings (serving size: 1½ cups).

POINTS: 6; **EXCHANGES:** 3 Starch, 1 Vegetable, 1 High-Fat Meat; **PER SERVING:** CAL 334 (19% from fat); PRO 17g; FAT 7.1g (sat 1.6g); CARB 50.8g; FIB 4.3g; CHOL 18mg; IRON 4.4mg; SOD 835mg; CALC 80mg

HOPPIN' JOHN WITH GREENS

- Cooking spray
- 4 ounces Canadian bacon, cut into 1-inch pieces
- 1¼ cups finely chopped onion (about 1 medium)
- 2 jalapeño peppers, seeded and finely chopped
- 2 garlic cloves, minced
- 2 cups fat-free, reduced-sodium chicken broth
- ½ cup water
- ½ (16-ounce) package prewashed collard greens, chopped (about 5 cups)
- 1 cup uncooked long-grain rice
- ¼ teaspoon crushed red pepper
- ¼ teaspoon salt
- 1 (15.8-ounce) can black-eyed peas, undrained
- Hot pepper sauce (optional)

1. Coat a Dutch oven with cooking spray; place over medium heat until hot. Add Canadian bacon and onion; cook 4 minutes, stirring constantly. Add jalapeño peppers and garlic; cook 3 minutes. Add chicken broth and next 5 ingredients; cover, reduce heat, and simmer 15 minutes. Add peas, and simmer 10 minutes or until liquid is absorbed. Serve with hot pepper sauce, if desired. **YIELD:** 6 servings (serving size: 1 cup).

POINTS: 4; **EXCHANGES:** 2½ Starch, 1 Vegetable, ½ Lean Meat; **PER SERVING:** CAL 241 (9% from fat); PRO 12.2g; FAT 2.3g (sat 0.7g); CARB 42.6g; FIB 7.3g; CHOL 9mg; IRON 2.6mg; SOD 792mg; CALC 135mg

NUTRITION

What's in for Takeout

Bringing dinner home is convenient, but is it smart? Here is our guide to healthful takeout.

Elizabeth Kiefling, a San Francisco production manager, usually stops for takeout after work. "I spend maybe five waking hours at home every day, so cooking isn't really a feasible option," she says.

Margaret Till, a working mom in Huntsville, Alabama, knows the routine. "I don't have time to cook a meal every night. So I pick up prepared foods from the grocery store or call ahead for takeout," she says.

According to a survey by the National Restaurant Association, more than three-quarters of Americans dine on takeout every month. To meet the demand, restaurants and grocery stores now offer everything from soup to dessert.

But convenience is not always healthful. A recent study found that women who chose food prepared away from home at least five times a week consumed an average of 300 more calories a day than those who prepared their dinner at home.

Fortunately, nutritious choices are becoming more available at the takeout counter. Felicia Busch, R.D., a spokesman for The American Dietetic Association, offers suggestions on what to choose for a healthful meal—and what to avoid.

PIZZA. Order a veggie pizza. If you really want meat, ask for Canadian bacon. If you have the option, get a whole-wheat crust. Serve with a salad made from prewashed lettuce in a bag, sliced plum tomatoes, and a splash of fat-free Italian dressing.

Resist high-fat toppings such as sausage, pepperoni, or extra cheese. Also, many pizzerias pour oil on a pizza before it goes in the oven to help the cheese brown and add flavor, but it's hardly necessary. Blot oil with a paper towel.

CHINESE. Choose lo mein, chow mein, and/or stir-fried vegetables. Order a large side of steamed rice and share, or save some for later. (The challenge with Chinese takeout is the portion size—those little boxes hold a lot of food.) "Order something with lots of vegetables or keep a large bag of frozen veggie stir-fry in the freezer to microwave when you get home," says Busch.

Say no to kung pao chicken or pork. Made with peanuts and oil, kung pao is one of the most high-fat entrées on any Chinese menu.

SUPERMARKET. Buy a rotisserie chicken, but remove the skin, which contains most of the fat. While you're at it, hit the produce section and grab a bag of prewashed mixed vegetables. Then pick up a loaf of whole-grain bread.

Avoid potato salad (at up to 475 calories and 35 grams of fat per cup), chicken salad, or tuna salad. These mayonnaise-based salads are high in fat and calories and low on healthful nutrients and fiber.

FAST FOOD. Consider a small burger or grilled chicken sandwich; order it with lettuce and tomato. Have a roast beef sandwich or turkey sub made with fresh vegetables. Hold the mayo and oil; mustard, ketchup, and barbecue sauce are good alternatives (but they are higher in sodium). A small order of fries (around 240 calories and 12 grams of fat) is okay, but a side salad with light dressing is a better choice.

Busch says, "Fast-food establishments make most of their money from soft drinks and fries. Nutritious options may be more expensive, but you're investing in your health, not the restaurant's bottom line."

TAKEOUT TIPS

If your favorite takeout food isn't mentioned here, you can still make sensible choices.

- Look for dishes that emphasize produce. Opt for fruit or vegetable sauces, relishes, chutneys, and salsas. These ingredients add flavor without fat.
- Incorporate salads into your meal. Choose greens such as romaine and radicchio, which are good sources of folate, vitamins A and C, and calcium.
- Know how food is prepared. Grilling, stir-frying, and baking add fewer calories than deep-frying or sautéing.
- Quit the clean-plate club. Eat the portion you want, saving the rest for another meal.
- Order a new food each time you get takeout. You'll get more variety in your diet and find new favorites as well.

Poultry

TORTILLA-AND-CHICKEN CASSEROLE

(pictured on page 94)

- 1 (28-ounce) can crushed tomatoes, undrained
- 1 medium onion, quartered
- 2 large garlic cloves, halved
- 1 (10-ounce) can diced tomatoes and green chiles, undrained
- 2 teaspoons ground cumin
- ½ teaspoon crushed red pepper
- ½ cup fat-free milk
- 1 (16-ounce) carton 50%-less-fat sour cream (such as Daisy)
- 18 (6-inch) corn tortillas, cut in half
- Cooking spray
- 1 (10.11-ounce) package ready-to-eat roasted chicken breast halves (such as Tyson), skinned, boned, and cut into bite-size pieces (about 2 cups)
- 2 cups (8 ounces) shredded reduced-fat Monterey Jack cheese

1. Preheat oven to 350°.
2. Place tomatoes, onion, and garlic in a food processor or blender; process until onion is minced.
3. Place tomato-onion mixture, diced tomatoes and green chiles, cumin, and crushed red pepper in a large nonstick skillet; bring to a boil. Reduce heat; simmer, uncovered, 15 minutes. Reserve 1 cup tomato sauce to serve with baked casserole. Set remaining tomato sauce aside.
4. Combine milk and sour cream in a bowl; stir with a whisk until blended.
5. Arrange 18 tortilla halves in a 13- x 9-inch baking dish coated with cooking spray; top with half of chicken, half of tomato sauce, and half of sour cream mixture. Arrange remaining tortilla halves over sour cream mixture; top with remaining chicken, half of tomato sauce, and sour cream mixture. Sprinkle with cheese. Bake at 350° for 30 minutes or until cheese melts. Top each serving with about 1 tablespoon reserved tomato sauce. **YIELD:** 12 servings.

POINTS: 5; **EXCHANGES:** ½ Starch, 1 Vegetable, 1 Low-Fat Milk, ½ Lean Meat, ½ Fat; **PER SERVING:** CAL 239 (30% from fat); PRO 15.4g; FAT 7.9g (sat 3.7g); CARB 26.1g; FIB 2.8g; CHOL 39mg; IRON 1.2mg; SOD 486mg; CALC 326mg

CHICKEN WITH CORNMEAL DUMPLINGS

(pictured on page 95)

Cornmeal Dumplings
- 1 teaspoon olive oil
- 1 cup chopped onion
- ½ cup sliced carrot
- ¼ cup chopped celery
- 1¼ cups diced, peeled baking potato (about 1 medium)
- 2 tablespoons all-purpose flour
- 3 (14½-ounce) cans fat-free, reduced-sodium chicken broth
- ½ cup frozen whole-kernel corn, thawed
- ½ cup frozen green peas, thawed
- 2 tablespoons chopped fresh or 2 teaspoons dried parsley
- 1 teaspoon chopped fresh or ¼ teaspoon dried thyme
- ¼ teaspoon pepper
- ½ (10.11-ounce) package ready-to-eat roasted chicken breast halves (such as Tyson), skinned, boned, and cut into bite-size pieces (about 1 cup)

1. Prepare Cornmeal Dumplings; cover and set aside.
2. Heat oil in a Dutch oven over medium heat. Add onion, carrot, and celery; cook, stirring constantly, 3 minutes. Add potato; sprinkle with flour, and cook 1 minute, stirring constantly. Gradually stir in broth. Bring to a boil; reduce heat, and simmer, uncovered, 15 minutes. Stir in corn and peas; simmer 10 minutes. Stir in parsley, thyme, and pepper.
3. Arrange dumplings over vegetable mixture. Cover, reduce heat, and simmer 12 minutes or until dumplings are done, turning once. Remove from pan with a slotted spoon; keep warm. Stir chicken into vegetable mixture; simmer 3 minutes or until thoroughly heated. Return dumplings to pan; simmer 1 minute. **YIELD:** 6 servings (serving size: 1 cup chicken mixture and 5 dumplings).

POINTS: 6; **EXCHANGES:** 3 Starch, 1 Vegetable, 1 Very Lean Meat; **PER SERVING:** CAL 306 (16% from fat); PRO 16.3g; FAT 5.4g (sat 2.1g); CARB 49.1g; FIB 4.2g; CHOL 60mg; IRON 2.7mg; SOD 1,108mg; CALC 123mg

CORNMEAL DUMPLINGS

- 1¼ cups all-purpose flour
- ½ cup cornmeal (not self-rising or cornmeal mix)
- 2 teaspoons baking powder
- ½ teaspoon salt
- 1 tablespoon chilled butter or stick margarine, cut into pieces
- ¾ cup low-fat buttermilk
- 1 large egg, lightly beaten

1. Combine first 4 ingredients in a large bowl. Cut in butter with a pastry blender or 2 knives until mixture resembles coarse meal. Stir in buttermilk and egg to form a soft dough. Roll dough into 1-inch balls with wet hands. **YIELD:** 6 servings (serving size: 5 dumplings).

LEMON CHICKEN WITH ANGEL HAIR PASTA AND ARTICHOKES

- ¼ teaspoon salt
- ¼ teaspoon pepper
- 4 (4-ounce) skinned, boned chicken breast halves
- 1 tablespoon olive oil
- 3 garlic cloves, minced
- 1 teaspoon grated lemon rind
- 2 (9-ounce) packages frozen artichoke hearts, thawed
- ¾ cup fat-free, reduced-sodium chicken broth
- ¼ cup fresh lemon juice
- ⅓ cup thinly sliced fresh basil leaves
- 4 cups hot cooked angel hair pasta (about 8 ounces uncooked pasta)

1. Sprinkle salt and pepper over chicken. Heat oil in a large nonstick skillet over medium-high heat. Add chicken; cook 3 minutes on each side or until browned. Remove chicken from skillet; set aside; and keep warm.
2. Add garlic and lemon rind to skillet; cook 30 seconds. Add artichokes, and cook, stirring constantly, 30 seconds.
3. Add chicken broth and lemon juice to skillet. Bring to a boil; return chicken to skillet. Cover, reduce heat, and simmer 8 minutes or until chicken is done. Stir in basil. Serve immediately over pasta. **YIELD:** 4 servings (serving size: 1 chicken breast half, 1 cup pasta, and ¾ cup artichoke mixture).

POINTS: 9; **EXCHANGES:** 3 Starch, 2 Vegetable, 3½ Very Lean Meat; **PER SERVING:** CAL 426 (13% from fat); PRO 37.2g; FAT 6.3g (sat 1.1g); CARB 54.9g; FIB 2.6g; CHOL 66mg; IRON 3.9mg; SOD 286mg; CALC 59mg

SPANISH-STYLE CHICKEN WITH RICE AND PEPPERS

(pictured on page 92)

- 1 tablespoon olive oil
- 1 pound skinned, boned chicken thighs
- ½ teaspoon salt
- ½ teaspoon pepper
- 1 (16-ounce) package frozen pepper stir-fry (such as Birds Eye)
- 1 cup uncooked rice
- 1 (14½-ounce) can diced tomatoes, undrained
- ½ teaspoon dried rosemary
- ½ cup dry sherry
- 1 cup water
- 2 tablespoons drained capers
- 2 tablespoons minced fresh parsley

1. Heat oil in a Dutch oven over medium-high heat. Sprinkle chicken with salt and pepper; add chicken to pan. Cook 2 to 3 minutes on each side or until browned.
2. Add pepper stir-fry and next 5 ingredients; stir well. Bring to a boil; cover, reduce heat, and simmer 22 minutes or until liquid is almost absorbed. Stir in capers and parsley. Cover and let stand 5 minutes.
YIELD: 4 servings.

POINTS: 7; **EXCHANGES:** 2½ Starch, 1½ Vegetable, 2 Lean Meat; **PER SERVING:** CAL 353 (19% from fat); PRO 24.4g; FAT 7.6g (sat 1.5g); CARB 44.3g; FIB 3.3g; CHOL 82mg; IRON 3.4mg; SOD 738mg; CALC 31mg

BUTTERMILK-BATTERED OVEN-FRIED CHICKEN

- 1½ teaspoons paprika
- 1 teaspoon salt
- ½ teaspoon pepper
- ½ teaspoon garlic powder
- ½ cup all-purpose flour
- 1 (4.3-ounce) package saltine crackers, crushed (41 crackers)
- ½ cup low-fat buttermilk
- 3 (6-ounce) skinned, bone-in chicken breast halves
- 3 (5-ounce) skinned chicken thighs
- Cooking spray

1. Preheat oven to 425°.
2. Combine first 4 ingredients in a small bowl. Place flour in a large heavy-duty, zip-top plastic bag; add 1½ teaspoons paprika mixture. Toss until thoroughly combined. Place cracker crumbs in a shallow dish; add remaining paprika mixture. Stir until well blended. Pour buttermilk into a small bowl.
3. Add chicken, 2 pieces at a time, to flour mixture; seal bag, and shake to coat chicken. Remove chicken from bag; dip in buttermilk. Dredge chicken in crumb mixture. Place on a baking sheet coated with cooking spray. Repeat procedure with remaining chicken and flour mixture.
4. Lightly coat chicken with cooking spray. Bake at 425° for 23 to 25 minutes or until chicken is done.
YIELD: 6 servings.

POINTS: 6; **EXCHANGES:** 1 Starch, 4½ Very Lean Meat; **PER SERVING:** CAL 280 (22% from fat); PRO 35.5g; FAT 6.8g (sat 1.9g); CARB 15.3g; FIB 0.7g; CHOL 112mg; IRON 2.5mg; SOD 739mg; CALC 57mg

GRILLED MAPLE-GLAZED CHICKEN

Use pure maple syrup, not pancake syrup, for this rich marinade.

2 skinned, bone-in chicken breast halves (about 1 pound)
2 skinned chicken thighs (about ½ pound)
2 skinned chicken drumsticks (about ½ pound)
1 cup maple syrup
⅓ cup bourbon
⅓ cup orange juice
2 tablespoons minced fresh sage
1 teaspoon coarsely ground black pepper
½ teaspoon salt
⅛ teaspoon ground red pepper
3 garlic cloves, crushed
Cooking spray

1. Combine all ingredients except cooking spray in a large heavy-duty, zip-top plastic bag; seal bag, and marinate in refrigerator at least 8 hours, turning bag occasionally.
2. Remove chicken from bag, reserving marinade. Place marinade in a saucepan. Bring to a boil; remove from heat. Coat grill rack with cooking spray; place chicken on rack over medium-hot coals (350° to 400°). Grill 6 to 8 minutes on each side or until done, basting frequently with reserved marinade. **YIELD:** 4 servings.

POINTS: 6; **EXCHANGES:** 2 Starch, 3 Lean Meat; **PER SERVING:** CAL 290 (17% from fat); PRO 25.5g; FAT 5.5g (sat 1.4g); CARB 34g; FIB 0.1g; CHOL 74mg; IRON 1.6mg; SOD 221mg; CALC 46mg

GRILLED ASIAN FIVE-SPICE CHICKEN

You can make the Lime Dipping Sauce ahead and store it in the refrigerator as the chicken marinates. But if you're pinched for time, this flavorful chicken can easily stand on its own without the sauce.

1 (3½-pound) chicken
1½ tablespoons brown sugar
3 tablespoons low-sodium soy sauce
3 tablespoons seasoned rice vinegar
1 teaspoon five-spice powder
½ teaspoon salt
¼ teaspoon ground red pepper
4 garlic cloves, peeled
3 shallots, halved
1 (1-inch) piece fresh ginger, halved
Cooking spray
Lime Dipping Sauce (optional)

1. Remove and discard giblets and neck from chicken. Rinse chicken with cold water, and pat dry. Remove skin, and trim excess fat; split chicken in half lengthwise. Place in a large heavy-duty, zip-top plastic bag, and set aside.
2. Combine brown sugar and next 8 ingredients in a food processor; process until smooth. Pour mixture over chicken; seal bag, and marinate in refrigerator at least 12 hours, turning bag occasionally.
3. Remove chicken from marinade, reserving marinade. Place marinade in a saucepan. Bring to a boil, and remove from heat. Coat grill rack with cooking spray; place chicken halves on rack over medium-hot coals (350° to 400°). Grill 20 minutes on each side or until done, basting frequently with reserved marinade. Serve with Lime Dipping Sauce, if desired. **YIELD:** 6 servings (serving size includes 2½ tablespoons sauce).

NOTE: Sharp kitchen scissors are the safest and easiest tool for cutting the chicken in half. Substitute 3½ pounds of chicken pieces for the whole chicken, if desired.

POINTS: 4; **EXCHANGES:** 3 Lean Meat; **PER SERVING:** CAL 184 (30% from fat); PRO 24.2g; FAT 6.2g (sat 1.7g); CARB 5.7g; FIB 0.1g; CHOL 73mg; IRON 1.3mg; SOD 649mg; CALC 21mg

LIME DIPPING SAUCE

⅓ cup water
¼ cup fresh lime juice
¼ cup low-sodium soy sauce
2 tablespoons sugar
1 tablespoon minced seeded green chile
1 garlic clove, minced

1. Combine all ingredients in a small bowl; stir well. Serve at room temperature with Grilled Asian Five-Spice Chicken. **YIELD:** 1 cup (serving size: 2½ tablespoons).

GOODS

Thrills at the Grill

Barbecue season heats up the selection of accessories for outdoor cooks.

Backyard chefs, reputed gadget lovers, now have a variety of gear to make outdoor cooking easier, safer, tastier, and more healthful. Nifty accessories such as fire starters, aromatic fuels, and professional-caliber tools transform the cookout to reflect modern tastes for fresher, lighter foods.

PROPANE SAFETY. Many Americans see outdoor cooking as an extension of their kitchens; with that comes an appreciation for safety. Overfill Protection Devices (OPDs) are required on new propane tanks for gas grills. If you have an older tank, it can be retrofitted with an OPD valve by a licensed dealer. If you participate in a tank exchange program, ask for an OPD-equipped tank; depending on the service provider, it may be a free upgrade or there may be a charge.

CHARCOAL STARTER. If you prefer cooking with charcoal, Weber's FireStarter cubes are a safe, odorless, nontoxic alternative to lighter fluid. These paraffin cubes light as easily as a birthday candle and get your fire going in minutes. They're perfect to use with natural hardwood charcoals such as hickory, mesquite, alder, maple, or pecan. Look for labels that say "natural" or "lump" charcoal or charwood; they're distributed by companies such as Weber, Wildfire, Red Seal, and Nature's Own.

WOOD FLAVORS. Charcoal Companion offers wood chips and dried smoking herbs, which make a natural charcoal fire even more flavorful. Wood chips work for gas grills, too; by adding these chips to a smoker tray, you get the authentic wood flavors of great barbecue.

You can also stoke your gas grill with briquettes that have hickory and mesquite wood blended with the ceramic binder. These briquettes impart wood flavor to foods for 10 to 12 grillings, after which they can be replaced or simply left on the grill. Gas briquette manufacturers include Woodstone and Charcoal Companion.

COOL TOOLS. Once you fire up your grill, new tools can ensure success. Nonstick grill pans with small holes are ideal for foods such as vegetables and seafood that tend to fall through the grill. Handsome enough for table service, Williams-Sonoma's nonstick grill basket has a removable handle and steep sides. Long-handled sealable baskets, such as ProGrill's large BBQ basket, hold foods in place when flipping and positioning over the fire. Grilla Gear's Kabob Rack keeps skewers from rolling around on the grate.

Grilling also requires long-handled tongs, spatulas, and sauce brushes. Williams-Sonoma's luxurious rosewood set includes spatula, tongs, fork, brush, and long-handled knife as well as a canvas carryall that doubles as an apron. Look for tongs that have a flexible spring and broad grippers such as the stainless tongs with rubber handles from ProGrill.

Every backyard chef who's been asked, "Is it done yet?" will appreciate Charcoal Companion's Perfect Temp 2 thermometer, which signals when food is done.

WHERE TO CALL. If you need help grillside, call the Weber Grill Line at 1-800-GRILL-OUT (between April 1 and Labor Day) or visit www.barbecuen.com, the site for "Barbecue'n on the Internet." To find a local retailer of Weber products, call 800-446-1071 or visit www.weber.com.

For information concerning the Williams-Sonoma catalog and products, call 877-812-6235 or visit www. williams-sonoma.com.

Another helpful Internet site is www.grillagear.com.

MOLASSES-SAUCED BARBECUED CHICKEN

This easy entrée is a family pleaser. Serve it with grilled corn on the cob (grill corn 15 to 20 minutes alongside the chicken).

½ cup ketchup
3 tablespoons molasses
2 tablespoons low-sodium Worcestershire sauce
2 tablespoons cider vinegar
2 tablespoons minced onion
1 tablespoon brown sugar
2 teaspoons liquid smoke
1 teaspoon chili powder
¾ teaspoon dry mustard
½ teaspoon coarsely ground pepper
Cooking spray
4 (4-ounce) skinned, boned chicken breast halves

1. Combine first 10 ingredients in a small bowl; stir well.
2. Coat grill rack with cooking spray; place chicken on rack over medium coals (300° to 350°). Grill, covered, 15 minutes or until done, turning and basting frequently with sauce. **YIELD:** 4 servings.

POINTS: 4; **EXCHANGES:** 1½ Starch, 3 Very Lean Meat; **PER SERVING:** CAL 220 (8% from fat); PRO 26.9g; FAT 1.9g (sat 0.4g); CARB 23.8g; FIB 0.8g; CHOL 66mg; IRON 2 mg; SOD 471mg; CALC 56mg

LEMON AND ROSEMARY ROASTED CHICKEN WITH POTATOES

(pictured on pages 92 and 93)

2 medium lemons
1 (3¼-pound) broiler-fryer
1½ tablespoons finely chopped fresh rosemary
6 garlic cloves, minced
1 teaspoon salt
¾ teaspoon pepper
2¼ pounds large red potatoes, cut into 2-inch pieces (about 5 cups)
3 tablespoons olive oil
Cooking spray

1. Preheat oven to 400°.
2. Remove yellow part of rind from lemons, using a vegetable peeler and leaving inner white skin on fruit; finely chop rind, and set aside. Squeeze juice from lemons; set juice aside. Reserve juiced lemon halves.
3. Remove and discard giblets and neck from chicken. Rinse chicken with cold water; pat dry. Trim excess fat. Stuff body cavity with reserved juiced lemon halves.
4. Combine reserved lemon rind, rosemary, and next 3 ingredients in a small bowl; stir in 2 tablespoons reserved lemon juice. Discard remaining lemon juice.
5. Combine potatoes and olive oil in a large bowl; toss well. Add 2 tablespoons lemon rind mixture to potatoes, tossing to coat; set aside.
6. Starting at neck cavity, loosen skin from breast and drumsticks by inserting fingers, gently pushing between skin and meat. Sprinkle remaining lemon rind mixture under loosened skin and rub over breast and drumstick meat.
7. Place chicken, breast side up, in a broiler pan on a rack coated with cooking spray. Arrange potatoes in a single layer around chicken. Bake at 400° for 1 hour or until meat thermometer inserted in meaty part of thigh registers 180°. Cover chicken loosely with foil; let stand 10 minutes. Discard skin. **YIELD:** 6 servings.

POINTS: 7; **EXCHANGES:** 1½ Starch, 3 Lean Meat, 1 Fat; **PER SERVING:** CAL 301 (39% from fat); PRO 26.2g; FAT 13.2g (sat 2.7g); CARB 19.3g; FIB 2.3g; CHOL 73mg; IRON 2.7mg; SOD 469mg; CALC 47mg

SPICY CHILI PITA PIZZAS

4 (6-inch) pita bread rounds
1 (15.5-ounce) can 99% fat-free turkey chili with beans (such as Hormel)
1½ cups (6 ounces) shredded reduced-fat Cheddar cheese
½ cup sliced pickled jalapeño peppers (about 24 slices)
1 cup diced tomato (about 1 medium)

1. Preheat oven to 450°.
2. Place pita bread rounds on a baking sheet; top each with about ⅓ cup chili. Sprinkle shredded cheese and jalapeño slices evenly over each pizza. Bake at 450° for 8 minutes or until cheese melts. Remove pizzas from oven; top each with ¼ cup tomato. **YIELD:** 4 servings.

POINTS: 8; **EXCHANGES:** 2 Starch, 1½ Low-Fat Milk, 1 Medium-Fat Meat; **PER SERVING:** CAL 403 (24% from fat); PRO 26.2g; FAT 10.7g (sat 5.4g); CARB 50.1g; FIB 3.3g; CHOL 48mg; IRON 6.2mg; SOD 979mg; CALC 474mg

"THE WORKS" DEEP-PAN PIZZA

- 1 (6.5-ounce) package pizza crust mix
- ⅓ cup yellow cornmeal
- ⅔ cup hot water (120° to 130°)
- Cooking spray
- 1 (8-ounce) can no-salt-added tomato sauce
- 1 teaspoon dried Italian seasoning
- 6 ounces turkey breakfast sausage, cooked and crumbled
- 1 (6-ounce) can sliced mushrooms, drained
- ⅓ cup drained pepperoncini pepper rings
- 1 cup (4 ounces) shredded part-skim mozzarella cheese

1. Preheat oven to 425°.
2. Combine first 3 ingredients in a bowl; stir with a fork until well blended. Shape dough into a ball; coat with cooking spray. Cover and let stand 5 minutes. Press dough in bottom and 1 inch up sides of a 10-inch cast-iron skillet coated with cooking spray; prick several times with a fork. Bake at 425° for 5 minutes.
3. Combine tomato sauce and Italian seasoning; spread over crust. Top with sausage, mushrooms, peppers, and cheese. Bake at 425° for 20 minutes or until cheese melts and crust is golden. Let stand 10 minutes before serving. **YIELD:** 6 servings (serving size: 1 slice).

POINTS: 6; **EXCHANGES:** 2 Starch, 1 Medium-Fat Meat, 1 Fat; **PER SERVING:** CAL 279 (31% from fat); PRO 14.5g; FAT 9.6g (sat 3.9g); CARB 33.2g; FIB 1.9g; CHOL 33mg; IRON 2.9mg; SOD 582mg; CALC 141mg

TURKEY-STUFFED ACORN SQUASH

- 3 (1-pound) acorn squash
- 1 tablespoon honey
- ¼ teaspoon ground cinnamon
- 1½ cups unsweetened apple cider
- ½ cup water
- ¾ cup long-grain rice, uncooked
- ¾ cup chopped red cooking apple
- 1 (3-inch) cinnamon stick
- ½ pound lean turkey sausage
- ⅔ cup chopped onion
- 1 tablespoon spicy brown mustard
- ⅛ teaspoon salt

1. Preheat oven to 375°.
2. Wash squash; cut in half lengthwise. Remove and discard seeds. Place squash halves, cut side down, in a 13- x 9-inch baking dish. Add water to dish to depth of ½ inch. Cover and bake at 375° for 35 to 40 minutes or until squash in tender. Drain, and let cool slightly. Scoop out pulp, leaving ½-inch-thick shells. Reserve squash pulp for another use. Brush squash shells with honey; sprinkle evenly with cinnamon.
3. Bring apple cider and ½ cup water to a boil in a medium saucepan; add rice, apple, and cinnamon stick. Cover; reduce heat, and simmer 20 to 25 minutes or until liquid is absorbed and rice is tender. Remove and discard cinnamon stick.
4. Cook sausage and onion in a medium nonstick skillet over medium heat until sausage is browned, stirring until it crumbles. Drain and pat dry with paper towels,
5. Combine rice mixture, sausage mixture, mustard, and salt; stir well, Spoon mixture evenly into squash shells; place in baking dish. Bake at 375° for 20 minutes or until thoroughly heated. **YIELD:** 6 servings.

POINTS: 6; **EXCHANGES:** 3 Starch, 2 Vegetable, 1 Fat; **PER SERVING:** CAL 292 (15% from fat); PRO 10.8g; FAT 5.0 g (sat .0.7g); CARB 54.2g; FIB 3.0g; CHOL 26mg; IRON 3.4mg; SOD 319mg; CALC 92mg

STUFFED SHELLS

(pictured on page 95)

Round out this hearty meal with a tossed salad and garlic bread.

- ¾ (12-ounce) package jumbo pasta shells (about 32 shells)
- 1 teaspoon olive oil
- 1 cup finely chopped onion
- 1 (10-ounce) package trimmed fresh spinach, coarsely chopped
- ¾ cup (3 ounces) grated fresh Romano cheese
- ⅓ cup chopped fresh or 2 tablespoons dried basil
- 1 teaspoon dried Italian seasoning
- ½ teaspoon salt
- 3 garlic cloves, minced
- 16 turkey-pepperoni slices (such as Hormel), chopped
- 1 (15-ounce) carton fat-free ricotta cheese
- 1 (15-ounce) carton whole-milk ricotta cheese
- 1 (26-ounce) jar fire-roasted tomato and garlic pasta sauce (such as Classico)
- 1 (8-ounce) can no-salt-added tomato sauce
- Basil sprigs (optional)

1. Preheat oven to 350°.
2. Cook pasta shells according to package directions, omitting salt and

(continued)

fat; drain. Rinse under cold water; drain and set aside.

3. Heat oil in a large nonstick skillet over medium heat. Add onion, and cook, stirring constantly, 5 minutes. Add spinach, and cook, stirring constantly, 3 minutes.

4. Combine spinach mixture, Romano cheese, and next 7 ingredients in a large bowl; stir well. Spoon about 1 heaping tablespoon spinach-cheese mixture into each cooked shell. Combine pasta sauce and tomato sauce; stir well. Spoon ½ cup sauce into a 13- x 9-inch baking dish. Arrange stuffed shells over sauce in baking dish; spoon remaining sauce over shells. Cover; bake at 350° for 35 minutes. Uncover; bake an additional 10 minutes. Let stand 5 minutes before serving. Garnish with basil, if desired. **YIELD:** 8 servings (serving size: 4 stuffed shells).

POINTS: 8; **EXCHANGES:** 1 Starch, 2½ Vegetable, 1 Medium-Fat Meat, 1½ Low-Fat Milk;
PER SERVING: CAL 400 (28% from fat); PRO 26.1g; FAT 12.4g (sat 6.6g); CARB 47.4g; FIB 4.1g; CHOL 49mg; IRON 3.5mg; SOD 747mg; CALC 423mg

GRILLED TURKEY TENDERLOINS WITH MANGO-PAPAYA SALSA

Mango-Papaya Salsa
- ¼ cup fresh lime juice
- 1 tablespoon olive oil
- ½ teaspoon salt
- ¼ teaspoon ground cumin
- ¼ teaspoon ground red pepper
- 2 (½-pound) turkey tenderloins

Cooking spray

1. Prepare Mango-Papaya Salsa; set aside.

2. Combine lime juice and next 5 ingredients in a large heavy-duty, zip-top plastic bag; seal bag, and marinate in refrigerator 30 minutes.

3. Remove turkey from bag, reserving marinade. Place marinade in a saucepan. Bring to a boil; remove from heat. Coat grill rack with cooking spray; place turkey on rack over medium-hot coals (350° to 400°). Grill, covered, 10 minutes on each side or until turkey is done, turning and basting frequently with reserved marinade. Cut turkey diagonally across grain into thin (¼-inch-thick) slices. Serve turkey with Mango-Papaya Salsa.
YIELD: 4 servings.

POINTS: 5; **EXCHANGES:** 1 Fruit, 3 Lean Meat;
PER SERVING: CAL 223 (35% from fat); PRO 24.4g; FAT 8.7g (sat 1.7g); CARB 12.3g; FIB 1.6g; CHOL 55mg; IRON 1.5mg; SOD 422mg; CALC 36mg

MANGO-PAPAYA SALSA

- ¾ cup diced peeled mango
- ¾ cup diced peeled papaya
- ½ cup diced red onion
- ½ cup diced plum tomato
- 3 tablespoons chopped fresh cilantro
- 2 tablespoons fresh lime juice
- 2 teaspoons olive oil
- 1½ teaspoons grated lime rind
- ⅛ teaspoon salt
- ⅛ teaspoon ground red pepper

1. Combine all ingredients in a medium bowl; toss gently. Cover and chill. **YIELD:** 2⅓ cups (serving size: about ½ cup).

TURKEY CUTLETS WITH TARRAGON

Serve these cutlets with parslied noodles, a mixed greens salad, and thin Italian breadsticks.

- 1 (1-pound) package turkey cutlets
- 2 garlic cloves, cut in half
- ¾ teaspoon dried tarragon
- ¼ teaspoon salt
- ¼ teaspoon pepper

Cooking spray
- 1 tablespoon extra-virgin olive oil
- ¼ cup lemon juice
- ¼ cup dry white wine
- 2 tablespoons chopped fresh parsley

1. Rub both sides of each turkey cutlet with garlic halves. Discard garlic halves.

2. Combine tarragon, salt, and pepper. Set aside.

3. Coat a large nonstick skillet with cooking spray; place over medium-high heat until hot. Add oil, tilting skillet to coat evenly. Add half of cutlets. Sprinkle half of tarragon mixture over cutlets. Cook 3 minutes on each side or until cutlets are done. Transfer cutlets to a serving platter; keep warm. Repeat procedure with remaining cutlets and tarragon mixture.

4. Add lemon juice and white wine to skillet. Increase heat to high, and cook about 1 minute, stirring constantly. Spoon wine mixture over turkey cutlets. Sprinkle with parsley.
YIELD: 4 servings.

POINTS: 4; **EXCHANGES:** 3½ Very Lean Meat, ½ Fat; **PER SERVING:** CAL 170 (28% from fat); PRO 27g; FAT 5.3g (sat 1.1g); CARB 2.3g; FIB 0.2g; CHOL 68mg; IRON 1.6mg; SOD 221mg; CALC 23mg

SUCCESSES

Proof Positive

TRACIE GALLOWAY • **HEIGHT** 5'4" • **BEFORE** 156 LBS. • **AFTER** 131 LBS.

Advice: Stay motivated—and positive—by occasionally splurging on a nonfood treat, such as a long, hot bath or a favorite magazine.

People can say the meanest things. "I had always been chubby as a child," remembers 28-year-old Tracie Galloway, who endured derogatory remarks about her weight for years.

Tracie camouflaged her weight with loose-fitting clothing until she went to college and encountered the freshman 15. "With the stress of being away from home, the weight just came on and it kept going," says Tracie.

Learning to care for herself on a student budget was hard. "I was not a healthful eater, and in college, money was tight," she says, which often meant cutting corners at the expense of good nutrition. As a "very insecure young person," Tracie found shelter and anonymity in being overweight.

She continued to hide behind her shield through college and then two years of marriage, while her weight crept up to 156. After a visit from her sister in 1995, Tracie was looking at photographs and thought, "I can't believe this is what I look like." A friend recommended that Tracie try Weight Watchers.

Tracie liked the organization's "realistic" approach. "You eat your own food and make lifestyle changes," she says. "I've learned to make more healthful choices, such as higher fiber and lower fat items."

Losing weight meant more than cutting back on calories. "I had a lot of negative attitudes about myself," she says. "But when you start to take care of your body, your attitudes become more positive. And when you have a more positive attitude about yourself, you take better care of yourself. It's really a cycle."

Part of that cycle was becoming physically active. Tracie was sedentary, but now she finds exercise a surprising pleasure as she lost weight and gained energy. "I got hooked because it makes you feel good and you can see results." Walking four times a week or working out to aerobics videos helped Tracie shed 25 pounds within a year.

> *"When you have a positive attitude about yourself, you take better care of yourself."*

But it wasn't easy. She says, "Sometimes you just have to take a step back, take a deep breath, and refocus; then keep going." That positive attitude has been the greatest benefit of losing weight, according to Tracie.

Before, Tracie says, "I felt like everything was happening to me. I felt out of control." Now she has taken charge of her life. She began a new career in childcare, is leading Weight Watchers sessions, and even enrolled in a watercolor class. Tracie says, "I've gained so much self-confidence and a passion for life."

Colorful Crunchy Slaw,
page 122

Apple Salad,
page 122

Oyster Po' Boy,
page 159

Pan-Seared Chicken Sandwich With Roasted Garlic Aioli, page 158

Smoked Turkey and Tortilla Soup, page 151

Citrus-Salmon Salad,
page 127

Lamb-Feta Burgers With Yogurt-Cucumber Sauce, page 157

Smoked Turkey-Bean Soup, page 150

Cincinnati Four-Way Chili, page 155

Fit at 50

RENÉE HURD • **HEIGHT** 5'5" • **BEFORE** 266 LBS. • **AFTER** 136 LBS.

Happiest moment: "I was so excited to buy my first Wonderbra. I don't have to go to a plus-size store. Now I buy whatever I want. I can even go to Victoria's Secret."

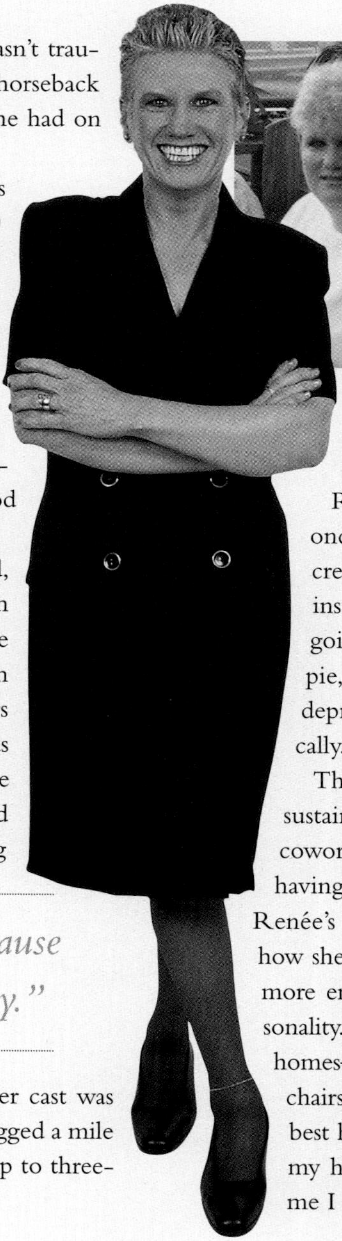

Reaching the half-century mark wasn't traumatic for Renée Hurd. Riding horseback on her birthday, she felt younger than she had on almost any other birthday of her life.

Renée reached her goal of 136 pounds just in time for her 50th, losing 130 pounds in 15 months. "Before, I wouldn't have thought of getting on a horse," she says. Instead, Renée was in the best shape ever thanks to a push from her physician. In December of 1996, Renée's doctor gave her medicine she didn't want to swallow: a lifetime prescription of drugs to lower her blood pressure and regulate her blood sugar.

But Renée never took a pill. Instead, she lost 35 pounds in three months with the help of Weight Watchers, though she was bedridden for most of that time with a broken ankle. "My Weight Watchers leader said, 'If you can lose 18 pounds while lying in bed, you're going to make your goal.' " Renée's family, friends, and coworkers offered support by bringing her healthful snacks and meals. Once her cast was off, Renée started walking. At first she logged a mile or two after work; eventually, she built up to three-mile walks.

"I never deprive myself, because you have to live realistically."

To celebrate Renée's landmark birthday, coworkers at the school where she works treated her to a tray of fresh fruit instead of a cake. "Everyone at work eats more healthfully because they see how it has changed me," Renée says. She credits her success to changes in her eating and cooking habits. "I can't call it a diet. I just became conscious of fruits and vegetables. Most important, keeping a daily journal keeps me in control."

Renée stopped eating many of the sweets she once craved. Now her treats are low-calorie ice creams and snacks baked with fruit purées instead of oil. "I plan my treats. If I know I'm going out for dinner, I know I'll want a piece of pie, so I plan around that," she says. "I never deprive myself, because you have to live realistically. I just plan those treats into my day."

The encouragement of friends and family has sustained Renée. When she lost 100 pounds, her coworkers gave her $100 to buy new clothes. Not having to shop in plus-size stores has boosted Renée's confidence. But what makes her happiest is how she feels. Once a size 28; now a size 8, Renée is more energetic and has a happier, more assured personality. "I was once afraid to go to other people's homes—I was too self-conscious to sit on their chairs," she says. "Now my doctor tells me I'm in the best health I've been in in ages. Seeing the look on my husband's face as he twirls me around reminds me I want to be here and healthy for a long time."

Salads

APPLE SALAD

(pictured on page 115)

Omit the pecans and blue cheese for a more kid-friendly fruit salad.

- 4 cups diced Red Delicious apple (about 2 medium)
- 1½ cups seedless green grapes, halved
- ½ cup finely chopped celery
- ½ cup finely shredded carrot (about 1 medium)
- 3 tablespoons fresh lemon juice
- ¼ cup plain fat-free yogurt
- 3 tablespoons honey
- ¼ cup chopped pecans, toasted
- ¼ cup (1 ounce) crumbled blue cheese

1. Combine first 5 ingredients in a large bowl, and toss well. Combine yogurt and honey in a small bowl; stir with a whisk until well blended. Pour over apple mixture; toss gently to coat. Sprinkle with pecans and blue cheese. **YIELD:** 6 servings (serving size: about 1 cup).

POINTS: 3; **EXCHANGES:** 1 Starch, 1 Fruit, 1 Fat; **PER SERVING:** CAL 163 (27% from fat); PRO 2.5g; FAT 4.8g (sat 1.3g); CARB 30.9g; FIB 3.2g; CHOL 4mg; IRON 0.5mg; SOD 86mg; CALC 63mg

COLORFUL CRUNCHY SLAW

(pictured on page 114)

For quicker preparation, use 4 cups preshredded coleslaw mix in place of cabbage and carrot.

- 2 cups thinly sliced green cabbage
- 2 cups thinly sliced red cabbage
- 1 cup thinly sliced fresh spinach leaves
- 1 cup shredded carrot
- 1 cup chopped sweet red pepper
- ½ cup julienne-cut peeled jícama
- ½ cup chopped onion
- ½ cup white wine vinegar
- ¼ cup sugar
- 2 tablespoons spicy brown mustard
- 1 tablespoon vegetable oil
- 1 teaspoon celery seeds
- ½ teaspoon salt
- ¼ teaspoon pepper

1. Combine first 7 ingredients in a large bowl. Combine vinegar and remaining 6 ingredients, stirring well. Pour dressing over cabbage mixture; stir well. Cover and chill at least 2 hours. **YIELD:** 6 servings (serving size: 1 cup).

POINTS: 2; **EXCHANGES:** 3 Vegetable, ½ Fat; **PER SERVING:** CAL 99 (27% from fat); PRO 1.9g; FAT 3g (sat 0.5g); CARB 17.1g; FIB 3.3g; CHOL 0mg; IRON 1.3mg; SOD 288mg; CALC 56mg

CAESAR SALAD

- ¼ cup (1 ounce) preshredded fresh Parmesan cheese
- ¼ cup low-fat buttermilk
- 2 teaspoons lemon juice
- 1½ teaspoons anchovy paste
- ¼ teaspoon Worcestershire sauce
- ⅛ teaspoon pepper
- 1 garlic clove
- ⅓ cup plain fat-free yogurt
- 2 (10-ounce) bags romaine salad or 12 cups sliced romaine lettuce
- 1 cup fat-free garlic-and-onion croutons
- 2 tablespoons (½ ounce) preshredded fresh Parmesan cheese

1. Combine first 7 ingredients in a blender; process until smooth. Pour into a bowl; stir in yogurt. Combine lettuce and croutons in a large bowl. Drizzle yogurt mixture over salad; toss gently to coat. Spoon salad into six individual bowls; sprinkle each with 1 teaspoon cheese. **YIELD:** 6 servings (serving size: 2 cups salad and 1 teaspoon cheese).

POINTS: 2; **EXCHANGES:** 2 Vegetable, ½ Fat; **PER SERVING:** CAL 92 (35% from fat); PRO 6.3g; FAT 3.6g (sat 1.7g); CARB 8.8g; FIB 1.6g; CHOL 7mg; IRON 1.3mg; SOD 441mg; CALC 162mg

BAKED POTATO SKINS ON CAESAR SALAD

Use reserved potato pulp for mashed potatoes or potato soup.

- 3 large baking potatoes (about 2 pounds)
- ¼ cup 50%-less-fat sour cream (such as Daisy)
- 1 cup fat-free creamy Caesar salad dressing, divided
- ¼ teaspoon freshly ground pepper
- 2 tablespoons horseradish mustard
- 1 cup (4 ounces) shredded reduced-fat sharp Cheddar cheese
- 4 slices bacon, cooked and crumbled
- 2 (10-ounce) bags romaine salad or 12 cups torn romaine lettuce
- ¼ cup sliced green onions

1. Bake potatoes at 425° for 1 hour or until done; let cool slightly. Increase oven temperature to 475°.
2. Cut each potato in half lengthwise; scoop out pulp, leaving a ¼-inch-thick shell. Reserve pulp for another use. Cut each shell lengthwise into four pieces.
3. Combine sour cream, 2 tablespoons salad dressing, and pepper; set aside.
4. Place potato shells on a baking sheet; spread shells evenly with horseradish mustard. Sprinkle evenly with cheese and top with crumbled bacon. Bake at 475° for 13 minutes or until shells are lightly browned and cheese melts.
5. Combine lettuce and remaining salad dressing; toss well. Place 2 cups lettuce mixture on each of six plates; top each with 4 potato pieces. Drizzle each with 1 tablespoon sour cream mixture and 2 teaspoons green onions. **YIELD:** 6 servings.

POINTS: 5; **EXCHANGES:** 2 Vegetable, 1½ Starch, 1 Fat, ½ Medium-Fat Meat; **PER SERVING:** CAL 250 (26% from fat); PRO 11.9g; FAT 7.3g (sat 3g); CARB 34.2g; FIB 2.9g; CHOL 20mg; IRON 1.6mg; SOD 742mg; CALC 230mg

SALAD OF VEGETABLES

(pictured on page 70)

- 9 cups torn red leaf lettuce (about 1 head)
- 1¾ cups peeled sliced cucumber
- 1¼ cups yellow bell or red bell pepper strips
- 1 cup sliced red onion
- 1½ cups chopped tomato, divided
- ¼ cup red wine vinegar
- 2 teaspoons extra-virgin olive oil
- 1 teaspoon dried oregano
- ½ teaspoon garlic powder
- ¼ teaspoon salt
- ¼ teaspoon freshly ground pepper

1. Combine first 4 ingredients in a large bowl; toss gently.
2. Place ¾ cup chopped tomato in a blender; process until smooth. Press puréed tomato through a sieve over a bowl, using back of a spoon; reserve tomato juice, and discard solids. Add remaining ¾ cup chopped tomato, vinegar, and remaining 5 ingredients to reserved tomato juice in bowl; stir until well blended. Pour dressing over salad, tossing gently to coat. **YIELD:** 6 servings (serving size: 2 cups).

POINTS: 1; **EXCHANGES:** 1½ Vegetable, ½ Fat; **PER SERVING:** CAL 53 (34% from fat); PRO 1.7g; FAT 2g (sat 0.3g); CARB 8.5g; FIB 2.3g; CHOL 0mg; IRON 1.3mg; SOD 107mg; CALC 46mg

SPINACH-FENNEL SALAD WITH GOAT CHEESE TOAST

Use long, slender French baguettes for these small cheese-topped toast slices.

- ¾ cup (3 ounces) goat cheese (at room temperature)
- 1 tablespoon fat-free milk
- 10 (¼-inch-thick) slices French baguette (about 4 ounces)
- 8 cups torn spinach
- 2 cups thinly sliced fennel bulb (about 2 small bulbs)
- 2 cups sliced mushrooms
- ¼ cup cider vinegar
- 3 tablespoons orange juice
- 1 teaspoon olive oil
- 1 teaspoon sugar
- ½ teaspoon salt

1. Combine goat cheese and milk; stir well. Spread evenly over bread slices. Place bread on a baking sheet; broil 2 minutes or until toasted.
2. Combine spinach, fennel, and mushrooms in a large bowl. Combine vinegar and remaining 4 ingredients; stir well. Pour over salad; toss gently to coat. Place 2 cups salad on each of five plates; top each with 2 bread slices. **YIELD:** 5 servings.

POINTS: 3; **EXCHANGES:** 2 Vegetable, 1 Starch, ½ Medium-Fat Meat; **PER SERVING:** CAL 166 (30% from fat); PRO 8.8g; FAT 6g (sat 3g); CARB 22.2g; FIB 4.7g; CHOL 16mg; IRON 4.4mg; SOD 633mg; CALC 225mg

ROASTED WINTER VEGETABLE SALAD

You can substitute the bottom of a broiler pan without the rack for the roasting pan.

- ½ cup fat-free Italian dressing, divided
- 3½ teaspoons olive oil, divided
- ¾ teaspoon salt, divided
- 4 cups chopped fennel bulb (about 4 small bulbs)
- 7 cups peeled, cubed acorn squash (about 2½ pounds)
- 2 medium onions, cut into ½-inch-thick wedges
- 1 teaspoon dried rosemary
- ¼ teaspoon ground red pepper
- Cooking spray
- 12 cups mixed baby salad greens
- 2 tablespoons balsamic vinegar

1. Preheat oven to 450°.
2. Combine ¼ cup salad dressing, 2 teaspoons olive oil, ½ teaspoon salt, fennel bulb, and next 4 ingredients in a large bowl, tossing to coat. Spread vegetable mixture evenly in a roasting pan coated with cooking spray. Roast at 450° for 45 minutes or until vegetables are tender, stirring occasionally. Set aside.
3. Place salad greens in a large bowl. Add remaining ¼ cup salad dressing, 1½ teaspoons olive oil, ¼ teaspoon salt, and balsamic vinegar; toss well. Add roasted vegetable mixture, tossing gently. **YIELD:** 12 servings (serving size: 1 cup).

POINTS: 1; **EXCHANGES:** ½ Starch, 1½ Vegetable; **PER SERVING:** CAL 77 (20% from fat); PRO 2.5g; FAT 1.7g (sat 0.2g); CARB 14.8g; FIB 2g; CHOL 0mg; IRON 1.6mg; SOD 299mg; CALC 103mg

SUGARED WALNUT, CHICKPEA, AND APPLE SALAD

- 1 tablespoon sugar
- 2 teaspoons butter or stick margarine
- 12 walnut halves (about ⅓ cup)
- 1 tablespoon apple juice
- ⅛ teaspoon ground red pepper
- Cooking spray
- ½ cup plain fat-free yogurt
- 2 tablespoons cider vinegar
- 1 tablespoon honey
- 2 teaspoons curry powder
- 2 teaspoons Dijon mustard
- ½ teaspoon salt
- 8 cups thinly sliced romaine lettuce
- 1 (19-ounce) can chickpeas (garbanzo beans), rinsed and drained
- 1 cup finely chopped red onion
- 2 medium Red Delicious apples, cut into wedges

1. Preheat oven to 350°.
2. Melt sugar and butter in a small skillet over low heat. Remove from heat; stir in walnuts, apple juice, and pepper. Spread walnut mixture evenly onto a baking sheet coated with cooking spray. Bake at 350° for 10 minutes, stirring after 5 minutes. Immediately scrape walnut mixture onto a sheet of foil coated with cooking spray, spreading walnut mixture evenly; let cool completely. Break mixture into pieces. Set aside.
3. Combine yogurt and next 5 ingredients in a small bowl.
4. Combine lettuce and ½ cup yogurt dressing, tossing to coat. Combine chickpeas, onion, and remaining dressing; toss well.
5. Divide romaine mixture evenly among four plates; top evenly with chickpea and walnut mixtures. Place apple wedges around edge of each salad. **YIELD:** 4 servings (serving size: about 2 cups lettuce, ¾ cup chickpea mixture, 3 walnut halves, and ½ apple).

POINTS: 7; **EXCHANGES:** 2 Starch, 2 Vegetable, 1½ Fat, 1 Fruit; **PER SERVING:** CAL 336 (27% from fat); PRO 12.9g; FAT 10.2g (sat 1.2g); CARB 52.7g; FIB 8.5g; CHOL 1mg; IRON 4.5mg; SOD 594mg; CALC 167mg

RICE SALAD WITH BACON AND PEAS

- 1 (6.2-ounce) package fast-cooking long-grain and wild rice mix (such as Uncle Ben's)
- 1 (10-ounce) package frozen petite green peas, thawed, or 2 cups fresh green peas
- 2 slices bacon, cooked and crumbled
- ½ cup reduced-calorie olive oil vinaigrette (such as Ken's Steak House)

1. Cook rice according to package directions, omitting salt and fat. Fluff with a fork; place rice in a large bowl, and let cool completely. Add peas, bacon, and vinaigrette; toss well. Cover and chill. **YIELD:** 4 servings (serving size: 1 cup).

POINTS: 6; **EXCHANGES:** 3 Starch, 1 Fat; **PER SERVING:** CAL 286 (28% from fat); PRO 9.3g; FAT 8.9g (sat 1.6g); CARB 44.2g; FIB 4g; CHOL 3mg; IRON 2.5mg; SOD 942mg; CALC 46mg

NUTRITION

Rethinking Cooking Oils

One of the most useful ingredients in the kitchen, oil is also one of the most maligned.

Oil used to be oil. Mom fried crispy chicken and made creamy salad dressing with it. But the oil didn't add a flavor of its own. These days, Mom's cooking is low fat. She's almost given up frying, but she hasn't given up oil.

Cooking healthfully and using oil are not mutually exclusive. Today's health-conscious cook uses oil as a flavorful condiment. For natural, full flavor, try unrefined oils pressed from fruits, seeds, or nuts. Flavor is removed from refined oils such as canola, providing a shelf-stable but tasteless product.

Unrefined oils are perishable, so buy small bottles and keep them refrigerated for no more than a few months. Use them sparingly near the end of a dish's cooking time—most unrefined oils have a low smoke point (the temperature at which oils burn), and high heat destroys the delicate flavor you paid for.

For daily use or for special occasions, we think oils are worth trying.

OLIVE OIL. Extra-virgin olive oil, the star of unrefined oils, comes from the first pressing of olives. Low in saturated fats (the kind you should avoid) and high in monounsaturated fats (the better kind), olive oil is an essential ingredient in heart-healthy cuisine. Don't be confused by the word "light"—in the case of olive oil, light refers to color and flavor, not calories.

WALNUT & HAZELNUT OILS. Walnut oil imparts an extraordinary nutty richness to salad dressings; just add a splash to any oil-and-vinegar dressing. Use either of these in baking; substitute a tablespoon or two for vegetable oil the next time you make blueberry muffins.

TOASTED SESAME OIL. Not to be confused with its refined but flavorless cousin, toasted sesame oil is a key ingredient in Chinese cooking. Almonds and a drop or two of this savory oil transform steamed asparagus into a sophisticated side dish.

ROASTED PEANUT OIL. This oil, which tastes a bit like natural peanut butter, is a spectacular addition to Southern, Thai, and Chinese cooking. Toss a teaspoon with noodles, add sesame seeds, and you get great flavor with little effort. Roasted peanut oil holds up well to heat, so it's okay to use it for light sautéing.

EXOTIC OILS. Worth sampling, toasted pumpkinseed oil has a robust, nutty flavor (try drizzling it over risotto). Just as intense, toasted pecan oil is excellent with fish or rice, or sprinkled lightly over a sweet potato instead of butter.

FLAVORED OILS. There's nothing like the taste that fresh herbs and spices add, but if you're short on time, use flavored oils such as basil, garlic, and chile oils instead to boost flavor. (Flavored oils are usually made from a combination of extra-virgin olive oil and canola infused with the herb or spice.) Chile oil adds a spicy kick to a favorite dish, and a few drops of truffle oil transforms plain poached eggs into a culinary triumph.

OIL AND YOU. All oil has the same number of calories and fat grams (a tablespoon has about 120 calories and 14 grams of fat), but it's not all the same kind of fat. To do your heart the most good, limit fat calories to 30% of your daily total (about 65 grams of fat for a 2,000 calorie-per-day diet). Get the bulk of your fat from oils made of mostly monounsaturated or polyunsaturated fats. High levels of saturated and trans fats are linked to heart disease, cancer, and stroke.

TYPES OF FATS IN OILS

Monounsaturated fats
canola oil • olive oil
peanut oil • pecan oil
sesame oil • hazelnut oil

Polyunsaturated fats
corn oil • pumpkinseed oil
safflower oil • sunflower oil
walnut oil

Saturated fats
butter • palm oil
coconut oil

Trans fats
margarine
hydrogenated or partially hydrogenated oil
(often found in commercially prepared baked goods and snack foods)

CURRIED CHICKPEA AND COUSCOUS SALAD

1 (5.6-ounce) package couscous with toasted pine nuts (such as Near East)
1 (15-ounce) can chickpeas (garbanzo beans), rinsed and drained
4 teaspoons curry powder
6 tablespoons light honey-mustard salad dressing (such as Maple Grove Farms)
½ cup sliced green onions
½ teaspoon pepper

1. Cook couscous according to package directions, omitting salt and fat; spread on a baking sheet, and let cool completely. Combine couscous, chickpeas, and remaining 4 ingredients in a large bowl; stir well. Cover and chill. **YIELD:** 4 servings (serving size: about 1 cup).

POINTS: 7; **EXCHANGES:** 4 Starch, 1 Fat; **PER SERVING:** CAL 337 (21% from fat); PRO 12.4g; FAT 7.7g (sat 1g); CARB 58.6g; FIB 5.1g; CHOL 0mg; IRON 3.4mg; SOD 708mg; CALC 70mg

FARFALLE SALAD

1 cup dried tomato halves, packed without oil
Boiling water
1 (1-pound) bunch fresh asparagus
8 ounces uncooked farfalle (bow tie pasta)
1 (2.8-ounce) jar pesto (such as Pesto Sanremo)
1 (6-ounce) package Italian-style chicken breast strips (such as Louis Rich Carving Board)
¼ teaspoon salt
½ teaspoon freshly ground pepper

1. Cut dried tomato halves into strips; place in a liquid measuring cup. Cover with boiling water; let stand 15 minutes or until soft. Drain, reserving ¼ cup liquid; set aside.
2. Snap off tough ends of asparagus spears; remove scales with a vegetable peeler, if desired. Cut asparagus into 2-inch pieces; set aside.
3. Cook pasta in boiling water 10 minutes, omitting salt and fat. Add asparagus to boiling pasta; boil 2 minutes or until pasta and asparagus are tender. Drain and rinse under cold water until cool; drain again.
4. Combine pasta, dried tomato strips, reserved tomato liquid, asparagus, pesto, and remaining 3 ingredients in a large bowl; toss well. Chill. **YIELD:** 7 servings (serving size: 1 cup).

POINTS: 5; **EXCHANGES:** 2 Starch, 1 Vegetable, 1 Very Lean Meat, 1 Fat; **PER SERVING:** CAL 273 (27% from fat); PRO 15.1g; FAT 8.2g (sat 1.5g); CARB 38.6g; FIB 4g; CHOL 17mg; IRON 4.9mg; SOD 782mg; CALC 125mg

TORTELLINI SALAD

1 (7-ounce) package cheese tortellini, uncooked (such as DaVinci)
1 cup grape or cherry tomatoes, halved
¼ cup reduced-calorie Caesar dressing (such as Ken's Steak House)
3 tablespoons chopped fresh oregano
½ teaspoon pepper

1. Cook tortellini according to package directions, omitting salt and fat. Drain and rinse under cold water. Combine tortellini, tomato, and remaining ingredients in a large bowl; toss well. Chill. **YIELD:** 3 servings (serving size: 1⅓ cups).

POINTS: 6; **EXCHANGES:** 2 Starch, 2 Vegetable, 1½ Fat; **PER SERVING:** CAL 284 (30% from fat); PRO 10.7g; FAT 9.4g (sat 3.4g); CARB 39.8g; FIB 1.9g; CHOL 40mg; IRON 2.8mg; SOD 915mg; CALC 128mg

SALAD NIÇOISE

1¼ pounds small round red potatoes, cut into 1-inch pieces
½ pound green beans, trimmed and cut into 2-inch pieces
1 (9-ounce) can solid white tuna in water, undrained
⅓ cup niçoise or kalamata olives, pitted and chopped
¼ cup reduced-calorie olive oil vinaigrette (such as Ken's Steak House)
½ teaspoon salt
½ teaspoon pepper

1. Place potato in a medium saucepan; cover with water. Bring to a boil; reduce heat, and simmer 10 minutes. Add beans, adding more water to cover, if necessary. Simmer 5 minutes or until vegetables are tender. Drain and rinse under cold water; let cool slightly. Set aside.
2. Drain tuna, reserving liquid. Flake tuna into bite-size pieces. Combine reserved liquid, olives, vinaigrette, salt, and pepper in a bowl. Add tuna, potato, and beans; toss gently. Chill. **YIELD:** 4 servings (serving size: 1¼ cups).

POINTS: 5; **EXCHANGES:** 1½ Starch, 2 Vegetable, 2 Very Lean Meat, ½ Fat; PER SERVING: CAL 268 (23% from fat); PRO 21.1g; FAT 6.8g (sat 1.1g); CARB 32.3g; FIB 4.1g; CHOL 27mg; IRON 2.7mg; SOD 836mg; CALC 56mg

CITRUS-SALMON SALAD

(pictured on page 117)

- 2 navel oranges
- 2 pink grapefruit
- 1 tablespoon olive oil
- 1 tablespoon honey
- 1 tablespoon Dijon mustard
- ¼ teaspoon salt
- ¼ teaspoon pepper
- 2 tablespoons Jamaican jerk seasoning
- 1 (1½-pound) skinned salmon fillet
- Cooking spray
- 5 cups fresh spinach leaves, torn
- ½ cup thinly sliced red onion
- 2 tablespoons sunflower seeds

1. Grate ½ teaspoon rind from orange (see Step 1 below); set grated rind aside.

2. Peel oranges and grapefruit as described in Step 2 below. Cut out citrus sections over a bowl, reserving juice (see Step 3 below). Set citrus sections aside. Squeeze membranes over bowl to extract additional juice. Discard membranes.

3. Combine 6 tablespoons citrus juice, grated rind, olive oil, and next 4 ingredients in a small bowl; stir well with a whisk. Cover dressing, and chill. Reserve remaining citrus juice for another use.

4. Rub Jamaican jerk seasoning over salmon. Place salmon on a broiler pan coated with cooking spray. Broil 14 minutes or until fish flakes easily when tested with a fork. Flake salmon into bite-size pieces; cover and chill at least 30 minutes.

5. Combine citrus sections, spinach, and onion in a large bowl. Drizzle dressing over salad, and toss gently to coat.

6. Divide salad evenly among five plates; top each salad evenly with salmon, and sprinkle with sunflower seeds. Serve immediately.

YIELD: 5 servings.

POINTS: 7; **EXCHANGES:** ½ Fruit, 2 Vegetable, 4 Lean Meat, 1 Fat; **PER SERVING:** CAL 342 (43% from fat); PRO 31g; FAT 16g (sat 2.6g); CARB 18g; FIB 5.1g; CHOL 89mg; IRON 3mg; SOD 797mg; CALC 105mg

PEELING CITRUS WITH EASE

Citrus is a sweet sensation in salad, but it's not always easy to work with. To get grated rind and perfectly peeled sections every time, follow these step-by-step directions.

1. Grate the rind from the citrus fruits, using a grater with small holes. Use short strokes and apply light pressure to avoid getting the white, bitter pith that lies under the colored rind.

2. Using a sharp knife, cut a small slice from both ends of the fruit. Place the fruit, cut side down, on a cutting board. Cut strips from the top, around the middle, and to the bottom just to reveal the citrus flesh, making sure that all of the white pith is removed.

3. Working over a bowl to collect the juice, cut along the side membranes of each citrus section, cutting to, but not through, the center of the fruit to release the sections. If the recipe calls for fresh citrus juice, squeeze the membranes to extract the juice; discard membranes.

THAI SALAD WITH GINGERED BEEF

- 1 (1-pound) lean flank steak
- 2 tablespoons grated peeled fresh ginger
- ½ teaspoon salt
- ½ teaspoon pepper
- Cooking spray
- 1 red bell pepper, seeded and cut into thin strips
- 1 (10-ounce) bag cabbage coleslaw
- ⅓ cup Thai peanut dressing (such as Bangkok Padang Peanut Sauce)

1. Trim fat from steak. Cut steak diagonally across grain into thin slices.
2. Combine ginger, salt, and pepper; toss with steak.
3. Coat a large nonstick skillet with cooking spray; place over medium-high heat until hot. Add half of beef, and cook 3 minutes, stirring often. Remove beef from pan. Set aside in a large bowl; keep warm. Repeat with additional cooking spray and remaining beef.
4. Coat pan with cooking spray; add red pepper, and cook 2 minutes. Add red pepper to beef strips; toss well.
5. Combine coleslaw and peanut dressing in a large bowl; stir well. Top coleslaw mixture with beef mixture. Let chill. Toss well before serving. **YIELD:** 4 servings (serving size: 1 cup).

POINTS: 7; **EXCHANGES:** 2 Vegetable, 3 Medium-Fat Meat; **PER SERVING:** CAL 293 (51% from fat); PRO 24.1g; FAT 16.5g (sat 6.2g); CARB 10.9g; FIB 2.2g; CHOL 60mg; IRON 2.9mg; SOD 697mg; CALC 42mg

GRILLED LEMON-HERB CHICKEN SALAD

- ¼ cup lemon juice
- 1 tablespoon dried basil
- 1 tablespoon dried parsley flakes
- 1 tablespoon minced garlic
- 1 tablespoon olive oil
- 6 (4-ounce) skinned, boned chicken breast halves
- 1 (12-ounce) bottle roasted red peppers, drained
- 3 tablespoons fat-free Italian dressing
- ¼ teaspoon salt
- ½ teaspoon pepper
- Cooking spray
- 1 (10-ounce) bag Mediterranean-blend salad greens or 12 cups mixed salad greens
- 1½ cups thinly sliced yellow bell pepper rings
- 1½ cups thinly sliced red onion, separated into rings
- 12 cherry tomatoes, halved

1. Combine first 5 ingredients in a large zip-top plastic bag. Add chicken to bag; seal bag. Marinate in refrigerator 8 hours.
2. Place roasted peppers and Italian dressing in a blender; process until smooth (dressing will be thick). Set aside.
3. Prepare grill. Remove chicken from bag; discard marinade. Sprinkle salt and pepper over chicken. Place chicken on grill rack coated with cooking spray; cover and grill 6 minutes on each side or until done. Cut each breast half diagonally into strips.
4. Divide salad greens evenly among six plates. Top each serving with 1 sliced breast half, ¼ cup yellow pepper, ¼ cup onion, 2 tomatoes, and ¼ cup roasted pepper dressing. **YIELD:** 6 servings.

POINTS: 4; **EXCHANGES:** ½ Starch, 1 Vegetable, 4 Very Lean Meat, ½ Fat; **PER SERVING:** CAL 230 (23% from fat); PRO 29.7g; FAT 6g (sat 1.3g); CARB 14.4g; FIB 3.7g; CHOL 72mg; IRON 3.4mg; SOD 867mg; CALC 98mg

CARIBBEAN CURRIED CHICKEN SALAD

Because this salad is tossed with fruit, it's best when assembled and served immediately.

- 2½ cups chopped cooked chicken breast (about 1 pound skinned, boned chicken breasts)
- 2 cups peeled, cubed honeydew melon
- 1¾ cups peeled, cubed mango
- ½ cup thinly sliced celery
- ⅓ cup reduced-fat mayonnaise
- 2 tablespoons chopped fresh cilantro
- 1½ teaspoons curry powder
- 2 teaspoons grated lime rind
- 2½ tablespoons fresh lime juice
- ½ teaspoon salt
- 8 Boston lettuce leaves

1. Combine first 4 ingredients in a medium bowl. Combine mayonnaise and next 5 ingredients in a small bowl; stir well. Pour over chicken salad; toss gently to coat. Spoon onto four lettuce-lined plates. Serve immediately. **YIELD:** 4 servings (serving size: 1¼ cups chicken salad and 2 lettuce leaves).

POINTS: 6; **EXCHANGES:** 1½ Fruit, 4 Very Lean Meat, 1½ Fat; **PER SERVING:** CAL 291 (30% from fat); PRO 27.8g; FAT 9.7g (sat 2.5g); CARB 24.3g; FIB 2.8g; CHOL 79mg; IRON 1.6mg; SOD 535mg; CALC 47mg

NUTRITION

Things That Go Gulp in the Night

Nibbling at night isn't a problem. It's the emotions behind the behavior that unravel a healthy lifestyle.

Stress is a fact of twenty-first century life. Juggling family, work, bills, and a host of other obligations is stressful, especially if you don't have enough help. In trying times, it's not unusual for the relative peace of evening to offer an opportunity to eat your way toward consolation.

Many of us do that. Nighttime nibblers snack for distraction from what is eating *them,* and often pay no attention to what they eat or how much. Before you know it, this bad habit packs on the pounds.

PLEASER PROBLEMS. Stress is not the only factor. The "pleaser" personality, for example, can play a role. Usually a woman, the pleaser lives for others, sacrificing her own needs and wants. It works until she's taken for granted or is made to feel that she can't do enough. Anxious and guilty, pleasers snack at night for reward and self-approval.

People frustrated at work often do the same thing. Lonely people fill up on snacks because TV and videos can't fill their evenings.

RELAXING ALTERNATIVES. Cheryl Hartsough, R.D., nutritionist and director of health programs at Colorado's Aspen Club, sums up the problem: stress, whatever its source may be. She says, "You reach for the bread because the body craves carbohydrates to stimulate production of serotonin, a natural relaxant. Marathon athletes get away with 'carbo-loading' because they are going to run 26 miles the next day. You're just watching TV." She suggests taking a long, hot bath instead or exercising enough to release those other natural relaxants—endorphins.

SLOWING DOWN. "I believe anything eaten after 7 p.m. is risky," Hartsough says, but not because of the food. Many people starve all day, skipping breakfast and skimping on lunch. They keep diet discipline with busyness and caffeine. But when they get home, they're ravenous and that leads to overeating.

"You eat for 20 minutes before the brain realizes the body is being fed," she says. "Chew every bite 20 times. If you finish a meal in less than 20 minutes, that's too fast."

Snacks aren't a sin to Hartsough. "If they're healthful—or even junky occasionally—that's okay if you have a plan," she says. "Charge the calories to your plan, so when you snack, you reach your limit instead of passing it."

FOCUS ON DINNER. "For many people, food is a source of comfort," says Tom Wadden, Ph.D., University of Pennsylvania professor of psychology. An effective tactic, Wadden says, is to concentrate on dinner. "The meal you've waited for all day should be worth the wait," he says. "Use your best china and silver to create a pleasing environment. A glass of wine with dinner is nice, and good table-talk protracts the meal and helps you to eat slowly."

The worst thing to do is to pay attention to something besides dinner. Combining TV and dinner is a bad habit, Wadden and Hartsough agree. Eating in front of the set is eating mindlessly. People who are unaware of their food don't enjoy it and aren't satisfied afterward.

There are exceptions. Amiable conversation is one. "For those who eat alone," Wadden says, "reading is a good way to slow down."

BEAT THE BINGE

The setting sun (and accompanying loss of willpower) isn't the only lifestyle villain. Dr. Tom Wadden, University of Pennsylvania professor of psychology, warns against these other "disinhibitors" that threaten diet plans.

1. Overeating: It encourages more overeating, undermining discipline and tempting you to give up.

2. Stress and fatigue: They create a need for self-indulgence.

3. Alcohol: In social settings, you're likely to have a second or third drink without thinking, as well as all those goldfish crackers.

Side Dishes

CONE OF PARADISE

(pictured on page 94)

This refreshing fruit blend is best eaten immediately because it becomes limp if refrigerated overnight.

- 1 mango, peeled
- 1 small cucumber, peeled
- ½ medium jícama, peeled
- ¼ fresh pineapple, peeled and cored
- ⅓ cup fresh lime juice
- ½ teaspoon salt
- ¼ teaspoon ground red pepper
- 5 lime wedges

1. Cut mango, cucumber, jícama, and pineapple into 4- x ½-inch strips; place in a large bowl.
2. Combine lime juice, salt, and red pepper; stir well. Pour juice mixture over fruit mixture; toss. Serve immediately with lime wedges. **YIELD:** 5 servings (serving size: 1 cup).

POINTS: 1; **EXCHANGE:** 1 Fruit;
PER SERVING: CAL 64 (6% from fat); PRO 0.9g; FAT 0.4g (sat 0.1g); CARB 16.4g; FIB 3.1g; CHOL 0mg; IRON 0.5mg; SOD 238mg; CALC 18mg

ARTICHOKES WITH BROWNED GARLIC AND LEMON DIPPING SAUCE

(pictured on page 143)

- 4 large artichokes
- 2 teaspoons butter or margarine
- 1 garlic clove, minced
- 2 tablespoons lemon juice
- 1 tablespoon white wine Worcestershire sauce
- ¼ cup water
- 1 tablespoon Dijon mustard
- Dash of ground white pepper

1. Wash artichokes by plunging up and down in cold water. Cut off stem ends; trim about ½ inch from top of each artichoke. Cut off artichoke stems; remove bottom leaves. Place artichokes, stem ends down, in an 11- x 7-inch baking dish; add water to depth of 1 inch. Cover with heavy-duty plastic wrap, and vent. Microwave at HIGH 10 minutes or until a leaf near the center of each artichoke pulls out easily. Drain. Remove fuzzy choke from center of each artichoke with a spoon.
2. Melt butter in a small saucepan; stir in garlic. Cook over medium heat, stirring constantly, until garlic is lightly browned. Add lemon juice and remaining 4 ingredients; heat just until hot. Serve as a dipping sauce with whole artichokes. **YIELD:** 4 servings (serving size: 1 artichoke and 2 tablespoons sauce).

POINTS: 1; **EXCHANGES:** 3 Vegetable, ½ Fat;
PER SERVING: CAL 91 (24% from fat); PRO 3.5g; FAT 2.4g (sat 1.3g); CARB 16.7g; FIB 6.5g; CHOL 5mg; IRON 2mg; SOD 28mg; CALC 66mg

ASPARAGUS WITH HONEY HORSERADISH DIJON SAUCE

- ¼ cup fat-free honey Dijon dressing (such as Marzetti)
- 1 tablespoon Dijon mustard
- 1 tablespoon prepared horseradish
- 1 pound asparagus spears
- Cooking spray
- ¼ teaspoon freshly ground pepper
- ½ cup (2 ounces) shaved Asiago or Romano cheese

1. Preheat oven to 400°.
2. Combine first 3 ingredients; set aside.
3. Snap off tough ends of asparagus; remove scales with a knife or vegetable peeler, if desired.
4. Place asparagus in a roasting pan; coat with cooking spray. Bake at 400° for 5 minutes. Turn asparagus spears; bake an additional 10 minutes or until tender and lightly browned.
5. Drizzle asparagus spears immediately with reserved dressing mixture; toss well. Sprinkle with pepper, and top with cheese. Serve warm or at room temperature. **YIELD:** 4 servings.

POINTS: 2; **EXCHANGES:** 2 Vegetable, 1 Fat;
PER SERVING: CAL 105 (37% from fat); PRO 7g; FAT 4.3g (sat 2.5g); CARB 10.3g; FIB 0.9g; CHOL 9mg; IRON 0.7mg; SOD 502mg; CALC 184mg

ROASTED SNAP BEANS

- Cooking spray
- 1 pound whole snap or string beans, trimmed
- 2 teaspoons extra-virgin olive oil
- ¼ teaspoon salt, divided
- ⅛ teaspoon pepper

1. Preheat oven to 500°.
2. Coat a jelly-roll pan with cooking spray. Place beans on pan, and arrange in a single layer. Drizzle with oil, and toss gently to coat. Sprinkle with ⅛ teaspoon salt. Bake on top rack of oven at 500° for 12 minutes or until beans are tender and beginning to brown, stirring once. Sprinkle with remaining ⅛ teaspoon salt and pepper. **YIELD:** 4 servings (serving size: ½ cup).

POINTS: 1; **EXCHANGES:** 1½ Vegetable, ½ Fat;
PER SERVING: CAL 54 (42% from fat); PRO 1.9g; FAT 2.5g (sat 0.4g); CARB 7.5g; FIB 2.2g; CHOL 0mg; IRON 1.1mg; SOD 153mg; CALC 39mg

REFRIED BLACK BEANS

(pictured on page 94)

These beans make a piquant side dish as well as a great filling for burritos.

1 tablespoon olive oil
½ cup chopped onion
½ cup chopped green bell pepper
2 garlic cloves, minced
½ cup tomato sauce
2 (15-ounce) cans black beans, drained
½ cup dry red wine
1 to 2 tablespoons hot sauce
1½ teaspoons ground cumin
1½ teaspoons dried oregano
½ teaspoon salt
1 tablespoon white vinegar
6 tablespoons fat-free sour cream
1 tablespoon chopped fresh cilantro
Cilantro sprigs (optional)

1. Heat oil in a large nonstick skillet over medium heat. Add onion, bell pepper, and garlic; cook, stirring constantly, 4 minutes or until tender. Add tomato sauce; cook 10 minutes or until most of liquid evaporates, stirring occasionally. Add black beans and next 5 ingredients; bring to a boil, stirring frequently. Partially mash bean mixture with a potato masher or fork. Add vinegar; reduce heat, and simmer 5 minutes or until thick, stirring occasionally. Top each serving with sour cream and chopped cilantro. Garnish with cilantro sprigs, if desired. **YIELD:** 6 servings (serving size: ½ cup refried beans, 1 tablespoon sour cream, and ½ teaspoon cilantro).

POINTS: 3; **EXCHANGES:** 1½ Starch, ½ Vegetable, ½ Very Lean Meat; **PER SERVING:** CAL 159 (18% from fat); PRO 9.3g; FAT 3.2g (sat 0.5g); CARB 25.6g; FIB 4.5g; CHOL 0mg; IRON 2.9mg; SOD 609mg; CALC 76mg

NEW ENGLAND BAKED BEANS

America's most famous bean dish was invented by the Puritan women of Boston. In addition to molasses and sweet brown sugar, this version gets its sweet tang from barbecue sauce. Rather than salt pork, we used turkey bacon.

3 cups dried Great Northern beans
8 cups water
1¼ cups chopped onion
1 cup barbecue sauce
¾ cup packed brown sugar
¼ cup molasses
1 tablespoon prepared mustard
½ teaspoon salt
¼ teaspoon pepper
⅛ teaspoon garlic powder
4 slices turkey bacon, cut crosswise into ¼-inch strips

1. Sort and wash beans; place in a large ovenproof Dutch oven. Cover with water to 2 inches above beans, and bring to a boil. Cook 2 minutes. Remove from heat; cover and let stand 1 hour.
2. Drain beans; return to Dutch oven. Add 8 cups water and onion; bring to a boil. Cover, reduce heat, and simmer 2 hours or until beans are tender.
3. Preheat oven to 350°.
4. Drain bean mixture; return to Dutch oven. Add barbecue sauce and remaining ingredients; stir well. Cover and bake at 350° for 1 hour. **YIELD:** 16 servings (serving size: ½ cup).

POINTS: 3; **EXCHANGES:** 2½ Starch, ½ Fat; **PER SERVING:** CAL 198 (11% from fat); PRO 9.6g; FAT 2.5g (sat 0.6g); CARB 34.4g; FIB 13.9g; CHOL 9mg; IRON 2.4mg; SOD 400mg; CALC 82mg

TEXAS CAVIAR

1½ cups seeded chopped tomato
⅓ cup thinly sliced green onions
2 tablespoons canned chopped green chiles
2 tablespoons white wine vinegar
1 tablespoon seeded minced jalapeño pepper
1 tablespoon chopped fresh cilantro
1 teaspoon olive oil
¼ teaspoon salt
¼ teaspoon ground cumin
⅛ teaspoon pepper
1 garlic clove, minced
1 (15.8-ounce) can black-eyed peas, drained
Jalapeño slices (optional)
Cilantro sprigs (optional)

1. Combine first 12 ingredients in a bowl. Cover and chill. Garnish with jalapeño slices and cilantro sprigs, if desired. **YIELD:** 6 servings (serving size: about ½ cup).

POINTS: 1; **EXCHANGES:** ½ Starch, ½ Vegetable; **PER SERVING:** CAL 62 (17% from fat); PRO 4g; FAT 1.2g (sat 0.2g); CARB 10g; FIB 1.4g; CHOL 0mg; IRON 1mg; SOD 210mg; CALC 20mg

TEXAS CAVIAR

This Texas "caviar" is made from black-eyed peas. Make it one to three days ahead so the flavors will blend. Serve this flavorful black-eyed pea and vegetable medley with grilled chicken or as an appetizer with baked tortilla chips.

BEETS WITH RASPBERRY-ORANGE GLAZE

- 2 pounds medium beets (without green tops)
- ½ cup seedless raspberry jam
- ⅓ cup cran-raspberry drink
- 1½ tablespoons reduced-calorie stick margarine
- ¼ teaspoon salt
- ¼ teaspoon ground ginger
- ¼ teaspoon grated orange rind
- ¾ teaspoon cornstarch
- 3 tablespoons thawed orange juice concentrate

1. Leave root and 1-inch stem on beets; scrub with a brush. Place in a large saucepan; cover with water, and bring to a boil. Cover, reduce heat, and simmer 35 minutes or until tender. Drain and rinse under cold water. Drain; let cool. Trim off beet roots; rub off skins. Cut beets into ¼-inch-thick slices.

2. Combine jam and next 5 ingredients in a large nonstick skillet; cook over medium-high heat until jam and margarine melt, stirring constantly. Add beets; cook until thoroughly heated, stirring frequently. Combine cornstarch and concentrate; stir until well blended. Add to beet mixture; cook until thick and bubbly, stirring constantly. YIELD: 10 servings (serving size: ½ cup).

NOTE: Substitute 3 (15-ounce) cans sliced beets, drained, if desired.

POINTS: 2; **EXCHANGES:** 1 Starch, 1½ Vegetable; **PER SERVING:** CAL 102 (11% from fat); PRO 1.6g; FAT 1.3g (sat 0.3g); CARB 22.5g; FIB 0.8g; CHOL 0mg; IRON 0.8mg; SOD 155mg; CALC 16mg

BROCCOLI AND CAULIFLOWER AU GRATIN

(pictured on page 143)

- 2 cups coarsely chopped fresh broccoli florets
- 2 cups coarsely chopped fresh cauliflower florets
- 1 cup fresh whole-wheat breadcrumbs
- 1 teaspoon olive oil
- ½ teaspoon paprika
- ¼ teaspoon salt
- ¼ teaspoon pepper
- 2 small garlic cloves, minced
- 1 tablespoon all-purpose flour
- ½ cup fat-free milk
- 1 cup (4 ounces) shredded reduced-fat sharp Cheddar cheese

Cooking spray

1. Preheat oven to 375°.

2. Steam broccoli and cauliflower, covered, 5 minutes or until crisp-tender. Drain well; set aside.

3. Combine breadcrumbs and next 5 ingredients; stir well, and set aside.

4. Place flour in a small saucepan. Gradually add milk, stirring with a whisk until blended. Bring to a boil over medium-high heat, and cook 1 minute or until thick, stirring constantly. Remove from heat; add cheese, stirring until cheese melts.

5. Combine vegetables and cheese sauce, stirring well to coat. Spoon mixture into a 1-quart baking dish coated with cooking spray. Sprinkle with breadcrumb mixture. Bake at 375° for 25 minutes or until breadcrumbs are lightly browned. Let stand 5 minutes before serving. YIELD: 4 servings.

POINTS: 3; **EXCHANGES:** ½ Starch, 1½ Vegetable, 1 Medium-Fat Meat; **PER SERVING:** CAL 153 (36% from fat); PRO 10.7g; FAT 6.2g (sat 2.7g); CARB 15g; FIB 2.9g; CHOL 1.5mg; IRON 1.2mg; SOD 411mg; CALC 270mg

GLAZED BRUSSELS SPROUTS AND BABY CARROTS

- 4 cups trimmed Brussels sprouts (about ¾ pound)
- 1 (16-ounce) package fresh baby-cut carrots
- 1 cup orange marmalade
- ½ teaspoon ground ginger
- ¼ teaspoon salt

1. Steam Brussels sprouts and carrots, covered, 10 minutes or until crisp-tender. Place in a serving bowl.

2. Combine marmalade, ginger, and salt; pour over vegetables, tossing to coat. Serve immediately. YIELD: 5 servings (serving size: 1 cup).

POINTS: 4; **EXCHANGES:** 3 Starch, 3 Vegetable; **PER SERVING:** CAL 225 (2% from fat); PRO 3.5g; FAT 0.4g (sat 0.1g); CARB 58g; FIB 5.9g; CHOL 0mg; IRON 1.6mg; SOD 202mg; CALC 79mg

SPROUTS TIP

Make sure your Brussels sprouts cook evenly by cutting an X in the stem end of each sprout.

CUMIN-AND-CORIANDER-SCENTED CARROT PURÉE

- 4 medium carrots, cut into 1-inch pieces (about ¾ pound)
- 1 (10-ounce) baking potato, peeled
- 1 teaspoon ground coriander
- ½ teaspoon ground cumin
- ½ teaspoon salt
- 2 teaspoons butter or margarine
- ¼ cup 2% reduced-fat milk
- 2 tablespoons 30%-less-fat sour cream (such as Breakstone)

1. Place carrot and potato in a large saucepan, and cover with water. Bring to a boil; reduce heat, and simmer, uncovered, 15 minutes or until vegetables are tender; drain. Place vegetables, coriander, and remaining ingredients in a food processor, and process until smooth. Reheat in a saucepan over medium heat, if necessary. **YIELD:** 4 servings (serving size: ¾ cup).

POINTS: 2; **EXCHANGES:** 1 Starch, 1 Vegetable, ½ Fat; **PER SERVING:** CAL 115 (26% from fat); PRO 2.5g; FAT 3.3g (sat 2g); CARB 19.7g; FIB 3.3g; CHOL 10mg; IRON 0.8mg; SOD 355mg; CALC 58mg

CHILE PEPPER CORN WITH CHEESE

- Cooking spray
- ½ teaspoon butter
- 1 Anaheim chile pepper, seeded and finely chopped
- 1 (10-ounce) package frozen whole-kernel corn, thawed
- ¼ teaspoon chili powder
- ¼ teaspoon ground cumin
- ⅛ teaspoon salt
- ⅛ teaspoon pepper
- ⅓ cup (1⅓ ounces) shredded reduced-fat sharp Cheddar cheese

1. Coat a large skillet with cooking spray. Place over medium-high heat until hot; add butter, tilting skillet to coat bottom. Add chile pepper, and cook 3 minutes or until crisp-tender. Add corn and next 4 ingredients; cook 2 minutes or until thoroughly heated. Remove from heat, and sprinkle with cheese. Let stand 2 minutes or until cheese melts. **YIELD:** 4 servings (serving size: ½ cup).

POINTS: 2; **EXCHANGES:** 1 Starch, ½ Fat; **PER SERVING:** CAL 95 (25% from fat); PRO 5g; FAT 2.6g (sat 1.2g); CARB 15.6g; FIB 1.8g; CHOL 6mg; IRON 0.5mg; SOD 143mg; CALC 89mg

MASHED POTATOES WITH FENNEL

- 3½ cups peeled cubed baking potato (about 1¾ pounds)
- 2 tablespoons reduced-calorie margarine
- ¾ cup chopped fennel bulb
- ½ cup chopped onion
- ½ teaspoon salt
- ⅛ teaspoon pepper

1. Place potato in a medium saucepan and cover with water; bring to a boil. Reduce heat, and simmer 15 minutes or until tender; drain, reserving ¼ cup liquid.
2. Melt margarine in a medium nonstick skillet over medium heat. Add fennel and onion; cook, stirring constantly, 12 minutes or until tender.
3. Combine potato, reserved potato liquid, fennel mixture, salt, and pepper in a medium bowl. Mash with a potato masher. **YIELD:** 3 servings (serving size: 1 cup).

POINTS: 4; **EXCHANGES:** 2 Starch, 1 Fat; **PER SERVING:** CAL 195 (24% from fat); PRO 7g; FAT 5.2g (sat 0.7g); CARB 33g; FIB 4.9g; CHOL 0mg; IRON 8.4mg; SOD 490mg; CALC 100mg

CHILI POTATOES

4 small baking potatoes (about 1½ pounds)
½ pound ground round
1 (16-ounce) can kidney beans, drained
1 (14½-ounce) can Mexican-style stewed tomatoes with jalapeño peppers and spices, undrained and chopped
1 (8-ounce) can no-salt-added tomato sauce
1 cup frozen chopped onion
1 tablespoon chili powder
1 teaspoon bottled minced garlic
½ teaspoon ground cumin
⅓ cup (1.3 ounces) shredded sharp Cheddar cheese

1. Pierce potatoes with a fork; arrange in a circle on paper towels in microwave oven. Microwave at HIGH 9 minutes or until done, turning and rearranging potatoes after 5 minutes. Let stand 5 minutes.
2. Cook meat in a large saucepan over medium-high heat until browned, stirring to crumble. Drain well; return meat to pan.
3. Add beans and next 6 ingredients; stir well. Cook over medium-high heat 8 minutes.
4. Split open each potato, and squeeze to open; fluff pulp with a fork. Spoon 1 cup chili mixture into center of each potato; sprinkle with cheese. YIELD: 4 servings (serving size: 1 potato, 1 cup chili mixture, and about 1 tablespoon cheese).

POINTS: 8; **EXCHANGES:** 3 Starch, 1 Vegetable, 2 Lean Meat; **PER SERVING:** CAL 397 (17% from fat); PRO 25.8g; FAT 7.4g (sat 3.4g); CARB 59.6g; FIB 9g; CHOL 45mg; IRON 6.3mg; SOD 600mg; CALC 144mg

CURRIED VEGETABLE STUFFED POTATOES

4 (8-ounce) baking potatoes
Cooking spray
1 teaspoon grated fresh ginger
3 cups frozen broccoli, onion, red pepper, and mushroom mix
1 (14.5-ounce) can no-salt-added stewed tomatoes, undrained and chopped
1½ teaspoons curry powder
¼ teaspoon salt
⅛ to ¼ teaspoon ground red or black pepper

1. Preheat oven to 400°.
2. Scrub potatoes; prick each several times with a fork. Bake at 400° for 45 minutes to 1 hour or until done.
3. Coat a large nonstick skillet with cooking spray; place over medium-high heat until hot. Add ginger, and cook, stirring constantly, 1 minute. Add broccoli mixture, and cook 4 minutes. Stir in tomatoes and remaining 3 ingredients. Cook an additional 4 minutes or until most of liquid evaporates.
4. Split open each potato, and squeeze to open; fluff pulp with a fork. Top potatoes with broccoli mixture. Serve immediately.
YIELD: 4 servings (serving size: 1 potato and about ⅔ cup broccoli mixture).

POINTS: 4; **EXCHANGES:** 2½ Starch, 2 Vegetable; **PER SERVING:** CAL 220 (2% from fat); PRO 7.7g; FAT 0.5g (sat 0.1g); CARB 48g; FIB 6.2g; CHOL 0mg; IRON 3.6mg; SOD 196mg; CALC 64mg

GRILLED POTATO AND ONION PACKET

1 (20-ounce) package precut new potato wedges (such as Simply Potatoes)
1 medium onion, cut into thin wedges and separated
¼ teaspoon grated lemon rind
3 tablespoons fresh lemon juice
2 tablespoons white wine Worcestershire sauce
1 tablespoon olive oil
1 garlic clove, crushed
2 teaspoons chopped fresh rosemary
1 teaspoon sugar
¼ teaspoon salt
¼ teaspoon coarsely ground pepper
1 large aluminum foil grilling bag (such as Reynold's Hot Bags)

1. Combine potatoes and onion in a large bowl. Combine lemon rind and next 8 ingredients. Pour lemon mixture over potato mixture; toss well to coat. Place potato and onion mixture in grilling bag, arranging potato mixture in a single layer. Pour any remaining lemon juice mixture over potato mixture.
2. Place grilling bag on grill rack over medium-hot coals (350° to 400°); cover and grill 15 minutes. Open bag and stir gently. Reseal bag, and grill an additional 15 minutes or until potatoes are tender.
YIELD: 8 servings (serving size: ½ cup).

POINTS: 1; **EXCHANGE:** 1 Starch; **PER SERVING:** CAL 75 (20% from fat); PRO 2.2g; FAT 1.7g (sat 0.2g); CARB 12.6g; FIB 2.3g; CHOL 0mg; IRON 0.4mg; SOD 185mg; CALC 11mg

CREAMY SCALLOPED POTATOES WITH BACON

- 3 hickory-smoked bacon slices
- 1½ cups thinly sliced onion, separated into rings
- 2 teaspoons chopped fresh or ½ teaspoon dried thyme
- 1 teaspoon sugar
- 1 teaspoon salt
- ½ teaspoon pepper
- ⅓ cup all-purpose flour
- 2½ cups fat-free milk
- ½ cup 50%-less-fat sour cream (such as Daisy)
- ¼ cup finely chopped fresh or 1½ tablespoons freeze-dried chives
- Cooking spray
- 4½ cups peeled, thinly sliced baking potatoes (about 2 pounds)
- Thyme sprigs (optional)

1. Preheat oven to 350°.
2. Cook bacon in a large nonstick skillet over medium heat until crisp. Remove bacon from skillet, reserving 1 teaspoon bacon fat in skillet; crumble bacon, and set aside. Add onion to bacon fat in skillet; cook, stirring constantly, 5 minutes. Add thyme and next 3 ingredients; cook, stirring constantly, 5 minutes. Sprinkle with flour; cook 1 minute, stirring constantly. Gradually stir in milk; bring to a simmer. Cook 5 minutes or until thick, stirring frequently. Remove from heat; stir in sour cream and chives.
3. Spread ½ cup sauce in an 8-inch square baking dish coated with cooking spray. Arrange one-third of potatoes over sauce, overlapping slices slightly. Spread ½ cup sauce over potatoes. Repeat layers twice with remaining potatoes and sauce, ending with sauce. Sprinkle with crumbled bacon. Cover and bake at 350° for 1 hour and 10 minutes or until potatoes are tender. Uncover and bake an additional 10 minutes. Garnish with thyme sprigs, if desired. **YIELD:** 6 servings.

POINTS: 5; **EXCHANGES:** 2 Starch, 1 Vegetable, ½ Skim Milk, ½ Fat; **PER SERVING:** CAL 248 (16% from fat); PRO 8.9g; FAT 4.5g (sat 2.5g); CARB 42g; FIB 3.1g; CHOL 13mg; IRON 1mg; SOD 525mg; CALC 174mg

TROPICAL SWEET POTATO CASSEROLE

- 4 pounds sweet potatoes, peeled and cubed
- 1 cup mashed banana
- 1 cup firmly packed brown sugar
- ½ cup canned coconut milk
- 1 (8-ounce) can crushed pineapple in juice, drained
- ⅛ teaspoon salt
- Cooking spray
- 1½ tablespoons flaked coconut

1. Place sweet potato in a large saucepan; cover with water. Bring to a boil; cook 20 minutes or until tender. Drain well; return sweet potato to pan. Beat at medium speed of a mixer until smooth; add banana and next 4 ingredients, beating well.
2. Preheat oven to 350°.
3. Pour sweet potato mixture into an 11- x 7-inch baking dish coated with cooking spray. Sprinkle mixture with flaked coconut. Bake at 350° for 30 minutes or until thoroughly heated. **YIELD:** 16 servings (serving size: ½ cup).

POINTS: 3; **EXCHANGES:** 2½ Starch, ½ Fruit; **PER SERVING:** CAL 189 (9% from fat); PRO 1.8g; FAT 1.9g (sat 1.5g); CARB 42.4g; FIB 3.4g; CHOL 0mg; IRON 1mg; SOD 41mg; CALC 33mg

SPINACH SOUFFLÉS WITH FONTINA

- 1 (10-ounce) package frozen chopped spinach, thawed, drained, and squeezed dry
- 1½ cups fat-free milk
- 3 tablespoons all-purpose flour
- ½ teaspoon salt
- ½ teaspoon dried Italian seasoning
- 1 large egg
- ½ cup (2 ounces) shredded fontina cheese

1. Preheat oven to 350°.
2. Combine first 6 ingredients in a food processor; process until smooth. Transfer mixture to a bowl, and add cheese, stirring until well blended.
3. Spoon into 4 (8-ounce) ramekins. Place in a 13- x 9-inch baking dish; add hot water to pan to a depth of 1 inch. Bake at 350° for 35 to 40 minutes or until puffy and set. Serve immediately. **YIELD:** 4 servings.

POINTS: 3; **EXCHANGES:** ½ Starch, 1 Vegetable, 1 Fat; **PER SERVING:** CAL 145 (38% from fat); PRO 11g; FAT 6.2g (sat 3.3g); CARB 12.2g; FIB 2.3g; CHOL 73mg; IRON 2.2mg; SOD 522mg; CALC 279mg

The Prime of Her Life

LORENE CONKLIN • **HEIGHT** 5'10" • **BEFORE** 272 LBS. • **AFTER** 172 LBS.

Most thankful for: Feeling healthy again.

Lorene Conklin had much to be thankful for at the party honoring her 30 years as assistant director of a community medical center. At 100 pounds lighter than when she joined Weight Watchers 15 months earlier, Lorene felt better, looked better, and marveled at how golden her golden years had become.

When Lorene weighed 272 pounds, simple daily routines were agonizing. She avoided the mall because she couldn't go from store to store without stopping to sit and rest. At home, going up and down steps was painful. In 1988 and 1990, she had knee replacement surgeries that were necessary in part because of her weight and inactivity.

Though she was uncomfortable, Lorene didn't think she was overweight. "I always felt I could carry a lot of pounds because I'm tall," she explains. But in July 1997, Lorene was horrified by photos of her 49th high school reunion in Matfield Green, Kansas. "I couldn't believe it was me standing there, looking so bloated and awful," she recalls.

"Is that you, Grandma? You look so young. I just don't believe it."

Lorene decided to join Weight Watchers, but not simply to lose pounds quickly. She wanted a change that would allow her to make the most of the best years of her life. She found that the ***1•2•3 Success®*** plan, an integral part of the Weight Watchers program, made meal planning easy. "I had fun with the journal, and experimented with breakfast, lunch, and dinner," she says.

Shedding 100 pounds has meant an incredible increase in Lorene's energy level. She rides a stationary bike at least 7 miles a day (an activity that she says has strengthened her knees tremendously), she and her husband travel, and they often shop in neighboring cities (but she no longer needs those rest breaks while shopping). Lorene also works about 20 hours a week.

Her schedule sounds demanding, but Lorene says that being active actually gives her more energy and has provided a big boost to her immune system. "I didn't have a cold or the flu at all this year, and I'm sure it has to do with the changes I made," she says. "My doctor keeps asking me what weight-loss pills I'm taking—I remind him that I've done it without them. I've never been happier or healthier."

And it shows. Recently, their children threw a 50th wedding anniversary for Lorene and her husband. When they arrived at the party, Lorene's only granddaughter looked at her blankly for a moment before recognizing her. "Grandma? Is that you, Grandma?" she asked. "You look so young. I just don't believe it." For Lorene, it's moments like these that remind her that it's never too late to enjoy a healthy life.

Frogmore Stew, page 153

Veal and Artichoke Stew, page 154

Beef Stew With
Ale, page 153

Roasted Vegetable Wrap, page 156

Creamy Potato and Garlic Soup, page 149

Cioppino, page 150

Winter Squash
and Rice Gratin,
page 145

Artichokes With Browned Garlic and Lemon Dipping Sauce, page 131

Broccoli and Cauliflower au Gratin, page 133

Mother's Day

DEIRDRE LARGE • **HEIGHT** 5'5" • **BEFORE** 186 LBS. • **AFTER** 136 LBS.

Tip: Deirdre and a friend treated weekly Weight Watchers meetings as Mommies' Days Out. "We loved doing something healthy for ourselves."

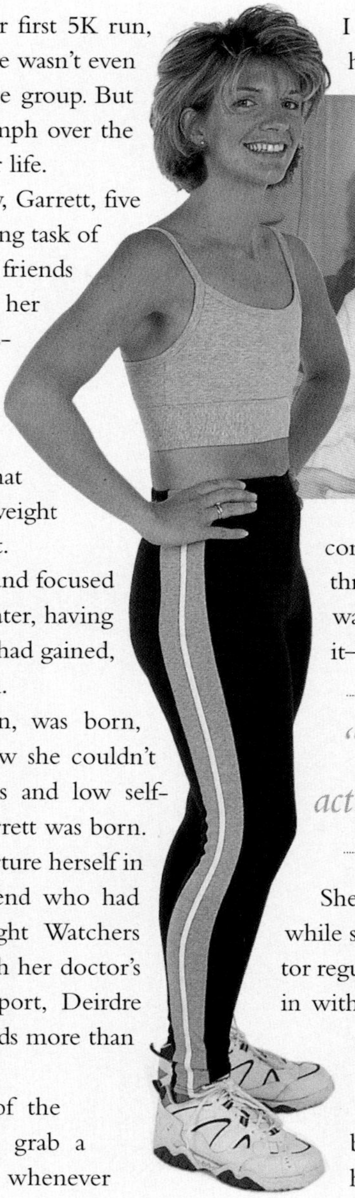

When Deirdre Large ran her first 5K run, she didn't win the race. She wasn't even one of the top finishers in her age group. But crossing the finish line was a triumph over the imbalance that once existed in her life.

After the birth of her first baby, Garrett, five years ago, Deirdre faced the daunting task of losing her "baby fat." Family and friends warned that dieting might affect her breast milk, but her doctor disagreed. "She said as long as I was careful, I would get all the essential nutrients the baby needed," Deirdre recalls. "But she also said that without much effort a lot of the weight would come off by itself." It didn't.

So Deirdre ignored the weight and focused on her baby. Seventeen months later, having lost only 22 of the 43 pounds she had gained, she found she was expecting again.

When her second son, Griffin, was born, Deirdre was ecstatic. But she knew she couldn't handle the weight-related sadness and low self-esteem she had suffered when Garrett was born.

Deirdre knew she needed to nurture herself in order to care for her sons. A friend who had breast-fed while attending Weight Watchers urged Deirdre to give it a try. With her doctor's approval and her husband's support, Deirdre signed up, weighing in at 50 pounds more than her prepregnancy weight.

She welcomed the structure of the ***1•2•3 Success®*** Plan. "I used to grab a peanut butter-and-jelly sandwich whenever I could," she says. "But Weight Watchers taught me how to reach for more healthful foods and to reach for them more regularly."

Deirdre learned to eat smaller portions and a variety of fruits and vegetables. "Initially it was tough," she admits. "But now I actually *prefer* fruits and vegetables."

And she figured out a way to make time for exercise without sacrificing time with her boys. She bought a double stroller and walked them around the neighborhood. The weight started coming off. "I looked forward to every day when the three of us would go out," says Deirdre. "The walking was such great exercise, and the kids absolutely loved it—even during the winter."

"Initially it was tough. But now I actually prefer fruits and vegetables."

She kept a close eye on her son's growth and health while she lost weight and breast-fed, and she saw her doctor regularly. "The leaders at Weight Watchers also checked in with me at every meeting," she says. "I got incredible support from them."

By learning more about her own body while watching her sons grow, Deirdre has learned to balance her needs with the demands of motherhood. "I'm staying fit for them and for me," she says.

WINTER SQUASH AND RICE GRATIN

(pictured on page 142)

2 cups chopped peeled butternut squash
¼ cup minced shallots
2 tablespoons butter
3 garlic cloves, minced
3 tablespoons all-purpose flour
1½ cups fat-free milk
1½ teaspoons chopped fresh sage
½ teaspoon salt
½ teaspoon ground white pepper
½ teaspoon ground nutmeg
⅛ teaspoon ground black pepper
1 cup cooked long-grain brown rice
¼ cup chopped fresh parsley
½ cup (2 ounces) shredded Gruyère or fontina cheese
Cooking spray
2 teaspoons garlic-and-herb-seasoned breadcrumbs

1. Preheat oven to 400°.
2. Cook squash and shallots in butter in a large nonstick skillet over medium heat 10 minutes or until tender, stirring frequently; add garlic, and cook 30 seconds. Stir in flour, and cook 1 minute or until flour is moistened. Gradually add milk, stirring until blended. Add sage and next 4 ingredients; stir well. Cook 2 to 3 minutes or until thickened. Stir in rice, parsley, and cheese.
3. Coat an 11- x 7-inch baking dish with cooking spray. Spoon mixture into baking dish. Sprinkle with breadcrumbs. Bake at 400° for 20 minutes or until bubbly. YIELD: 5 servings (serving size: ¾ cup).
NOTE: You can spoon squash mixture evenly into 5 (8-ounce) au gratin dishes, and bake 15 minutes or until bubbly.

POINTS: 5; **EXCHANGES:** 1½ Starch, 1 Vegetable, 2 Fat; **PER SERVING:** CAL 216 (38% from fat); PRO 8.5g; FAT 9.2g (sat 5.3g); CARB 26g; FIB 1.9g; CHOL 26mg; IRON 1.3mg; SOD 391mg; CALC 251mg

SQUASH SAUTÉ

2 teaspoons olive oil
1¼ cups sliced onion (about 1 medium onion)
1 cup red bell pepper strips
3 garlic cloves, minced
4 cups sliced yellow squash (about 1 pound)
1 tablespoon chopped fresh or 1 teaspoon dried basil
½ teaspoon lemon pepper
¼ teaspoon salt
2 tablespoons grated Parmesan cheese

1. Heat oil in a large nonstick skillet over medium-high heat. Add onion, bell pepper, and garlic; cook, stirring constantly, 2 minutes. Add squash; cook, stirring constantly, 6 minutes or until vegetables are crisp-tender. Stir in basil, lemon pepper, and salt. Remove from heat, and sprinkle with Parmesan cheese. Serve immediately. YIELD: 5 cups (serving size: 1 cup).

POINTS: 1; **EXCHANGES:** 1½ Vegetable, ½ Fat; **PER SERVING:** CAL 64 (39% from fat); PRO 2.6g; FAT 2.8g (sat 0.7g); CARB 8.6g; FIB 2.6g; CHOL 2mg; IRON 0.9mg; SOD 192mg; CALC 58mg

PASTA WITH FRESH GARLIC OIL

Drain cooked pasta immediately, but don't worry about rinsing. You don't have to rinse cooked pasta unless it's specifically stated in the recipe or unless you're preparing a cold pasta salad.

4 ounces uncooked vermicelli
1 tablespoon extra-virgin olive oil
2 teaspoons lemon juice
1 garlic clove, minced
½ teaspoon dried basil
½ teaspoon salt
⅛ teaspoon freshly ground pepper
2 tablespoons chopped fresh parsley

1. Cook pasta according to package directions, omitting salt and fat. Drain; set aside, and keep warm.
2. Combine olive oil and next 5 ingredients in a small bowl. Combine pasta, oil mixture, and parsley, tossing well. YIELD: 4 servings (serving size: ½ cup pasta).

POINTS: 3; **EXCHANGES:** 1½ Starch, ½ Fat; **PER SERVING:** CAL 138 (25% from fat); PRO 3.8g; FAT 3.9g (sat 0.5g); CARB 21.9g; FIB 0.8g; CHOL 0mg; IRON 1.3mg; SOD 296mg; CALC 13mg

ONION AND RICE PILAF

- 2 tablespoons vegetable oil
- 1 teaspoon mustard seeds
- 1 teaspoon ground turmeric
- ¾ teaspoon curry powder
- 2 tablespoons grated fresh ginger
- 2 jalapeño peppers, seeded and minced
- 1 pound onions, thinly sliced into half circles
- 1 teaspoon sugar
- ¾ teaspoon salt
- 4 cups cooked basmati rice, cooked without salt or fat
- ¼ cup lime juice
- 2 tablespoons water
- 2 tablespoons chopped lightly salted roasted cashews

1. Heat oil in a large Dutch oven over medium-high heat. Add mustard seeds, and stir. Cover and cook until seeds pop. Stir in turmeric and next 4 ingredients, coating well with oil mixture. Reduce heat to medium, and cook, stirring frequently, until onion is tender and beginning to brown.

2. Add sugar, salt, and rice, stirring until smooth. Cook 3 minutes or until thoroughly heated. Add lime juice and water; stir 30 seconds. Mound rice mixture on a serving platter; top with chopped cashews. **YIELD:** 6 servings (serving size: 1 cup onion and rice mixture and 1 teaspoon cashews).

POINTS: 5; **EXCHANGES:** 2½ Starch, 1 Vegetable, 1 Fat; **PER SERVING:** CAL 245 (24% from fat); PRO 4.4g; FAT 6.4g (sat 1.1g); CARB 42.9g; FIB 2.4g; CHOL 0mg; IRON 1.9mg; SOD 314mg; CALC 37mg

SPANISH RICE

Serve this spicy rice dish alongside Steak Fajitas with Cilantro and Olive Salsa (page 98).

- 2 teaspoons vegetable oil
- 1 cup chopped onion
- 1 cup chopped green bell pepper
- 2 garlic cloves, minced
- 1⅔ cups uncooked instant rice
- 2 (14½-ounce) cans diced tomatoes, undrained
- 1 (5½-ounce) can tomato juice
- 2 teaspoons chili powder
- 1 teaspoon ground cumin
- ½ teaspoon hot sauce
- ¼ cup chopped fresh cilantro

1. Place a large saucepan over medium-high heat until hot; add oil. Add onion, bell pepper, and garlic; cook, stirring constantly, until tender. Stir in rice and next 5 ingredients. Bring to a boil; cover, reduce heat, and simmer 7 minutes or until liquid is absorbed. Remove from heat. Let stand, covered, 5 minutes. Stir in cilantro. **YIELD:** 6 servings (serving size: 1 cup).

POINTS: 3; **EXCHANGES:** 1½ Starch, 2 Vegetable, ½ Fat; **PER SERVING:** CAL 168 (11% from fat); PRO 4.2g; FAT 2g (sat 0.4g); CARB 34.5g; FIB 4g; CHOL 0mg; IRON 2.5mg; SOD 402mg; CALC 47mg

SOUTHERN CORN BREAD STUFFING

- ½ (19-ounce) package corn bread mix
- 1 cup fat-free milk
- 1 large egg
- Cooking spray
- 1 cup diced onion
- ½ cup diced celery
- 1 large egg, lightly beaten
- ½ teaspoon ground sage
- ½ teaspoon poultry seasoning
- ¼ teaspoon pepper
- 4 (1-ounce) slices day-old white bread, cubed
- 1 (14½-ounce) can fat-free, reduced-sodium chicken broth

1. Preheat oven to 400°.

2. Combine corn bread mix, milk, and egg in a large bowl, stirring well.

3. Pour batter into an 8-inch square baking pan coated with cooking spray. Bake at 400° for 18 to 20 minutes or until a wooden pick inserted in center comes out clean. Let corn bread cool slightly. Crumble corn bread into a large bowl; set aside. Reduce oven temperature to 375°.

4. Coat a large nonstick skillet with cooking spray; add onion and celery. Cook, stirring constantly, 4 minutes or until tender.

5. Add vegetables, beaten egg, sage, poultry seasoning, pepper, and cubed bread to crumbled corn bread. Add broth, stirring just until moistened. Pour mixture into a 1-quart baking dish, and bake, uncovered, at 375° for 30 minutes or until golden. **YIELD:** 5 cups (serving size: ½ cup).

POINTS: 3; **EXCHANGES:** 2 Starch, ½ Fat; **PER SERVING:** CAL 164 (16% from fat); PRO 5.7g; FAT 2.9g (sat 0.4g); CARB 27.9g; FIB 1.1g; CHOL 43mg; IRON 1.8mg; SOD 651mg; CALC 50mg

NUTRITION

Perfect Portions

Familiarity breeds content when it comes to keeping serving sizes under control.

Eating healthfully often requires making changes in what we eat. Equally important is managing serving size or portion control. You may be eating the right stuff, but your efforts won't succeed if you are eating incorrect amounts.

Portion size can be deceptive. The next time you reach for a bagel, weigh it first. A big, chewy bagel can tip the scales at 5 ounces. According to the U.S. Department of Agriculture's Food Guide Pyramid, that bagel equals five servings of bread. A steak as big as your face is far larger than the recommended 3 ounces, which is roughly as big as your palm.

KEEPING COUNT. Serving sizes—and number of servings—are the foundation of the Food Guide Pyramid. (To learn more about the Pyramid, visit www.usda.gov/cnpp.)

Keeping track is important when foods cross boundaries. For instance, ½ cup of spaghetti with ½ cup of tomato sauce and three 1-ounce meatballs constitutes one serving of grain (pasta), one vegetable (tomato sauce), one meat (meatballs), and one fat (meatballs, again).

SIZE MATTERS

Here are some tips for picking perfect portion sizes every time.

- Think small when you set the table. Buy 4-ounce juice glasses and small bowls that hold 1 cup of soup.
- Serve meals on luncheon plates.
- Use the proper utensils—measuring cups and spoons or food scales—to familiarize yourself with recommended portion sizes.
- Order appetizers in restaurants. You can have a varied meal—in smaller, more appropriate portions—by ordering starters rather than full-size (or oversize) entrées.

WHAT RIGHT LOOKS LIKE. Most people have unrealistic ideas of what a portion is, says Mary Abbott Hess, M.S., R.D., former president of The American Dietetic Association (ADA). For example, a restaurant serving of pasta might be 3 cups. "A person might count that serving as one portion, when it's really *six* standard portions," explains Hess.

Jackie Newgent, a nutritional consultant, has clients visualize portions in ways that relate to them. "If someone's a tennis player, I say that 1 cup is roughly the size of a tennis ball." A 3-ounce fish fillet is the size of a checkbook, and 1 ounce of cheese is the size of your thumb.

CHECK LABELS. The Nutrition Facts chart required on all packaged food labels is helpful, but only when you take into account the portion size it lists. Read the label carefully. Don't assume that the bottle of fruit juice or the bag of trail mix equals one serving; it's common for a pack of granola bars, for instance, to contain two servings.

WHAT COUNTS AS A SERVING?

Serving sizes indicated here are based on both suggested and usually consumed portions.

Bread, Cereal, Rice, and Pasta

- 1 slice of bread
- 1 ounce of ready-to-eat cereal
- ½ cup of cooked cereal, rice, or pasta

Vegetables and Fruit

- 1 cup of raw leafy vegetables or other raw vegetables
- ½ cup of cooked vegetables
- ½ cup of vegetable juice
- 1 medium apple, banana, or orange
- ½ cup of chopped, cooked, or canned fruit
- ½ cup of fruit juice

Milk, Yogurt, and Cheese

- 1 cup of milk or yogurt
- 1½ ounces of natural cheese
- 2 ounces of process cheese

Meat, Poultry, Fish, Dry Beans, Eggs, and Nuts

- 2 to 3 ounces cooked lean meat, poultry, or fish
- ½ cup of cooked dry beans or 1 egg counts as 1 ounce of lean meat; 2 tablespoons of peanut butter or ⅓ cup of nuts also count as 1 ounce of meat

Newgent recommends that every so often you take out your measuring cups and scales to test your portion sizes. This gives you a visual guide to follow. You might be surprised at your servings. "They tend to get bigger and bigger when we're not paying attention," she says.

Soups & Sandwiches

PEACH-APRICOT SOUP

Fresh apricots are available in June and July. If you want to make this soup in other months, substitute six drained canned unsweetened apricot halves.

¼ cup cognac
2 tablespoons dried cranberries (such as Craisins)
2 cups orange juice
3 medium peaches, peeled, halved, and pitted
3 medium apricots, peeled, halved, and pitted

1. Combine cognac and cranberries in a bowl; let stand 15 minutes, stirring occasionally.
2. Place cognac and cranberries in a blender; process until cranberries are finely chopped. Add orange juice, peaches, and apricots; process until peach mixture is smooth and cranberries are minced. Cover and chill. Serve chilled. YIELD: 4 servings (serving size: 1¼ cups).
NOTE: You can omit the cognac and use 2¼ cups orange juice, if desired.

POINTS: 3; EXCHANGES: 2 Fruit, ½ Starch; PER SERVING: CAL 157 (2% from fat); PRO 1.8g; FAT 0.3g (sat 0g); CARB 29.7g; FIB 2.5g; CHOL 0mg; IRON 0.4mg; SOD 2mg; CALC 20mg

CREAMY POTATO AND GARLIC SOUP

(pictured on page 140)

1 tablespoon olive oil
1½ cups chopped onion
2 pounds baking potatoes, peeled and cut into ½-inch pieces
4 large garlic cloves
3 cups fat-free, reduced-sodium chicken broth
1½ cups fat-free milk
½ teaspoon salt
⅛ teaspoon pepper
1 cup plain croutons
Additional pepper (optional)

1. Heat oil in a large saucepan over medium heat. Add onion; cook, stirring constantly, 4 minutes or until tender. Stir in potato, garlic, and broth; bring to a boil. Cover, reduce heat, and simmer 15 minutes. Add milk; cook 4 minutes, stirring frequently. Stir in salt and pepper.
2. Place one-third of potato mixture in a food processor or blender; process until smooth. Pour puréed mixture into a large bowl; repeat procedure twice with remaining potato mixture. Ladle soup into individual bowls; top evenly with croutons. Sprinkle each serving with additional pepper, if desired. YIELD: 4 servings (serving size: 1¾ cups).

POINTS: 4; EXCHANGES: 2 Starch, ½ Skim Milk, ½ Fat; PER SERVING: CAL 216 (17% from fat); PRO 11g; FAT 4g (sat 0.7g); CARB 38g; FIB 4.6g; CHOL 1.8mg; IRON 6.3mg; SOD 835mg; CALC 189mg

RICE NOODLE SOUP WITH ESCAROLE AND SHRIMP

We loved this soup served with thin, crispy Oriental rice crackers.

2 ounces uncooked bean threads (cellophane noodles), broken in half
2 (14½-ounce) cans vegetable broth
½ pound medium shrimp, peeled, deveined, and chopped
1 cup thinly sliced escarole
2 tablespoons chopped fresh cilantro

1. Cook noodles according to package directions; drain.
2. Bring broth to a boil in a medium saucepan. Add shrimp; reduce heat, and simmer 3 minutes. Add escarole; cook 30 seconds. Stir in noodles. Sprinkle cilantro evenly over each serving. Serve warm. YIELD: 5 servings (serving size: 1 cup).

POINTS: 2; EXCHANGES: 1 Starch, 1 Very Lean Meat; PER SERVING: CAL 107 (13% from fat); PRO 9.4g; FAT 1.6g (sat 0.2g); CARB 13.1g; FIB 0.3g; CHOL 69mg; IRON 1.4mg; SOD 890mg; CALC 43mg

ESCAROLE

The mildest member of the endive family, escarole has broad, slightly curved green leaves.

CIOPPINO

(pictured on page 141)

See page 63 for tips on debearding mussels and page 74 for step-by-step photos on peeling and deveining shrimp.

- 2 tablespoons olive oil
- 2 cups chopped onion
- 1¾ cups chopped fennel bulb (about 1 small bulb)
- 1 cup chopped green bell pepper
- 4 garlic cloves, minced
- 3 tablespoons red wine vinegar
- 1 teaspoon saffron threads
- ¼ teaspoon crushed red pepper
- 3 (14½-ounce) cans diced tomatoes, undrained
- 1 cup dry white wine
- 1 (8-ounce) bottle clam juice
- 1 tablespoon chopped fresh or 1 teaspoon dried thyme
- 2 pounds small clams in shells (about 24), scrubbed
- 1 pound mussels (about 16), scrubbed and debearded
- 1 pound medium shrimp, peeled and deveined
- 8 ounces lump crabmeat, shell pieces removed

1. Heat oil in a large nonstick skillet over medium-high heat. Add onion and next 3 ingredients; cook, stirring constantly, 5 minutes or until crisp-tender. Add vinegar, saffron, and red pepper; cook 3 minutes or until vinegar evaporates.

2. Add tomatoes and next 3 ingredients; bring to a boil. Reduce heat, and simmer 15 minutes. Add clams; cover and cook 10 minutes or until shells open. Discard any unopened shells. Add mussels; cook 5 minutes or until shells open. Discard any unopened shells. Add shrimp and crabmeat; cook 4 minutes or until shrimp are done. **YIELD:** 8 servings (serving size: 2 cups).

POINTS: 5; **EXCHANGES:** 3½ Vegetable, 3 Very Lean Meat, 1½ Fat; **PER SERVING:** CAL 252 (24% from fat); PRO 29g; FAT 7g (sat 1g); CARB 18g; FIB 2.1g; CHOL 130mg; IRON 8.7mg; SOD 631mg; CALC 162mg

QUICK VEGETABLE SOUP

Pick up whole wheat rolls and low-fat vanilla ice cream to round out the meal.

- 2 cups frozen vegetable soup mix with tomatoes
- ¾ cup bottled home-style savory beef gravy
- ½ cup water
- ¼ cup dry red wine
- ¼ teaspoon pepper
- 1 (14½-ounce) can diced tomatoes with garlic and onion, undrained

1. Combine all ingredients in a large saucepan; bring to a boil. Cover, reduce heat, and simmer 30 minutes. **YIELD:** 4 servings (serving size: 1 cup).

POINTS: 2; **EXCHANGES:** ½ Starch, 2 Vegetable; **PER SERVING:** CAL 99 (14% from fat); PRO 6.3g; FAT 1.5g (sat 0g); CARB 16.2g; FIB 2.3g; CHOL 0mg; IRON 1.4mg; SOD 941mg; CALC 44mg

SMOKED TURKEY-BEAN SOUP

(pictured on page 118)

- 2 cups water
- ¾ cup chopped onion
- ¾ cup chopped carrot
- ¼ cup chopped celery
- ¼ teaspoon pepper
- 1 bay leaf
- 3 (15.8-ounce) cans Great Northern beans, rinsed and drained
- 1 (14½-ounce) can fat-free, reduced-sodium chicken broth
- 1 (10-ounce) whole smoked turkey leg
- 2 teaspoons white wine vinegar

1. Combine all ingredients except vinegar in a Dutch oven. Bring to a boil; reduce heat, and simmer, uncovered, 1 hour and 15 minutes. Stir in vinegar; discard bay leaf. Remove turkey leg from soup; discard skin. Remove meat from bone; discard bone. Shred meat into bite-size pieces. Add turkey to soup. **YIELD:** 6 servings (serving size: 1 cup).

POINTS: 3; **EXCHANGES:** 2 Starch, ½ Vegetable, 1 Very Lean Meat; **PER SERVING:** CAL 205 (8% from fat); PRO 15.6g; FAT 1.8g (sat 0.5g); CARB 32.9g; FIB 8.5g; CHOL 15mg; IRON 2.4mg; SOD 913mg; CALC 84mg

SMOKED TURKEY AND TORTILLA SOUP

(pictured on page 116)

- 6 (6-inch) corn tortillas, cut into ¼-inch strips
- Cooking spray
- 2 teaspoons olive oil
- 1 cup chopped onion
- 3 garlic cloves, minced
- 2 (14½-ounce) cans diced tomatoes with garlic and onion, undrained
- 4 cups fat-free, reduced-sodium chicken broth
- 2 teaspoons dried oregano
- 2 teaspoons ground cumin
- ¼ teaspoon crushed red pepper
- ¼ teaspoon black pepper
- 1 green bell pepper, diced
- 1⅓ cups chopped smoked turkey breast (about ¾ pound)
- 1 cup frozen whole-kernel corn
- 1 (4-ounce) can whole green chiles, drained and sliced
- ½ cup chopped fresh cilantro

1. Preheat oven to 350°.
2. Spread tortilla strips on a baking sheet coated with cooking spray. Bake at 350° for 20 minutes or until golden, stirring after 10 minutes. Set aside.
3. Heat oil in a Dutch oven over medium-high heat. Add onion and garlic; cook, stirring constantly, 2 minutes. Add tomatoes and next 6 ingredients; bring to a boil. Reduce heat, and simmer 10 minutes.
4. Add turkey, corn, and chiles to pan; bring to a boil. Reduce heat, and simmer 15 minutes.
5. Ladle soup into individual bowls, and top with tortilla strips and cilantro. **YIELD:** 6 servings (serving size: 1½ cups).

POINTS: 4; **EXCHANGES:** 1 Starch, 3 Vegetable, 1 Very Lean Meat, ½ Fat; **PER SERVING:** CAL 214 (13% from fat); PRO 15g; FAT 3g (sat 0.4g); CARB 34g; FIB 3.7g; CHOL 20mg; IRON 3mg; SOD 1,489mg; CALC 94mg

SAUSAGE AND TORTELLINI SOUP

- ½ pound sweet Italian turkey sausage
- ¾ cup chopped onion
- 2 garlic cloves, minced
- 2 (14½-ounce) cans diced tomatoes with basil, garlic, and oregano, undrained
- 2 (14½-ounce) cans fat-free, reduced-sodium chicken broth
- ½ teaspoon fennel seeds
- ½ teaspoon coarsely ground pepper
- 1 (9-ounce) package fresh cheese tortellini, uncooked
- 2 cups torn fresh spinach

1. Remove casings from sausage. Cook sausage, onion, and garlic in a large Dutch oven over medium heat until sausage is browned, stirring to crumble. Drain well; return to pan.
2. Add tomatoes and next 3 ingredients; bring to a boil. Cover; reduce heat, and simmer 15 minutes. Add tortellini; cover and simmer 6 minutes, stirring occasionally. Stir in spinach; cook 2 minutes. **YIELD:** 8 servings (serving size: 1 cup).

POINTS: 4; **EXCHANGES:** 1½ Starch, 1 Vegetable, 1 Medium-Fat Meat; **PER SERVING:** CAL 198 (25% from fat); PRO 14g; FAT 5.5g (sat 2.1g); CARB 27g; FIB 2.3g; CHOL 47mg; IRON 2.7mg; SOD 1,192mg; CALC 128mg

CONGEE

Congee (pronounced KON-jee) is a spicy rice soup popular in many Asian cuisines.

- ⅓ cup rice vinegar
- 1 garlic clove, minced
- 2 teaspoons Thai chili paste
- ¼ teaspoon crushed red pepper
- ¾ pound skinned, boned chicken thighs, cut into bite-size pieces
- 2 garlic cloves, minced
- Cooking spray
- 4 cups chicken broth
- ⅔ cup jasmine or long-grain rice, uncooked
- 1 (2-inch) piece ginger, halved
- 1 teaspoon Thai fish sauce (nam pla)
- ⅓ cup chopped dry-roasted peanuts
- ½ cup chopped fresh cilantro

1. Combine first 4 ingredients.
2. Place chicken and garlic in a bowl; coat with cooking spray, and toss well. Heat a large saucepan over medium-high heat; add chicken mixture. Cook, stirring constantly, 5 minutes or until chicken is done.
3. Add broth and next 3 ingredients. Bring to a boil; cover, reduce heat to medium-low, and simmer 25 minutes or until rice is tender. Discard ginger.
4. Divide rice mixture evenly among 4 bowls; top evenly with reserved vinegar mixture, peanuts, and cilantro. **YIELD:** 4 servings (serving size: 1¼ cups).

POINTS: 7; **EXCHANGES:** 2 Starch, 3 Lean Meat, ½ Fat; **PER SERVING:** CAL 331 (30% from fat); PRO 27.3g; FAT 11g (sat 2.2g); CARB 29.4g; FIB 1.8g; CHOL 71mg; IRON 3.4mg; SOD 1,015mg; CALC 52mg

CHICKEN-CORN CHOWDER

4 bacon slices
1 cup chopped onion
1 cup diced carrot
2 garlic cloves, minced
2 cups peeled diced red potato
1 (10.11-ounce) package ready-to-eat roasted chicken breast halves (such as Tyson), skin removed, boned and diced
½ teaspoon salt
½ teaspoon pepper
4¼ cups 2% reduced-fat milk, divided
¼ cup all-purpose flour
2 cups frozen whole-kernel corn, thawed
1½ cups (6 ounces) shredded reduced-fat sharp Cheddar cheese, divided

1. Cook bacon in a Dutch oven over medium-high heat until crisp. Remove bacon from pan; crumble and set aside.
2. Add onion, carrot, and garlic to pan; cook, stirring constantly, 5 minutes. Add potato, chicken, salt, pepper, and 4 cups milk; bring to a boil. Cover, reduce heat to medium, and simmer 20 minutes or until potatoes are tender, stirring occasionally.
3. Place flour in a small bowl; gradually add remaining ¼ cup milk, stirring until smooth. Add flour mixture to chicken mixture. Bring to a boil over medium-high heat. Reduce heat, and simmer, uncovered, 5 minutes, stirring frequently.
4. Add corn and 1 cup shredded cheese to chicken mixture; stir until cheese melts. Divide mixture evenly among 9 bowls; top with crumbled bacon and remaining ½ cup shredded cheese.
YIELD: 9 servings (serving size: 1 cup).

POINTS: 7; **EXCHANGES:** 1½ Starch, ½ Low-Fat Milk, 2 Medium-Fat Meat; **PER SERVING:** CAL 302 (41% from fat); PRO 20.2g; FAT 13.8g (sat 15.1g); CARB 26.1g; FIB 2.3g; CHOL 48mg; IRON 0.7mg; SOD 567mg; CALC 318mg

CREAMY VEGETABLE CHOWDER

1 (16-ounce) package frozen baby corn blend, unthawed
4 cups 1% low-fat milk
1 tablespoon salt-free garlic-herb seasoning
1 teaspoon garlic paste
½ teaspoon salt
1¼ cups instant potato flakes
¾ cup (3 ounces) shredded sharp Cheddar cheese

1. Place baby corn blend under running hot water 1 minute to thaw partially. Combine baby corn blend, milk, and next 3 ingredients in a large saucepan. Bring mixture to a simmer over medium heat; slowly stir in potato flakes. Cook, uncovered over medium heat, stirring constantly, 5 minutes or until slightly thickened. Add cheese; stir until cheese melts. **YIELD:** 6 servings (serving size: 1 cup).

POINTS: 5; **EXCHANGES:** 1½ Starch, ½ Skim Milk, ½ High-Fat Meat; **PER SERVING:** CAL 230 (29% from fat); PRO 11.8g; FAT 7.4g (sat 4.1g); CARB 27.9g; FIB 2.3g; CHOL 21mg; IRON 0.3mg; SOD 423mg; CALC 306mg

SHRIMP GUMBO

4 bacon slices
2 tablespoons vegetable oil
½ cup all-purpose flour
2 cups chopped onion
1 cup chopped green bell pepper
⅔ cup chopped celery
5 garlic cloves, minced
2 cups hot water
1 cup frozen cut okra, thawed
1 (14½-ounce) can diced tomatoes, undrained
1 tablespoon Cajun seasoning
2 (8-ounce) bottles clam juice
2 bay leaves
1¼ pounds medium shrimp, peeled and deveined
1 (8-ounce) container Standard oysters, undrained
1½ to 3 teaspoons hot sauce
5 cups hot cooked long-grain rice

1. Cook bacon in a Dutch oven over medium heat until crisp. Remove bacon from pan, reserving 3 tablespoons drippings in pan; crumble bacon, and set aside.
2. Add oil to bacon drippings; place over medium heat. Add flour; cook, stirring constantly, 10 minutes or until very brown. Slowly add onion and next 3 ingredients; reduce heat to medium-low, and cook, stirring constantly, 4 minutes. Slowly add water, stirring well. Add okra and next 4 ingredients. Bring to a boil; reduce heat, and simmer, uncovered, 45 minutes, stirring occasionally.
3. Add shrimp and oysters; cook 10 minutes or until seafood is done. Stir in hot sauce. Discard bay leaves. Spoon ½ cup rice into each serving bowl; add 1 cup gumbo. Sprinkle each evenly with crumbled bacon.

YIELD: 10 servings (serving size: 1 cup gumbo and ½ cup rice).

POINTS: 7; **EXCHANGES:** 2½ Starch, 1½ Very Lean Meat, 1½ Fat; **PER SERVING:** CAL 306 (29% from fat); PRO 17.4g; FAT 9.8g (sat 2.9g); CARB 38g; FIB 2.1g; CHOL 88mg; IRON 4.5mg; SOD 890mg; CALC 85mg

FROGMORE STEW

(pictured on page 138)

- 6 cups water
- 2 (8-ounce) bottles clam juice
- 2 pounds small red potatoes (about 10 potatoes)
- 2 tablespoons Old Bay seasoning
- 1 teaspoon dried thyme
- 4 garlic cloves, minced
- 2 bay leaves
- ½ teaspoon salt
- 2 teaspoons hot sauce
- 2 pounds smoked turkey sausage, cut into 20 pieces
- 5 ears corn, (about 3 pounds) each cut crosswise into 4 pieces
- 2 pounds unpeeled medium shrimp

1. Combine first 9 ingredients in a 10-quart stock pot; bring to a boil. Simmer, uncovered, 15 minutes or until potatoes are just tender. Add sausage; cook 5 minutes. Add corn and shrimp; cover and cook 4 minutes or until shrimp are done. Drain. Discard bay leaves, and serve immediately. **YIELD:** 10 servings (serving size: 1 potato, 2 pieces sausage, 2 pieces corn, and 2½ ounces unpeeled shrimp).

POINTS: 8; **EXCHANGES:** 3½ Starch, 3 Very Lean Meat, ½ Fat; **PER SERVING:** CAL 414 (22% from fat); PRO 31g; FAT 10g (sat 4.5g); CARB 54g; FIB 6.7g; CHOL 153mg; IRON 13.9mg; SOD 1,321mg; CALC 72mg

BEEF STEW WITH ALE

(pictured on page 139)

- ¼ cup all-purpose flour
- ½ teaspoon salt
- ⅛ teaspoon pepper
- 1½ pounds lean boned round steak, cut into 1-inch cubes
- Cooking spray
- 1 teaspoon canola or vegetable oil
- 3 cups chopped onion
- 1½ pounds baking potato, peeled and cut into 1-inch pieces
- 1 pound carrots, sliced
- ½ teaspoon dried rosemary
- ½ teaspoon dried thyme
- 1 (14½-ounce) can fat-free, reduced-sodium chicken broth
- 1 (12-ounce) bottle ale
- 1 tablespoon cider vinegar
- 1 teaspoon Worcestershire sauce
- 1 bay leaf

1. Combine flour, salt, and pepper in a shallow dish; stir well. Dredge beef in flour mixture.
2. Coat a Dutch oven with cooking spray; add oil, and place pan over medium-high heat until hot. Add meat and any remaining flour mixture; cook 6 minutes or until meat is browned, stirring occasionally (pan will be dry).
3. Add onion, potato, and carrot to meat mixture; cook 2 minutes, stirring constantly. Stir in rosemary and remaining ingredients; bring to a boil. Cover, reduce heat, and simmer 1½ hours. Discard bay leaf. **YIELD:** 5 servings (serving size: 2 cups).

POINTS: 8; **EXCHANGES:** 2 Starch, 3 Vegetable, 3 Lean Meat; **PER SERVING:** CAL 406 (18% from fat); PRO 35g; FAT 8g (sat 2.7g); CARB 45g; FIB 5.6g; CHOL 79mg; IRON 4.3mg; SOD 750mg; CALC 56mg

SIRLOIN VEGETABLE STEW

- ¾ pound lean boneless top sirloin steak, cut into 1-inch pieces
- ¼ teaspoon salt
- ¼ teaspoon pepper
- Cooking spray
- 1 (16-ounce) bag frozen stewing vegetables
- 1 (16-ounce) bag frozen pepper stir-fry, thawed
- 1 (8-ounce) package fresh whole mushrooms
- ¼ cup dry red wine
- ¼ cup water, divided
- 1 tablespoon Worcestershire sauce
- 1 tablespoon beef-flavored bouillon granules
- 2 teaspoons cornstarch
- 2 tablespoons ketchup

1. Heat a Dutch oven over medium-high heat. Sprinkle steak with salt and pepper; coat with cooking spray. Add steak to pan; cook 2 minutes or until browned, stirring frequently. Add stewing vegetables, next 3 ingredients, 3 tablespoons water, Worcestershire sauce, and bouillon granules; bring to a boil. Cover, reduce heat, and simmer 12 minutes or until vegetables are tender.
2. Combine cornstarch and remaining 1 tablespoon water; stir in ketchup until smooth. Add ketchup mixture to steak mixture; bring to a boil. Cook, stirring constantly, 1 to 2 minutes or until slightly thickened. **YIELD:** 4 servings (serving size: 1½ cups).

POINTS: 4; **EXCHANGES:** 1 Starch, 2 Vegetable, 2 Lean Meat; **PER SERVING:** CAL 229 (22% from fat); PRO 21.3g; FAT 5.5g (sat 1.9g); CARB 23.2g; FIB 3.4g; CHOL 52mg; IRON 3.9mg; SOD 1,090mg; CALC 26mg

VEAL AND ARTICHOKE STEW

(pictured on page 138)

3 tablespoons all-purpose flour
½ teaspoon salt
1½ pounds lean boned veal shoulder roast, cut into 1-inch cubes
1 tablespoon canola or vegetable oil
1 cup chopped onion
2½ cups fat-free, reduced-sodium chicken broth
2 tablespoons lemon juice
½ teaspoon lemon pepper
½ teaspoon dried tarragon
2 (9-ounce) packages frozen artichoke hearts

1. Combine flour and salt in a shallow dish; stir well. Dredge veal in flour mixture.
2. Heat oil in a Dutch oven over medium-high heat; add veal, and cook 6 minutes, stirring occasionally. Add onion; cook 2 minutes, stirring constantly. Stir in broth, lemon juice, lemon pepper, and tarragon; bring to a boil. Cover, reduce heat, and simmer 1 hour. Add artichoke hearts, and bring to a boil. Reduce heat, and simmer, uncovered, 10 minutes or until veal and artichoke hearts are tender and sauce thickens. **YIELD:** 6 servings (serving size: 1 cup).

POINTS: 4; **EXCHANGES:** 2 Vegetable, 3½ Very Lean Meat, 1 Fat; **PER SERVING:** CAL 205 (26% from fat); PRO 26g; FAT 6.1g (sat 1.5g); CARB 11g; FIB 1.1g; CHOL 98mg; IRON 1.6mg; SOD 621mg; CALC 36mg

AFRICAN LAMB AND PEANUT STEW

1½ pounds boned leg of lamb, trimmed and cut into 1-inch cubes
Cooking spray
2 teaspoons peanut oil
4 cups thinly sliced onion
8 garlic cloves, minced
1 tablespoon ground coriander
1 tablespoon ground cumin
1 teaspoon ground red pepper
4 cups water
1 large peeled sweet potato, cut into 1-inch pieces
2 large carrots, cut into 1-inch pieces
⅓ cup reduced-fat chunky peanut butter
¼ cup tomato paste
2 (14½-ounce) cans diced tomatoes, drained
1 teaspoon salt
1 teaspoon freshly ground black pepper
2 cups sliced fresh or frozen cut okra
4 cups hot cooked long-grain rice

1. Heat a large Dutch oven over medium-high heat. Coat lamb with cooking spray. Add lamb to pan; cook 5 minutes or until browned, stirring frequently. Drain in a colander; set aside. Wipe drippings from pan with a paper towel.
2. Recoat Dutch oven with cooking spray; add oil. Place over medium-high heat. Add onion and garlic; cook 2 minutes, stirring constantly. Return lamb to pan, and add coriander, cumin, and red pepper. Cook 2 minutes, stirring constantly.
3. Add water and next 7 ingredients; stir well, and bring to a boil. Cover, reduce heat, and simmer 30 minutes. Add okra, and cook an additional 5 minutes.
4. Spoon rice into individual bowls; top with stew. **YIELD:** 7 servings (serving size: 2 cups stew and about ½ cup rice).

POINTS: 10; **EXCHANGES:** 4 Starch, 2½ Medium-Fat Meat; **PER SERVING:** CAL 472 (24% from fat); PRO 29.6g; FAT 12.5g (sat 3.3g); CARB 61.2g; FIB 7.1g; CHOL 65mg; IRON 4.8mg; SOD 698mg; CALC 137mg

DUMP-AND-STIR CHILI

This chili takes about 25 minutes to make—start to finish—and feeds a crowd. Serve with fat-free sour cream and shredded fat-free Cheddar cheese, if desired.

2 (15-ounce) cans 99% fat-free turkey chili without beans
2 (15-ounce) cans no-salt-added pinto beans, undrained
2 (14½-ounce) cans no-salt-added diced tomatoes, undrained
1 (10-ounce) can diced tomatoes and green chiles, undrained
3 tablespoons instant minced onion
1 tablespoon chili powder

1. Combine all ingredients in a large Dutch oven, and bring to a boil. Cover, reduce heat, and simmer 10 minutes. Uncover and simmer an additional 10 minutes, stirring occasionally. **YIELD:** 11 servings (serving size: 1 cup).

POINTS: 3; **EXCHANGES:** 1½ Starch, ½ Vegetable, 1 Very Lean Meat; **PER SERVING:** CAL 170 (6% from fat); PRO 14.1g; FAT 1.2g (sat 0.4g); CARB 25.6g; FIB 7.3g; CHOL 0mg; IRON 2.5mg; SOD 591mg; CALC 95mg

CINCINNATI FOUR-WAY CHILI

(pictured on page 119)

- 1 pound lean ground beef
- 2 cups chopped onion
- 2 garlic cloves, minced
- 2 teaspoons chili powder
- 2 teaspoons unsweetened cocoa
- 1½ teaspoons ground cumin
- ¾ teaspoon ground cinnamon
- 1 teaspoon salt
- ¼ teaspoon ground red pepper
- ¼ teaspoon black pepper
- 2 (14½-ounce) cans diced tomatoes, undrained
- ¾ cup brewed coffee
- ¾ cup water
- 5 cups hot cooked spaghetti (about 10 ounces uncooked pasta), cooked without salt or fat
- 1 (16-ounce) can kidney beans, rinsed and drained
- ⅓ cup diced onion
- 1 cup (4 ounces) shredded reduced-fat Cheddar cheese
- ⅔ cup oyster crackers

1. Cook beef in a Dutch oven over medium heat 5 minutes or until no longer pink, stirring to crumble. Add chopped onion and next 8 ingredients; cook 3 minutes, stirring constantly. Add tomatoes, coffee, and water; bring to a boil. Reduce heat, and simmer 45 minutes.

2. Divide spaghetti evenly among 7 plates; top with chili. Sprinkle each serving evenly with beans, diced onion, cheese, and crackers. **YIELD:** 7 servings (serving size: about ¾ cup pasta, about ¾ cup chili, about ¼ cup beans, about 2¼ teaspoons onion, about 2¼ tablespoons cheese, and about 1½ tablespoons crackers).

POINTS: 8; **EXCHANGES:** 3½ Starch, 2½ Lean Meat; **PER SERVING:** CAL 409 (22% from fat); PRO 27g; FAT 10g (sat 4.5g); CARB 51g; FIB 5.8g; CHOL 48mg; IRON 5.3mg; SOD 1,162mg; CALC 191mg

REUBEN ROLL-UP

You'll find presliced lean corned beef with the lunch meat in most grocery stores. We used a product by Hormel that has only 1.75 grams of fat per slice.

- 3 cups thinly sliced cabbage
- ¼ cup fat-free Thousand Island dressing
- 1 teaspoon caraway seeds
- 8 (1-ounce) slices pumpernickel-rye bread
- 6 ounces thinly sliced lean corned beef
- 4 (⅔-ounce) slices low-fat process Swiss cheese, each cut in half

Cooking spray

1. Combine first 3 ingredients in a bowl; toss well, and set aside.

2. Place 2 bread slices on work surface with flat, bottom crusts together and overlapping slightly. Flatten bread slices to ⅛-inch thickness, using a rolling pin, seaming 2 bread slices together (cover bread to keep from drying). Repeat procedure 3 times with remaining 6 bread slices.

3. Divide corned beef evenly among bread. Divide cheese slices evenly over corned beef, and spread cabbage mixture evenly over cheese slices. Beginning with 1 long edge, roll up each sandwich, jelly-roll fashion, so seam of bread is in the middle of each sandwich (secure with wooden picks, if necessary).

4. Coat a large nonstick skillet with cooking spray; place over medium-high heat until hot. Place 2 sandwiches in skillet; cook until lightly browned on all sides, gently turning with tongs. **YIELD:** 4 servings.

POINTS: 5; **EXCHANGES:** 2½ Starch, 1½ Lean Meat; **PER SERVING:** CAL 276 (20% from fat); PRO 18.3g; FAT 6g (sat 2.1g); CARB 38.6g; FIB 3.3g; CHOL 25mg; IRON 2.8mg; SOD 1,320mg; CALC 181mg

CRÊPE TORTE

- 1 (5-ounce) package ready-to-use crêpes (such as Melissa's)
- 1 pound thinly sliced deli mesquite-smoked turkey breast
- 1 cup trimmed arugula leaves
- 1 (6-ounce) container light crunchy garden vegetable spread (such as Fleur de Lait)
- 1 cup freshly grated carrot

1. Place 1 crêpe on a large plate; top with one-third of turkey. Place 1 crêpe on top of turkey; cover with one-third of arugula leaves, and another crêpe. Spread one-third of vegetable spread on top; sprinkle with one-third of grated carrot. Repeat layers twice, ending with a crêpe. Wrap in plastic wrap, and chill 4 hours or overnight. Cut into wedges, and serve. **YIELD:** 6 servings.

POINTS: 6; **EXCHANGES:** 1½ Starch, 3 Lean Meat; **PER SERVING:** CAL 280 (33% from fat); PRO 24.8g; FAT 10.1g (sat 5.3g); CARB 21.8g; FIB 0.5g; CHOL 108mg; IRON 1.1mg; SOD 1,102mg; CALC 183mg

DAGWOOD SANDWICH

Named after Dagwood Bumstead, a character in the "Blondie" comic strip, this thick sandwich is piled high with a variety of meats and cheeses.

- 3 tablespoons nonfat mayonnaise
- 4 (2½-ounce) submarine rolls
- 2 tablespoons spicy hot mustard
- 8 small green leaf lettuce leaves
- 4 (1-ounce) slices smoked turkey breast, cut in half diagonally
- 4 (¾-ounce) slices fat-free Swiss cheese, cut in half diagonally
- 4 slices small red onion
- 4 (1-ounce) slices turkey ham, cut in half diagonally
- 4 (¾-ounce) slices fat-free sharp Cheddar cheese, cut in half diagonally
- 4 gherkin pickles

1. Spread mayonnaise evenly on top half of each roll. Spread mustard evenly on bottom half of each roll. Place 1 lettuce leaf on bottom of each roll; top with 2 half slices of smoked turkey. Layer Swiss cheese, onion, lettuce, turkey ham, and Cheddar cheese on lettuce, dividing evenly among rolls. Place top of roll on cheese.
2. Secure 1 pickle on top of each sandwich with a wooden pick. **YIELD:** 4 servings.

POINTS: 6; **EXCHANGES:** 3 Starch, 1 Vegetable, 2 Very Lean Meat; **PER SERVING:** CAL 326 (13% from fat); PRO 24.9g; FAT 4.6g (sat 1.5g); CARB 50.5g; FIB 2.5g; CHOL 24mg; IRON 3.4mg; SOD 1,688mg; CALC 380mg

ROASTED VEGETABLE WRAP

(pictured on page 140)

- 4 cups sliced yellow squash (about 3 medium)
- 3 cups (1-inch) sliced asparagus (about 1 pound)
- 1⅓ cups vertically sliced red onion (about 1 small)
- Olive oil-flavored cooking spray
- ¼ teaspoon salt
- ¼ teaspoon pepper
- 1 (15.5-ounce) can cannellini beans or other white beans, undrained
- 1 tablespoon red wine vinegar
- 2 tablespoons sun-dried tomato sprinkles
- ½ teaspoon dried oregano
- 6 (8-inch) flour tortillas
- ¾ cup (3 ounces) crumbled feta cheese

1. Preheat oven to 500°.
2. Place first 3 ingredients on a jelly-roll pan coated with cooking spray. Lightly coat vegetables with cooking spray, and sprinkle with salt and pepper. Bake at 500° for 12 minutes. Drain vegetables in a colander to remove excess moisture; set aside.
3. Drain beans, reserving 2 tablespoons liquid. Place beans, reserved 2 tablespoons liquid, and vinegar in a food processor; process until smooth. Stir in tomato sprinkles and oregano.
4. Warm tortillas according to package directions. Spread about ¼ cup bean mixture over each tortilla, leaving a ¼-inch margin around edge of tortillas. Divide vegetables evenly down the center of each tortilla, and sprinkle evenly with feta cheese; roll up. Wrap bottom of rolled sandwiches in wax paper or parchment paper to secure. **YIELD:** 6 servings.

POINTS: 6; **EXCHANGES:** 2½ Starch, 2 Vegetable, ½ Medium-Fat Meat; **PER SERVING:** CAL 294 (21% from fat); PRO 12.3g; FAT 6.8g (sat 2.8g); CARB 46.4g; FIB 5.9g; CHOL 13mg; IRON 3.3mg; SOD 794mg; CALC 121mg

PEPPERONI AND VEGETABLE LOAF

- 1 (1-pound) unsliced loaf French bread (such as Francisco International)
- ¼ cup reduced-fat mayonnaise
- 4 (1-ounce) slices reduced-fat sharp Cheddar cheese
- 24 slices turkey pepperoni
- 1 (16-ounce) jar giardiniera vegetables (such as Vigo), well drained and chopped

1. Slanting knife at an angle, cut a 3- x 1½-inch oval piece out of top of loaf (to make a hollow loaf). Set top aside.
2. Spread mayonnaise in cut surface of loaf. Layer cheese, pepperoni, and vegetables in loaf; top with reserved top, pressing firmly to pack. Wrap tightly in heavy-duty plastic wrap, and chill at least 4 hours. Cut loaf crosswise into 8 pieces.
YIELD: 8 servings.

POINTS: 5; **EXCHANGES:** 2 Starch, ½ Medium-Fat Meat, 1 Fat; **PER SERVING:** CAL 245 (27% from fat); PRO 10.8g; FAT 7.4g (sat 0.9g); CARB 30.1g; FIB 1.7g; CHOL 20mg; IRON 1.6mg; SOD 1,480mg; CALC 169mg

STEAK-AND-POTATO WRAP

¾ pound lean, boned sirloin steak, cut into thin strips
1 (8-ounce) package presliced fresh mushrooms
¼ cup minced shallots
2 garlic cloves, minced
Cooking spray
½ cup dry red wine
¼ teaspoon dried thyme
¼ teaspoon freshly ground pepper
½ cup bottled home-style savory beef gravy
3 cups frozen shredded hash brown potatoes
¼ teaspoon salt
5 (8-inch) fat-free flour tortillas
2½ cups thinly sliced romaine lettuce

1. Place a large nonstick skillet over medium-high heat until hot. Add steak; sauté until browned. Drain well. Place steak in a medium bowl; set aside. Wipe skillet clean with paper towels.
2. Place skillet over medium-high heat until hot. Coat mushrooms, shallots, and garlic with cooking spray; add to skillet. Cook, stirring constantly, until tender. Add wine, thyme, and pepper; cook 8 minutes or until most of liquid evaporates. Remove from heat; stir in gravy. Add mixture to steak in bowl; stir well, and set aside. Wipe skillet clean with paper towels.
3. Place skillet over medium-high heat until hot. Coat potatoes with cooking spray. Add potatoes to skillet, spreading to an even layer; add salt. Cook 5 minutes (do not stir). Turn potatoes over, and cook an additional 5 minutes (do not stir). Add potatoes to steak mixture in bowl, and stir well.
4. Warm tortillas according to package directions. Spoon steak mixture evenly down the center of each tortilla, and top with lettuce; roll up. Wrap bottom of rolled sandwiches in wax paper or parchment paper to secure. YIELD: 5 servings.

POINTS: 5; **EXCHANGES:** 2 Starch, 1 Vegetable, 1½ Lean Meat; **PER SERVING:** CAL 274 (14% from fat); PRO 21.1g; FAT 4.2g (sat 1.3g); CARB 38.1g; FIB 2.7g; CHOL 42mg; IRON 4mg; SOD 656mg; CALC 25mg

LAMB-FETA BURGERS WITH YOGURT-CUCUMBER SAUCE

(pictured on page 118)

1 pound lean ground lamb
⅓ cup finely chopped onion
1 garlic clove, minced
2 tablespoons fine, dry breadcrumbs
2 teaspoons chopped fresh oregano
2 teaspoons chopped fresh mint
¼ teaspoon salt
¼ teaspoon pepper
¼ cup crumbled peppercorn feta cheese
Cooking spray
2 (6-inch) pita bread rounds, cut in half
4 red leaf lettuce leaves
4 (½-inch-thick) slices tomato
Yogurt-Cucumber Sauce

1. Combine first 8 ingredients in a large bowl. Divide mixture into 8 equal portions, shaping into ¼-inch-thick patties. Spoon 1 tablespoon feta cheese onto each of 4 patties (do not spread to edges); top with remaining patties, pressing edges to seal well.
2. Coat grill rack with cooking spray; place on grill over medium-hot coals (350° to 400°). Place patties on grill rack, and grill, covered, 6 to 8 minutes on each side or until done.
3. Wrap pita halves in heavy-duty foil. Add foil-wrapped pita halves to grill rack, and grill 2 minutes or until pitas are warm, turning foil pouch occasionally.
4. Line each pita half with lettuce. Place 1 slice tomato and 1 patty in each pita half. Drizzle 2 tablespoons Yogurt-Cucumber Sauce over each pita half. YIELD: 4 servings (serving size: ½ pita round, 1 burger, and 2 tablespoons sauce).

POINTS: 7; **EXCHANGES:** 1½ Starch, ½ Vegetable, 3½ Lean Meat; **PER SERVING:** CAL 327 (30% from fat); PRO 31.3g; FAT 11.0g (sat 4.4g); CARB 24.2g; FIB 1.6g; CHOL 88mg; IRON 3.2mg; SOD 504mg; CALC 141mg

YOGURT-CUCUMBER SAUCE

⅓ cup plain low-fat yogurt
¼ cup shredded seeded unpeeled cucumber, drained
2 teaspoons finely chopped fresh mint
2 teaspoons lemon juice

1. Combine all ingredients in a small bowl; stir well. YIELD: ½ cup.

ROASTED CHICKEN-AND-CORN WRAP

1 (11-ounce) can vacuum-packed corn with red and green peppers (such as Mexicorn), drained
1 teaspoon chili powder, divided
1½ teaspoons garlic-flavored vegetable oil
¼ teaspoon salt
2 (4-ounce) skinned, boned chicken breast halves
⅓ cup fat-free sour cream
¼ cup tomatillo or other green salsa
1½ cups cooked long-grain rice
½ cup (2 ounces) shredded reduced-fat Monterey Jack cheese
1 tablespoon fresh lime juice
10 (6-inch) corn tortillas

1. Preheat oven to 400°.
2. Spread corn over 1 end of a jelly-roll pan. Bake at 400° for 10 minutes. Combine ¾ teaspoon chili powder, oil, and salt; brush on both sides of chicken breast halves. Place chicken on pan with corn; bake an additional 20 minutes or until chicken is done and corn is lightly charred, stirring corn after 10 minutes. Remove chicken from pan; coarsely chop.
3. Combine sour cream and salsa in a medium bowl; stir well. Add chopped chicken, corn, remaining ¼ teaspoon chili powder, rice, cheese, and lime juice; stir well.
4. Warm tortillas according to package directions. Spoon about ½ cup chicken mixture down the center of each tortilla; roll up. Wrap bottom of rolled sandwiches in wax paper or parchment paper to secure. YIELD: 5 servings (serving size: 2 sandwiches).

POINTS: 7; **EXCHANGES:** 3½ Starch, 1½ Very Lean Meat, ½ Fat; **PER SERVING:** CAL 369 (14% from fat); PRO 21.3g; FAT 5.7g (sat 1.9g); CARB 56.7g; FIB 5.2g; CHOL 34mg; IRON 1.9mg; SOD 690mg; CALC 244mg

PAN-SEARED CHICKEN SANDWICH WITH ROASTED GARLIC AIOLI

(pictured on page 116)

2 whole garlic heads
Olive oil-flavored cooking spray
¼ cup grated Parmesan cheese
¼ cup reduced-fat mayonnaise
4 (4-ounce) skinned, boned chicken breast halves
¼ teaspoon salt
¼ teaspoon pepper
Cooking spray
4 (2-ounce) sandwich buns, split
4 red leaf lettuce leaves
4 (½-inch-thick) slices tomato

1. Remove white papery skin from garlic heads (do not peel or separate the cloves). Coat each head with cooking spray; wrap separately in foil. Bake at 350° for 1 hour; let cool 10 minutes. Separate cloves; carefully snip or cut 1 end of each clove. Squeeze cloves over a small bowl to extract garlic pulp. Discard skins.
2. Sprinkle Parmesan cheese over garlic pulp; mash with a fork until blended. Stir in mayonnaise until blended. Cover tightly with plastic wrap pressed onto surface of aioli; chill.
3. Place chicken breasts between 2 sheets of heavy-duty plastic wrap or wax paper; flatten to ¼-inch thickness, using a meat mallet or rolling pin (if chicken breasts are very large, cut in half, crosswise). Sprinkle salt and pepper over 1 side of each chicken breast.
4. Place a large nonstick skillet over medium-high heat until hot. Coat chicken breasts with cooking spray. Add chicken breasts, seasoned side down; cook 2 minutes on each side or until done. Remove from pan, and keep warm. Coat cut sides of buns with cooking spray; place in skillet, cut sides down, and cook until lightly toasted.
5. Spread 1 tablespoon garlic aioli over toasted sides of each bun. Divide chicken evenly among bottom halves of buns; top with lettuce, tomato, and top halves of buns. Serve immediately. YIELD: 4 servings.

POINTS: 9; **EXCHANGES:** 4 Very Lean Meat, 2 Starch, 1 Vegetable, 1½ Fat;
PER SERVING: CAL 403 (28% from fat); PRO 37g; FAT 13g (sat 3.1g); CARB 36g; FIB 1.2g; CHOL 87mg; IRON 3.5mg; SOD 709mg; CALC 182mg

OYSTER PO'BOY

(pictured on page 115)

- ⅓ cup white cornmeal
- ⅓ cup fine, dry breadcrumbs
- 1½ teaspoons Cajun seasoning
- 2 (8-ounce) containers Select oysters, well drained
- Cooking spray
- 1 tablespoon vegetable oil, divided
- 1 (8-ounce) unsliced loaf French bread
- ¼ cup reduced-fat mayonnaise
- 3 tablespoons Creole mustard
- 1½ cups thinly sliced romaine lettuce
- 1 medium tomato, thinly sliced

1. Combine first 3 ingredients in a bowl; stir well. Dredge oysters in cornmeal mixture.
2. Coat a large nonstick skillet with cooking spray, and place over medium heat until hot; add 1½ teaspoons oil. Add half of oysters, and cook 3 minutes on each side or until oysters are done and breading is golden. Repeat with remaining oil and oysters.
3. Cut bread in half horizontally, and spread mayonnaise and mustard evenly over cut sides of bread. Arrange lettuce and tomato slices over bottom half of loaf. Top with cooked oysters and top half of loaf. Cut loaf into 4 pieces. Serve immediately. **YIELD:** 4 servings.

POINTS: 7; **EXCHANGES:** 3 Starch, 1 Vegetable, ½ Lean Meat, 1 Fat; **PER SERVING:** CAL 351 (24% from fat); PRO 14.3g; FAT 9.3g (sat 1.7g); CARB 50.7g; FIB 3.2g; CHOL 52mg; IRON 8.4mg; SOD 1,070mg; CALC 90mg

GOODS

Picking Pots and Pans

Here's what you need to know in choosing the right cookware.

Whether it's a saucepan or a skillet, everyone seems to have a favorite pan, a piece that cooks everything from stir-fry to burgers. But no one pot or pan can do it all.

Varied shapes, materials, and prices can make selecting pots and pans a daunting experience. And as attractive as boxed sets are, they often include at least one piece you'll never use, making the bargain no bargain at all. Instead of buying a set, think about how *you* cook; certain materials work better with certain foods. Here's the rundown on the four basic materials: aluminum, stainless steel, cast iron, and copper.

ALUMINUM. Lightweight and a good conductor of heat, which disperses evenly throughout the pan, aluminum cookware is first rate.

Anodized aluminum is electrochemically sealed and offers a harder surface. Add a nonstick coating—such as Anolon, Calphalon Nonstick, or Circulon—and you can cook with little or no oil.

Always purchase heavy-gauge aluminum. The heavier the gauge, the longer it lasts, the more evenly it distributes heat, and the more it costs.

STAINLESS STEEL. Stainless steel is easy to clean and durable. But it's also a poor conductor of heat. That's why quality stainless steel pans have an aluminum core. These are general-purpose pans for everyday cooking.

CAST IRON. Cast iron is almost indestructible (if it's seasoned and washed correctly). It heats slowly, but holds heat very well and distributes it evenly. A well-seasoned cast-iron skillet is nearly nonstick.

Cast iron is heavy, which is what helps it hold heat and cook evenly. But that also makes it unwieldy. Lift a piece before purchasing to decide if you can comfortably work with it.

Enameled cast iron, which has a glasslike coating bonded to the metal, is more expensive and not as nonstick as regular cast iron, but it's almost as good and easier to care for. (Le Creuset is one popular brand.)

COPPER. The luster of copper pots signals that a true chef resides in your home. But chances are you don't have time to cook—you're busy polishing those beautiful pots, which tarnish easily and quickly. Copper conducts heat well and is ideal for making sauces because it heats and cools quickly.

STOCKING UP. No home should be without these essential pieces of cookware, no matter what your cooking style.

- 10- to 12-inch nonstick skillet, anodized aluminum or stainless steel
- 6- to 8-quart Dutch oven, enameled cast iron or stainless steel
- 2- to 3-quart saucepan with steamer (stainless steel, copper, or anodized aluminum).

One day's menu provides at least two servings of milk and at least five servings of fruits and/or vegetables.

	MONDAY	TUESDAY	WEDNESDAY	THURSDAY
BREAKFAST	**whole-wheat English muffin,** 1 (2-ounce), split and toasted, topped with 1 tablespoon *each of* honey and peanut butter **fat-free milk,** 1 cup **orange,** 1	**Raisin-Nut Oatmeal** (Cook ½ cup quick-cooking oats in 1 cup fat-free milk according to package directions; top with 2 tablespoons raisins and 1 tablespoon *each of* chopped walnuts and cinnamon-sugar. [*POINTS:* 7]) **orange juice,** 1 cup	**shredded wheat,** 2 large biscuits, topped with 2 tablespoons raisins and 1 tablespoon *each of* chopped walnuts and brown sugar **fat-free milk,** 1 cup **banana,** 1	**Cinnamon-Toasted Muffin** 1 (2-ounce) whole-wheat English muffin, split, and spread with 1½ tablespoons light butter and sprinkled with 1 tablespoon cinnamon-sugar. Broil until toasted. [*POINTS:* 5] **fat-free milk,** 1 cup **banana,** 1
LUNCH	**Tuna Pita** (Combine ½ [6-ounce] can tuna packed in water, drained, 1 tablespoon reduced-fat mayonnaise, and ⅛ teaspoon *each of* dried dill and pepper; stir well. Cut 1 [2-ounce] whole-wheat pita in half; line each half with a romaine lettuce leaf and 1 plum tomato, sliced. Stuff evenly with tuna mixture. [*POINTS:* 6]) **cucumber spears,** 1 cup, with 2 tablespoons fat-free Caesar salad dressing **apple,** 1	**Chicken Pizzas** (Split 1 [2-ounce] whole-wheat English muffin, and spread with ¼ cup prepared hummus. Top halves evenly with ½ cup thinly sliced fresh spinach, 1 ounce thinly sliced roasted chicken breast, and 6 tablespoons shredded part-skim mozzarella cheese. Broil until toasted. [*POINTS:* 8]) **frozen seedless red grapes,** 1 cup	**Veggie Burrito** (Spread 2 [8-inch] flour tortillas with ¼ cup prepared hummus; top evenly with 8 slices cucumber, 3 tablespoons shredded part-skim mozzarella cheese, and ¼ cup *each of* shredded carrot, chopped plum tomato, and thinly sliced fresh spinach. Roll up burritos. Serve with ½ cup salsa. [*POINTS:* 5]) **coconut cream pie fat-free yogurt,** 8 ounces	**Chicken Caesar Salad** (Combine 2 cups sliced romaine lettuce, 1 plum tomato, chopped, 2 ounces thinly sliced roasted chicken breast, and 2 tablespoons fat-free Caesar salad dressing; toss well. Sprinkle with 3 tablespoons shredded part-skim mozzarella cheese. [*POINTS:* 5]) **whole-wheat pita,** 1 (2-ounce), with ¼ cup prepared hummus
DINNER	**Curried-Apricot Pork** (Combine 2 tablespoons apricot preserves and ⅛ teaspoon curry powder; stir well. Spread over a 4-ounce lean, boned center-cut pork loin chop. Bake at 350° for 25 minutes or until done. [*POINTS:* 7]) **cooked couscous,** 1 cup **steamed asparagus,** 12 spears **seedless red grapes,** 1 cup	**broiled sirloin steak,** 3 ounces **baked potato,** 1 (8-ounce), with ¼ cup fat-free sour cream **cooked green beans,** 1 cup	**Shrimp Fettuccine** (Place 1 teaspoon olive oil in a nonstick skillet coated with cooking spray; place over medium-high heat until hot. Add 6 ounces peeled medium shrimp, 2 green onions, chopped, and 1 garlic clove, minced; sauté 5 minutes or until done. Add 3 tablespoons dry white wine and ⅛ teaspoon *each of* salt and pepper; sauté 1 minute. Add 1 cup hot cooked fettuccine and 1 teaspoon olive oil; toss well. [*POINTS:* 10]) **steamed asparagus,** 12 spears	**Bean and Rice Burritos** (Combine ½ cup hot cooked brown rice, ⅓ cup drained canned black beans, and 2 tablespoons salsa; stir well. Spoon down center of 1 [8-inch] flour tortilla; roll up. [*POINTS:* 4]) **Cucumber-Orange Salad** (Combine 1 cup orange sections, ½ cup peeled sliced cucumber, 1 teaspoon *each of* olive oil and vinegar, and a dash *each of* salt and pepper; toss well. [*POINTS:* 1])
SNACK	**blueberry fat-free yogurt,** 8 ounces **gingersnaps,** 2	**strawberry fat-free yogurt,** 8 ounces	**mango,** 1, served with a lime wedge	**fat-free cereal bar,** 1 **fat-free milk,** 1 cup
POINTS	***POINTS*** for the day: 30 **Exchanges:** 10½ Starch, 3 Vegetable, 3 Fruit, 3 Very Lean Meat, 3 Lean Meat, ½ High-Fat Meat, 2 Skim Milk, 1 Fat	***POINTS*** for the day: 28 **Exchanges:** 8½ Starch, 3 Vegetable, 4 Fruit, 2 Skim Milk, 1 Very Lean Meat, 3 Lean Meat, 2 Fat	***POINTS*** for the day: 28 **Exchanges:** 8 Starch, 3 Vegetable, 4 Fruit, 3 Very Lean Meat, 1 Lean Meat, 2 Skim Milk, 4 Fat	***POINTS*** for the day: 26 **Exchanges:** 10½ Starch, 3 Vegetable, 3 Fruit, 3 Very Lean Meat, 1 Lean Meat, 2 Skim Milk, 3½ Fat

7-DAY MENU PLANNER

WEEK 1

	FRIDAY	SATURDAY	SUNDAY
BREAKFAST	**cooked oatmeal,** 1 cup, with 1 tablespoon *each of* chopped walnuts and cinnamon-sugar **fat-free milk,** 1 cup **orange,** 1	**scrambled eggs,** 1 egg and 1 egg white in 2 teaspoons light butter **high-fiber whole-wheat bread,** 1 slice, toasted, with 1½ teaspoons light butter **orange juice,** 1 cup	**shredded wheat,** 2 large biscuits, topped with 1 banana, sliced, and 1 tablespoon brown sugar **fat-free milk,** 1 cup
LUNCH	**chili,** fast food, 8 ounces **saltines,** 6 **side salad,** fast food, with 2 tablespoons fat-free French dressing **banana,** 1	**Peanut Butter and Jelly Sandwich** (Spread 1 tablespoon peanut butter and 2 tablespoons jelly evenly over 2 slices high-fiber whole-wheat bread. [*POINTS:* 5]) **Carrot-Raisin Salad** (Combine 1 cup shredded carrot and 2 tablespoons *each of* raisins and vanilla fat-free yogurt*; stir well. [*POINTS:* 1]) *Save remaining portion of (8-ounce) carton yogurt for snack (below). **fat-free milk,** 1 cup	**baked ham,** 2 ounces **baked sweet potato,** 1 large, with 1 tablespoon *each of* chopped walnuts, brown sugar, and light butter **steamed broccoli,** 1 cup **pear,** 1
DINNER	**Warm Lamb Salad** (Cut 3 ounces lean leg of lamb into ½-inch cubes. Place a nonstick skillet over medium-high heat until hot. Add lamb; sauté 3 minutes or until browned. Combine lamb, 2 cups sliced romaine lettuce, 1 cup sliced cucumber, 2 steamed small red potatoes, quartered, and 1 plum tomato, chopped. Drizzle with 3 tablespoons fat-free Caesar salad dressing. [*POINTS:* 7])	**Cayenne Chicken and Black Beans** (Sprinkle 1 [4-ounce] skinned, boned chicken breast half with ½ teaspoon ground cumin and ⅛ teaspoon *each of* salt and ground red pepper; broil 5 minutes on each side or until done. Top with ½ cup salsa and ⅓ cup drained canned black beans. [*POINTS:* 5]) **cooked brown rice,** ½ cup **steamed broccoli,** 1 cup **mango,** 1	**Tortellini With Pasta Sauce** (Cook 1 cup refrigerated cheese tortellini according to package directions; top with ½ cup tomato-and-basil pasta sauce and 1 tablespoon Parmesan cheese. [*POINTS:* 8]) **green salad,** 1 cup, with 1 tablespoon fat-free Caesar salad dressing **apple,** 1
SNACK	**Cinnamon-Banana Smoothie** (Process 8 ounces vanilla fat-free yogurt, 1 banana, and 1 teaspoon cinnamon-sugar in a blender until smooth. [*POINTS:* 4])	**vanilla fat-free yogurt,** *remaining carton from lunch (above) **apple,** 1, sprinkled with 1 tablespoon cinnamon-sugar	**cappuccino-flavored fat-free yogurt,** 8 ounces **graham cracker squares,** 2
POINTS	***POINTS*** for the day: 30 **Exchanges:** 8½ Starch, 4 Vegetable, 3 Fruit, 2 Lean Meat, 2 Medium-Fat Meat, 2 Skim Milk, 1 Fat	***POINTS*** for the day: 28 **Exchanges:** 7 Starch, 3 Vegetable, 6 Fruit, 4½ Very Lean Meat, 1 Medium-Fat Meat, ½ High-Fat Meat, 2 Skim Milk, 1 Fat	***POINTS*** for the day: 30 **Exchanges:** 9 Starch, 3 Vegetable, 3 Fruit, 3 Lean Meat, 2 Skim Milk, 2 Fat

One day's menu provides at least two servings of milk and at least five servings of fruits and/or vegetables.

	MONDAY	TUESDAY	WEDNESDAY	THURSDAY
BREAKFAST	**Cheese Toast** (Toast 1 slice high-fiber whole-wheat bread; top with 3 tablespoons shredded reduced-fat Cheddar cheese. Broil until cheese melts. [*POINTS*: 2]) **apple,** 1 **fat-free milk,** 1 cup	**Honey-Raisin Oatmeal** (Combine 1 cup cooked oatmeal, 2 tablespoons raisins, and 1½ teaspoons *each of* light butter and honey. [*POINTS*: 6]) **fat-free milk,** 1 cup	**Strawberry Smoothie** (Combine 1 cup fat-free milk, ¾ cup sliced strawberries, 2 ice cubes, and 1 teaspoon strawberry jam in a blender; process until smooth. [*POINTS*: 2]) **cinnamon-raisin bagel,** 1 (2-ounce), with 1 tablespoon light cream cheese	**bran flakes,** 1½ cup **fat-free milk,** 1 cup **banana,** 1
LUNCH	**Beans and Greens Salad** (Combine 2 cups sliced romaine lettuce, ½ cup drained canned chickpeas [garbanzo beans], 3 tablespoons crumbled feta cheese, 6 cherry tomatoes, ½ cup sliced cucumber, and 2 tablespoons *each of* chopped red onion and sliced ripe olives. Drizzle with 3 tablespoons fat-free balsamic vinaigrette. [*POINTS*: 7]) **whole-wheat pita bread,** ½ (1 [2-ounce]) **seedless red grapes,** 1 cup	**lentil soup,** 1 (19-ounce) can (*POINTS*: 3) **Spinach Salad** (Combine 1 cup torn fresh spinach, ½ cup red bell pepper strips, ¼ cup shredded carrot, and 2 tablespoons fat-free balsamic vinaigrette. [*POINTS*: 1]) **saltine crackers,** 6, with 1 ounce reduced-fat sharp Cheddar cheese **strawberries,** 1 cup	**Turkey-Ham Sandwich** (Layer 1 ounce thinly sliced turkey-ham, 2 romaine lettuce leaves, ¼ cup cucumber slices, 2 tomato slices, 2 red onion slices, and 2 teaspoons prepared mustard between 2 slices high-fiber whole-wheat bread. [*POINTS*: 2]) **carrot and celery sticks,** 1 cup **seedless red grapes,** 1 cup **low-fat brownie,** 1 (1½ ounces)	**Lentil Salad** (Combine 2 cups torn romaine lettuce, ½ cup drained cooked lentils, ¼ cup *each of* chopped tomato, red onion, and yellow bell pepper, and 1 teaspoon *each of* extra-virgin olive oil and red wine vinegar. [*POINTS*: 3]) **whole-wheat pita bread,** 2 ounces, with ¼ cup hummus **cantaloupe chunks,** 1 cup
DINNER	**Baked Pesto Salmon** (Brush 2 teaspoons prepared pesto over 1 [6-ounce] skinned salmon fillet; bake at 350° for 20 minutes or until fish flakes easily when tested with a fork. [*POINTS:* 6]) **baked potato,** 1 (8-ounce), with 1½ teaspoons light butter **steamed asparagus,** 12 spears, with 1 lemon wedge	**Baked Barbecue Chicken** (Brush 2 tablespoons barbecue sauce over 1 [6-ounce] skinned, bone-in chicken breast half; bake at 400° for 45 minutes or until done. [*POINTS*: 5]) **coleslaw,** 1 cup very thinly sliced green cabbage with 1 tablespoon fat-free coleslaw dressing **cooked corn on the cob,** 1 small ear, with 1½ teaspoons light butter **orange sections,** 1 cup	**Bean and Cheese Tacos** (Fill each of 2 [¾-ounce] taco shells with 2 tablespoons drained canned black beans, 3 tablespoons shredded reduced-fat sharp Cheddar cheese, 2 tablespoons salsa, and ½ cup thinly sliced iceberg lettuce. [*POINTS*: 7]) **Jícama-Orange Salad** (Arrange 1 cup thinly sliced romaine lettuce on plate; top with ½ cup *each of* orange sections and diced peeled jícama. Drizzle with ½ teaspoon *each of* olive oil and white wine vinegar. [*POINTS*: 1]	**Shrimp Stir-Fry** (Coat a nonstick skillet with cooking spray; place over medium-high heat. Add 6 ounces peeled shrimp, 1 cup torn spinach, ½ cup *each of* sliced green onions and broccoli, ¼ cup chicken broth, and 2 teaspoons soy sauce; stir-fry until shrimp are done. [*POINTS*: 3]) **cooked brown rice,** 1 cup **Cucumber Salad** (Combine ½ cup sliced cucumber, 1 teaspoon *each of* olive oil and rice vinegar, and a pinch of white pepper. [*POINTS*: 1])
SNACK	**Yogurt Crunch** (Stir 2 tablespoons nutlike cereal nuggets into 1 [8-ounce] container vanilla fat-free yogurt. [*POINTS*: 3])	**fig bar cookies,** 2 **fat-free milk,** 1 cup	**fat-free milk,** 1 cup **banana,** 1, with 1 tablespoon peanut butter	**apple pie à la mode fat-free yogurt,** 8 ounces **gingersnaps,** 2
POINTS	***POINTS*** for the day: 27 **Exchanges:** 6 Starch, 4 Vegetable, 2 Fruit, 1 Very Lean Meat, 5 Lean Meat, 2 Medium-Fat Meat, 2 Skim Milk, 1 Fat	***POINTS*** for the day: 28 **Exchanges:** 10 Starch, 3½ Vegetable, 3 Fruit, 2 Very Lean Meat, 4 Lean Meat, 1 Medium-Fat Meat, 1 Fat	***POINTS*** for the day: 26 **Exchanges:** 6½ Starch, 4 Vegetable, 4 Fruit, ½ Very Lean Meat, 1 Lean Meat, 2 Medium-Fat Meat, ½ High-Fat Meat, 2 Skim Milk, 2 Fat	***POINTS*** for the day: 26 **Exchanges:** 11 Starch, 4 Vegetable, 2 Fruit, 6 Very Lean Meat, 2 Skim Milk, 1 Fat

7-DAY MENU PLANNER

WEEK 2

	FRIDAY	SATURDAY	SUNDAY
BREAKFAST	**cinnamon-raisin bagel,** 1 (2-ounce), with 1 tablespoon tub-style light cream cheese **fat-free milk,** 1 cup **pear,** 1	**pancakes,** 2 (4-inch), topped with ½ cup blueberries and 2 tablespoons low-calorie syrup **fat-free milk,** 1 cup	**whole-wheat English muffin,** 1 (2 ounce), split and toasted, with 1½ teaspoons light butter **poached egg,** 1 **fat-free milk,** 1 cup
LUNCH	**Pasta Toss** (Combine 1 cup hot cooked rotelle pasta, ½ cup canned crushed tomatoes, ¼ cup sliced fresh basil; toss. Sprinkle with 2 teaspoons grated Parmesan cheese. [*POINTS*: 4]) **Spinach Salad** (Combine 2 cups torn spinach, ½ cup sliced mushrooms, ¼ cup sliced red onion, and 1 hard-cooked egg, sliced. Drizzle with 2 tablespoons fat-free balsamic vinaigrette. [*POINTS*: 3]) **strawberries,** 1 cup	**English Muffin Pizza** (Split 1 [2-ounce] whole-wheat English muffin; top evenly with 1 tablespoon low-fat pasta sauce, 2 tablespoons *each of* sliced mushrooms, chopped green bell pepper, chopped onion, and 3 tablespoons shredded part-skim mozzarella cheese; broil until thoroughly heated. [*POINTS*: 6]) **green salad,** 2 cups shredded romaine lettuce with ¼ cup croutons and 2 tablespoons fat-free balsamic vinaigrette **apple,** 1	**Breaded Pork Chop** (Brush 2 teaspoons Dijon mustard over both sides of 1 [6-ounce] lean, center-cut pork chop; press 1½ tablespoons dry breadcrumbs onto both sides of chop. Panfry over medium-high heat in a nonstick skillet coated with cooking spray 6 minutes on each side. [*POINTS*: 8]) **mashed potatoes,** ½ cup **steamed green beans,** 1 cup **pear,** 1
DINNER	**Oriental Steak** (Marinate 1 [4-ounce] filet mignon in 3 tablespoons soy sauce and 1 teaspoon dark sesame oil. Broil 3 minutes on each side or until desired degree of doneness. [*POINTS*: 6]) **steamed broccoli florets,** 1 cup, sprinkled with 1 teaspoon toasted sesame seeds **cooked Oriental noodles,** ½ cup	**Garlic-Rosemary Lamb Chops** (Rub 2 [3-ounce] lean lamb loin chops with 2 minced garlic cloves and 1 teaspoon dried rosemary. Broil until desired degree of doneness. [*POINTS*: 6]) **cooked couscous,** 1 cup **steamed green beans,** 1 cup	**Skillet Rice and Beans** (Heat 1 teaspoon olive oil over medium-high heat. Add ½ cup *each of* chopped onion, red bell pepper, and green bell pepper; sauté. Add 1 cup tomato juice, ¼ cup *each of* drained canned kidney beans and black beans, and ½ teaspoon dried basil; stir in 1 cup cooked rice. Cook until thoroughly heated. [*POINTS*: 8]) **cantaloupe chunks,** 1 cup
SNACK	**animal crackers,** 13 **fat-free milk,** 1 cup	**popcorn,** 94% fat-free microwave-popped, 1 large bag **fat-free milk,** 1 cup	**cappuccino parfait** (Layer 1 [8-ounce] carton cappuccino-flavored fat-free yogurt alternately with 6 reduced-fat chocolate wafers, crumbled. [*POINTS*: 3])
POINTS	***POINTS*** for the day: 29 **Exchanges:** 8 Starch, 5 Vegetable, 2 Fruit, 3½ Lean Meat, 1 Medium-Fat Meat, 1½ Fat	***POINTS*** for the day: 25 **Exchanges:** 8½ Starch, 4 Vegetable, 1½ Fruit, 4 Lean Meat, 2 Skim Milk	***POINTS*** for the day: 30 **Exchanges:** 6½ Starch, 3½ Vegetable, 2 Fruit, 1 Very Lean Meat, 3 Lean Meat, 1 Medium-Fat Meat, 2 Skim Milk, ½ Fat

One day's menu provides at least two servings of milk and at least five servings of fruits and/or vegetables.

	MONDAY	TUESDAY	WEDNESDAY	THURSDAY
BREAKFAST	**1% low-fat cottage cheese,** ⅓ cup, with 1 cup sliced strawberries and 2 teaspoons sugar **fat-free milk,** 1 cup	**whole-wheat bagel,** 2 ounces, with 2 tablespoons tub-style light cream cheese **orange juice,** 1 cup	**Peanut Butter-Banana-Raisin Bread** (Spread 1 tablespoon peanut butter over 1 slice raisin bread. Top with 1 sliced banana. [*POINTS:* 6]) **fat-free milk,** 1 cup	**bran flakes,** 1½ cups **banana,** 1 **fat-free milk,** 1 cup
LUNCH	**Quick Vegetable Pizza** (Spread ¼ cup tomato low-fat pasta sauce over 1 [4-ounce] Italian cheese-flavored pizza crust. Top with ¼ cup *each of* chopped tomato, onion, and zucchini; sprinkle with 3 tablespoons grated Parmesan cheese. Bake at 450° for 6 minutes or until cheese melts. [*POINTS:* 8]) **apple slices,** 1 cup	**Philly Swiss Melt** (Place a nonstick skillet coated with cooking spray over medium heat; sauté ½ cup *each of* sliced onion and red bell pepper for 4 minutes. Spread 2 teaspoons reduced-fat mayonnaise over cut sides of 2 [1-ounce] slices French bread. Layer 2 ounces thinly sliced lean deli-style roast beef, sautéed vegetables, and 1 [¾-ounce] slice Swiss cheese on 1 slice bread; broil until cheese melts. Top with remaining bread slice. [*POINTS:* 10]) **carrot sticks,** 1 cup **fat-free milk,** 1 cup	**Cannellini-Macaroni Soup** (Sauté 1 minced garlic clove, and ¼ cup *each of* chopped onion and zucchini in 1 teaspoon olive oil in a saucepan for 1 minute. Add 1½ cups chicken broth; bring to a boil. Add ½ cup low-fat pasta sauce, ⅓ cup drained canned cannellini beans, ¼ cup uncooked macaroni, and ¼ teaspoon Italian seasoning. Reduce heat, and simmer 10 minutes. Sprinkle with 1 tablespoon grated Parmesan cheese. [*POINTS:* 4]) **saltines,** 6 **seedless green grapes,** 1 cup	**Pineapple-Swiss Sandwich** (Spread 2 teaspoons reduced-fat mayonnaise over 2 slices raisin bread. Place 1 [¾-ounce] slice Swiss cheese, 3 canned pineapple slices, and ½ cup alfalfa sprouts onto 1 bread slice. Top with remaining bread slice. [*POINTS:* 6]) **carrot sticks,** 1 cup
DINNER	**Cajun Chicken Salad** (Brush 1 [4-ounce] skinned, boned chicken breast half with 2 teaspoons lemon juice and 1 teaspoon olive oil, and sprinkle with ½ teaspoon Cajun seasoning. Broil 10 minutes, turning once. Combine 3 cups sliced romaine lettuce, ½ cup red bell pepper strips, and 1 hard-cooked egg, chopped; toss with 2 tablespoons fat-free red wine vinaigrette. Top with chicken breast and 1 tomato, cut into wedges. [*POINTS:* 5]) **French bread,** 2 ounces, with 1½ teaspoons light butter	**broiled lamb,** 3 ounces **Pesto Linguine** (Toss 1 cup cooked linguine with 2 teaspoons *each of* pesto sauce and lemon juice. Sprinkle with 1 tablespoon grated Parmesan cheese. [*POINTS:* 5]) **steamed yellow squash,** 1 cup	**Quick Beef and Rice** (Sauté 1 minced garlic clove and ½ cup *each of* chopped onion and red bell pepper in a nonstick skillet for 3 minutes. Stir in 1 cup hot cooked brown rice, 1 ounce chopped lean deli-style roast beef, and a dash *each of* allspice and cinnamon. [*POINTS:* 6]) **French bread,** 2-ounces **fat-free milk,** 1 cup	**Pan-Seared Tuna** (Rub 1 [6-ounce] tuna steak with 1 teaspoon *each of* olive oil and lemon juice; sprinkle with salt and pepper. Place a nonstick skillet over medium-high heat until hot; add tuna. Cook 2 minutes on each side or until medium-rare. [*POINTS:* 5]) **steamed new potatoes,** 8 ounces **green salad,** 2 cups, with 2 tablespoons fat-free red wine vinaigrette
SNACK	**blueberry fat-free yogurt,** 8 ounces	**lemon chiffon fat-free yogurt,** 8 ounces **apple,** 1	**Strawberry-Orange Juice** (Combine ½ cup orange juice and 1 cup sliced strawberries in a blender; process until smooth. [*POINTS:* 2])	**saltines,** 6, with 1 tablespoon peanut butter **fat-free milk,** 1 cup
POINTS	***POINTS*** for the day: 25 **Exchanges:** 7½ Starch, 5 Vegetable, 4 Fruit, 4 Very Lean Meat, 1 Lean Meat, 1 Medium-Fat Meat, 2 Skim Milk, 1½ Fat	***POINTS*** for the day: 30 **Exchanges:** 6 Starch, 3 Fruit, 4 Vegetable, 5½ Lean Meat, 2 Skim Milk, 1 High-Fat Milk, 1 Fat	***POINTS*** for the day: 27 **Exchanges:** 9 Starch, 2 Vegetable, 5 Fruit, 1 Very Lean Meat, 1½ Lean Meat, ½ High-Fat Meat, 2 Skim Milk, 1 Fat	***POINTS*** for the day: 27 **Exchanges:** 8 Starch, 3½ Vegetable, 2½ Fruit, 5 Very Lean Meat, 1 High-Fat Meat, 2 Skim Milk, 1½ Fat

7-DAY MENU PLANNER

WEEK 3

	FRIDAY	SATURDAY	SUNDAY
BREAKFAST	**banana,** 1 **vanilla fat-free yogurt,** 8 ounces	**Raisin Bread French Toast** (Combine 3 tablespoons *each of* fat-free milk and egg substitute, and a dash *each of* salt and vanilla extract; stir well. Dip 2 slices raisin bread into milk mixture. Melt 1 teaspoon light butter in a nonstick skillet over medium heat; add bread. Cook 7 minutes or until browned, turning after 3 minutes. Serve with 2 tablespoons maple syrup. [*POINTS:* 8]) **orange juice,** 1 cup	**Fruit and Cheese Bagel** (Combine ⅓ cup 1% low-fat cottage cheese, ¼ cup sliced fresh strawberries, and 2 teaspoons honey in a blender; process until smooth. Spread over 1 [2-ounce] whole-wheat bagel. [*POINTS:* 3]) **orange juice,** 1 cup
LUNCH	**Ham and Egg Bagel Sandwich** (Cook 1 large egg in a nonstick skillet coated with cooking spray until firm, stirring constantly. Spread 1 teaspoon reduced-fat mayonnaise over bottom half of 1 [2-ounce] whole-wheat bagel, top with egg, 1 ounce sliced lean ham, and top half of bagel. [*POINTS:* 5])	**Lamb-Vegetable Salad** (Combine 3 cups sliced romaine lettuce, ½ cup chopped tomato, 2 ounces thinly sliced broiled lamb, and 2 tablespoons *each of* grated Parmesan cheese and fat-free red wine vinaigrette; toss well. [*POINTS:* 5]) **fat-free milk,** 1 cup	**Tuna-Stuffed Tomato** (Combine 2 ounces drained water-packed tuna, 2 tablespoons chopped carrot, 2 teaspoons reduced-fat mayonnaise, 1 teaspoon Dijon mustard, and a dash of celery seeds; stir well. Cut a tomato into 4 wedges, cutting to, but not through, bottom of tomato; stuff with tuna salad. [*POINTS:* 3]) **fat-free milk,** 1 cup **saltines,** 6
DINNER	**Pesto-Cannellini Pizza** (Spread 2 teaspoons pesto sauce over 1 [4-ounce] Italian cheese-flavored pizza crust; top with ⅓ cup *each of* drained canned cannellini beans and chopped zucchini. Sprinkle with 3 tablespoons grated Parmesan cheese. Bake at 450° for 6 minutes. [*POINTS:* 11]) **spinach salad,** 2 cups torn fresh spinach, with 1 tablespoon fat-free red wine vinaigrette **fat-free milk,** 1 cup	**Ham With Pineapple-Bourbon Sauce** (Combine ¼ cup undrained pineapple tidbits in juice, 1 tablespoon *each of* raisins and bourbon, and 1 teaspoon honey; bring to a boil, and spoon over 2 [1-ounce] slices ham. [*POINTS:* 4]) **steamed fresh spinach,** 1 cup **steamed yellow squash,** 1 cup **French bread,** 2 ounces	**Kung Pao Chicken** (Toss 4 ounces boned cubed chicken breast with 2 teaspoons *each of* soy sauce and fat-free red wine vinaigrette, ⅛ teaspoon red pepper, and 1 minced garlic clove. Heat 1 teaspoon vegetable oil over medium-high heat. Add ½ cup *each of* chopped onion and sliced mushrooms, and chicken mixture; sauté 5 minutes. Top with 2 tablespoons *each of* chopped green onions and peanuts. [*POINTS:* 6]) **cooked brown rice,** 1 cup **cantaloupe chunks,** 1 cup
SNACK	**Fruit Sundae** (Combine ½ cup each of sliced fresh strawberries and pineapple tidbits in juice; spoon over ½ cup fat-free vanilla ice cream. [*POINTS:* 3])	**Chunky Strawberry Yogurt** (Stir ½ cup sliced strawberries into 8 ounces vanilla fat-free yogurt. [*POINTS:* 3])	**coconut cream pie fat-free yogurt,** 8 ounces **gingersnaps,** 2
POINTS	***POINTS*** for the day: 26 **Exchanges:** 8 Starch, 2 Vegetable, 3 Fruit, 1 Very Lean Meat, 2½ Lean Meat, 1 Medium-Fat Meat, 2 Skim Milk, 2 Fat	***POINTS*** for the day: 25 **Exchanges:** 6 Starch, 7½ Vegetable, 4 Fruit, ½ Very Lean Meat, 5 Lean Meat, 2½ Skim Milk, ½ Fat	***POINTS*** for the day: 26 **Exchanges:** 8½ Starch, 3 Vegetable, 4 Fruit, 7½ Very Lean Meat, 2 Skim Milk, 1½ Fat

One day's menu provides at least two servings of milk and at least five servings of fruits and/or vegetables.

	MONDAY	TUESDAY	WEDNESDAY	THURSDAY
BREAKFAST	**Cheese Omelet** (Combine 2 eggs, 2 tablespoons of water, and a dash *each of* salt and pepper; stir. Pour into a small nonstick skillet; cook over medium heat 1 minute or until almost set. Sprinkle 3 tablespoons shredded reduced-fat sharp Cheddar cheese over omelet; fold in half. [*POINTS*: 5]) **whole-wheat English muffin,** 1 (2 ounce), split and toasted with 1½ teaspoons *each of* light butter and orange marmalade **fat-free milk,** 1 cup	**Maple Oatmeal** (Combine 1 cup cooked oatmeal with 2 tablespoons raisins, 1 tablespoon maple syrup, and 1 teaspoon light butter. [*POINTS*: 5]) **fat-free milk,** 1 cup	**Egg and Cheese Sandwich** (Combine 1 large egg and 3 tablespoons shredded reduced-fat sharp Cheddar cheese; stir well. Cook in a nonstick skillet coated with cooking spray over medium heat until set, stirring occasionally. Spread over 1 slice high-fiber whole wheat bread; top with another slice of bread. [*POINTS*: 6]) **orange juice,** ½ cup	**cooked oatmeal,** 1 cup, with 1 tablespoon cinnamon-sugar **Marmalade-Broiled Grapefruit** (Spread 1 teaspoon orange marmalade over cut side of 1 grapefruit half; top with 1 teaspoon brown sugar. Broil 5 minutes or until hot and bubbly. [*POINTS*: 1]) **fat-free milk,** 1 cup
LUNCH	**minestrone soup,** (1 [16-ounce] can. [*POINTS*: 4]) **saltine crackers,** 6 **strawberries,** 1 cup **fat-free milk,** ½ cup	**Hummus-Veggie Wrap** (Spread 2 tablespoons hummus over 1 [8-inch] flour tortilla; top with ¼ cup *each of* sliced red bell pepper, zucchini, and yellow squash. Sprinkle with 3 tablespoons crumbled feta cheese; roll up. [*POINTS*: 5]) **frozen seedless red grapes,** 1 cup	**Tomato and Cheese Quesadilla** (Sprinkle ¼ cup chopped tomato, 3 tablespoons *each of* crumbled feta cheese and chopped red bell pepper, and 1 tablespoon chopped onion over 1 [8-inch] flour tortilla. Fold tortilla in half, and coat with cooking spray. Cook over medium heat until lightly browned, turning once. Serve with 2 tablespoons fat-free sour cream. [*POINTS*: 5]) **grapefruit sections,** ½ cup	**Sloppy Joe** (Cook 4 ounces ground round, ¼ cup chopped onion, and 1 minced garlic clove over medium-high heat until beef is browned, stirring to crumble; drain. Return meat to pan and stir in ½ cup tomato sauce and ½ teaspoon chili powder; cook until thoroughly heated. Serve on 1 [2-ounce] whole-wheat bun. [*POINTS:* 9]) **vegetarian baked beans,** ½ cup
DINNER	**Portobello Mushroom Sandwich** (Brush 1 teaspoon *each of* olive oil, balsamic vinegar, and soy sauce over 1 large portobello mushroom cap. Broil 2 minutes on each side. Place mushroom, 2 tomato slices, 1 onion slice, and 1 [¾-ounce] slice Swiss cheese on bottom half of 1 [2-ounce] whole-wheat bun. Top with remaining bun half. [*POINTS:* 6]) **Apple-Spinach Salad** (Combine 2 cups fresh spinach with 1 apple, sliced, and 2 tablespoons fat-free balsamic vinaigrette [*POINTS:* 1]) **roasted potato wedges,** 1 cup	**Baked Orange Roughy** (Drizzle 1 teaspoon *each of* olive oil and lemon juice over 1 [6-ounce] orange roughy fillet. Sprinkle with ½ teaspoon lemon pepper. Bake at 350° for 20 minutes or until fish flakes easily when tested with a fork. [*POINTS:* 4]) **cooked brown rice,** 1 cup **Spinach Salad** (Combine 2 cups torn spinach, 2 tablespoons toasted walnuts, and 2 tablespoons fat-free balsamic vinaigrette. Sprinkle with 1 tablespoon grated Parmesan cheese. [*POINTS:* 4])	**Roasted Vegetable Pasta** (Combine 1 onion, quartered, ½ cup *each of* sliced yellow squash and sliced zucchini, and 2 tablespoons balsamic vinegar in a baking dish. Bake at 400° for 20 minutes or until lightly browned; Toss with 1 cup hot cooked spaghetti, and 1 cup low-fat pasta sauce. [*POINTS*: 7]) **Garlic Bread** (Top 1 soft breadstick with 1 teaspoon light butter and a dash of garlic salt; bake until thoroughly heated. [*POINTS*: 3]) **fat-free milk,** 1 cup	**cheese pizza,** ⅛ of a 12-inch pizza **Caesar Salad** (Combine 2 cups torn romaine lettuce and 2 tablespoons fat-free Caesar dressing; toss well. Sprinkle with ¼ cup fat-free croutons and 1 tablespoon grated Parmesan cheese. [*POINTS:* 2]) **cucumber spears,** 1 cup
SNACK	**Banana Pudding** (Layer 3 reduced-fat vanilla wafers, ½ cup *each of* sliced banana and vanilla sugar-free instant pudding [prepared with fat-free milk] in the bottom of a 10-ounce custard cup; repeat layers. [*POINTS*: 4])	**Tropical Parfait** (Layer 1 [8-ounce] container coconut creme pie fat-free yogurt alternately with1 kiwifruit, sliced, in a parfait glass. [*POINTS*: 2])	**strawberry fat-free yogurt,** 8 ounces	**Cranberry-Apple Ice Cream Float** (Combine ½ cup cranberry juice cocktail and ¼ cup sparkling apple juice. Serve over ½ cup reduced-fat ice cream. [*POINTS:* 5])
POINTS	***POINTS*** for the day: 30 **Exchanges:** 11½ Starch, 4½ Vegetable, 3 Fruit, 4 Medium-Fat Meat, 2 Skim Milk, 1 Fat	***POINTS*** for the day: 27 **Exchanges:** 8 Starch, 3½ Vegetable, 3 Fruit, 5 Very Lean Meat, ½ Lean Meat, 1 Medium-Fat Meat, 2 Skim Milk, 3 Fat	***POINTS*** for the day: 27 **Exchanges:** 8 Starch, 3 Vegetable, 1½ Fruit, 3 Medium-Fat Meat, 2 Skim Milk, 1½ Fat	***POINTS*** for the day: 30 **Exchanges:** 10½ Starch, 5 Vegetable, 2½ Fruit, 3½ Lean Meat, 2 Medium-Fat Meat, 2 Skim Milk, 2 Fat

7-DAY MENU PLANNER

WEEK 4

	FRIDAY	SATURDAY	SUNDAY
BREAKFAST	**Strawberry Smoothie** (Combine 1 cup sliced strawberries, ½ cup fat-free milk, and 8 ounces vanilla fat-free yogurt in a blender; process until smooth. [*POINTS:* 3])	**Banana-Nut Pancakes** (Top 2 [4-inch] pancakes with ½ cup sliced banana and 1 tablespoons *each of* toasted walnuts and maple syrup. [*POINTS:* 7]) **fat-free milk,** 1 cup	**Breakfast Sandwich** (Combine 1 egg, 1 egg white, and 1 tablespoon water; cook 30 seconds in a nonstick skillet. Stir in 1 cooked, crumbled meatless breakfast patty; cook until set. Spoon over bottom half of 1 [2-ounce] whole-wheat English muffin; top with remaining muffin half. [*POINTS:* 7]) **fat-free milk,** 1 cup
LUNCH	**Greek Salad** (Combine 2 cups torn romaine lettuce, ¼ cup crumbled feta cheese, 2 tablespoons sliced ripe olives, and 2 tablespoons fat-free balsamic vinaigrette; toss well. Top with 2 pepperoncini peppers. [*POINTS:* 3]) **hummus,** ¼ cup **whole-wheat pita bread,** 1 (2-ounce)	**Turkey and Swiss Sandwich** (Spread 1 tablespoon reduced-fat mayonnaise and 2 teaspoons Dijon mustard evenly over 2 slices high-fiber whole wheat bread. Place 2 ounces thinly sliced smoked turkey, 1 [¾-ounce] slice Swiss cheese, 2 tomato slices, and 2 lettuce leaves on 1 bread slice; top with remaining bread slice. [*POINTS:* 6]) **frozen seedless red grapes,** 1 cup	**Bow-Tie Pasta Pepper Toss** (Combine 1 cup cooked bow-tie pasta, ½ cup *each of* drained canned chickpeas [garbanzo beans], chopped red bell pepper, chopped green bell pepper, ¼ cup chopped tomato, 3 tablespoons crumbled feta cheese, and 2 tablespoons fat-free balsamic vinaigrette; toss to coat. [*POINTS:* 7]) **kiwifruit,** 1
DINNER	**cooked chicken breast,** 3 ounces, sprinkled with ½ teaspoon Creole seasoning **Red Beans and Rice** (Cook ¼ cup *each of* chopped onion and chopped green bell pepper over medium heat until vegetables are tender. Stir in ½ cup drained canned red beans, 2 tablespoons water, ½ teaspoon chili powder, and ¼ teaspoon hot sauce; cook until thoroughly heated. Serve over ½ cup hot cooked brown rice. [*POINTS:* 4]) **corn bread,** 2 ounces **fat-free milk,** 1 cup **lemon sorbet,** ½ cup	**Pork Tenderloin With Chutney Sauce** (Combine 2 tablespoons chutney and 1 tablespoon apple juice; stir well. Serve with 3 ounces roasted pork tenderloin. [*POINTS:* 5]) **Lemon-Pepper Linguine** (Combine ½ cup hot cooked linguine, ½ teaspoon freshly ground pepper, and 1 teaspoon *each of* extra-virgin olive oil and lemon juice; toss well. [*POINTS:* 3]) **steamed spinach,** 1 cup **pear,** 1	**broiled lamb chop,** 3 ounces, with 1 teaspoon pesto **Romaine Salad** (Combine 2 cups sliced romaine lettuce, ¼ cup fat-free croutons, and 2 tablespoons fat-free Caesar dressing; toss well. Sprinkle with 1 teaspoon grated Parmesan cheese. [*POINTS:* 2]) **steamed broccoli,** 1 cup
SNACK	**popcorn,** 94% fat-free microwave-popped, 1 large bag	**Cinnamon-Sugar Toasted Tortilla** (Lightly coat 1 [8-inch] flour tortilla with cooking spray. Sprinkle with 2 teaspoons cinnamon-sugar. Bake at 350° for 5 minutes or until crisp. [*POINTS:* 3]) **fat-free milk,** 1 cup	**vanilla fat-free yogurt,** 8 ounces **apple,** 1
POINTS	***POINTS*** for the day: 26 **Exchanges:** 9½ Starch, 3½ Vegetable, 2 Fruit, 4 Very Lean Meat, 1 Medium-Fat Meat, 2½ Skim Milk, 1½ Fat	***POINTS*** for the day: 30 **Exchanges:** 7½ Starch, 3 Vegetable, 3 Fruit, 2 Very Lean Meat, 3 Lean Meat, 1 Medium-Fat Meat, 2 Skim Milk, 2 Fat	***POINTS*** for the day: 26 **Exchanges:** 5 Starch, 5½ Vegetable, 2 Fruit, 4 Very Lean Meat, 3 Lean Meat, 2 Medium-Fat Meat, 2 Skim Milk, ½ Fat

One day's menu provides at least two servings of milk and at least five servings of fruits and/or vegetables.

	MONDAY	TUESDAY	WEDNESDAY	THURSDAY
BREAKFAST	**whole-grain frozen waffles,** 2 (4-inch), toasted, with 2 tablespoons maple syrup and 1 teaspoon light butter **blueberries,** ½ cup **fat-free milk,** 1 cup	**Breakfast Bagel** (Split and toast 1 [2-ounce] whole-wheat bagel; spread with 2 tablespoons tub-style light cream cheese and top with 1 ounce smoked salmon. [*POINTS*: 5]) **strawberries,** 1 cup **fat-free milk,** 1 cup	**bran flakes** 1½ cups **banana,** 1 **fat-free milk,** 1 cup	**Cheese Bagel** (Sprinkle 3 tablespoons shredded reduced-fat sharp Cheddar cheese over cut sides of 1 [2-ounce] whole-wheat bagel; broil until cheese melts. [*POINTS*: 4]) **fat-free milk,** 1 cup
LUNCH	**Tuna Sandwich** (Combine 2 ounces drained water-packed tuna and 1 tablespoon *each of* reduced-fat mayonnaise and pickle relish. Spread over 1 slice high-fiber whole-wheat bread and top with lettuce leaf, 2 slices tomato, and another slice of bread. [*POINTS*: 4]) **baked potato chips,** 1 ounce **carrot and celery sticks,** ½ cup each **apple,** 1	**Bean Burrito** (Warm ½ cup canned fat-free refried beans; spread over 1 [8-inch] flour tortilla. Top with ¼ cup shredded lettuce, ¼ cup chopped tomato, and 1 tablespoon fat-free sour cream; roll up. [*POINTS*: 4]) **salsa,** ½ cup **baked tortilla chips,** 1 ounce **cantaloupe,** 1 cup	**canned chicken noodle soup,** 2 cups **Pimiento Cheese Sandwich** (Spread 2 tablespoons pimiento-cheese over 1 slice of high-fiber whole-wheat bread; top with another slice of bread. [*POINTS*: 3]) **celery sticks,** ½ cup **seedless red grapes,** 1 cup	**Chicken Sandwich** (Marinate 1 [4-ounce] skinned, boned chicken breast half in ¼ cup fat-free Italian dressing. Broil 7 minutes on each side or until done. Place on bottom half of 1 [2-ounce] hamburger bun; top with 1 lettuce leaf, 2 slices tomato, and top half of bun. [*POINTS*: 7]) **cucumber spears,** 1 cup with 2 tablespoon fat-free Italian dressing **apple,** 1, with 2 tablespoons fat-free caramel sundae syrup
DINNER	**Chicken Dijon** (Combine 2 teaspoons creamy-mustard mayonnaise blend, ⅛ teaspoon each of dried thyme and pepper; spread over 1 [4-ounce] skinned, boned chicken breast half. Dredge in 1½ tablespoons dry breadcrumbs; bake at 375° for 45 minutes. [*POINTS*: 5]) **cooked brown rice,** 1 cup **steamed broccoli,** 1 cup, with 1 lemon wedge	**Oven-Baked Orange Roughy** (Spread 1½ teaspoons of reduced-fat mayonnaise over both sides of 1 [6-ounce] fillet; dredge in a mixture of 2 tablespoons dry breadcrumbs and 1 teaspoon Creole seasoning. Bake at 350° for 20 minutes or until fish flakes easily when tested with a fork. [*POINTS*: 4]) **baked potato,** 1 (8-ounce), with 1½ teaspoons light butter **Vegetable Sauté** (Melt 1½ teaspoons light butter in a nonstick skillet over medium-high heat; sauté ¼ cup *each of* diced zucchini, red bell pepper, and whole-kernel corn 5 minutes or until vegetables are tender. [*POINTS*: 2])	**Beef and Vegetable Stir-Fry** (Coat a nonstick skillet with cooking spray; place over medium-high heat. Stir-fry 4 ounces sliced flank steak, ½ cup *each of* broccoli florets, sliced carrot, and sliced mushrooms. Drizzle with 2 teaspoons soy sauce and ½ teaspoon sesame oil. [*POINTS*: 8]) **cooked Oriental noodles,** ½ cup **pear,** 1	**Beans and Rice** (Combine ½ cup drained canned black beans, 2 teaspoons lime juice, and ¼ teaspoon chili powder; cook over medium-low heat until thoroughly heated. Serve over ½ cup brown rice. Top with 1 tablespoon *each of* chopped fresh cilantro and fat-free sour cream. [*POINTS*: 4]) **Citrus Salad** (Combine 1 cup sliced romaine lettuce, ½ cup orange sections, and ¼ cup sliced avocado; drizzle with 2 tablespoons fat-free red wine vinaigrette. [*POINTS*: 4])
SNACK	**creme caramel fat-free yogurt,** 8 ounces **reduced-fat vanilla wafers,** 6	**apple,** 1 **fat-free milk,** 1 cup	**reduced-fat vanilla wafers,** 6 **fat-free milk,** 1 cup	**lemon fat-free yogurt,** 8 ounces
POINTS	***POINTS*** for the day: 26 **Exchanges:** 10 Starch, 3½ Vegetable, 2 Fruit, 5 Very Lean Meat, 2 Skim Milk, 1½ Fat	***POINTS*** for the day: 29 **Exchanges:** 8 Starch, 2 Vegetable, 3 Fruit, 6 Very Lean Meat, 1 Lean Meat, 2 Skim Milk, 2 Fat	***POINTS*** for the day: 29 **Exchanges:** 9 Starch, 2 Vegetable, 3 Fruit, 3 Lean Meat, ½ High-Fat Meat, 2 Skim Milk	***POINTS*** for the day: 27 **Exchanges:** 7½ Starch, 2½ Vegetable, 21/2 Fruit, 4 Very Lean Meat, 1 Medium-Fat Meat, 2 Skim Milk, 1 Fat

7-DAY MENU PLANNER

WEEK 5

	FRIDAY	SATURDAY	SUNDAY
BREAKFAST	**Peanut Butter-Raisin Toast** (Spread 1 tablespoon peanut butter over 1 slice high-fiber whole-wheat bread; top with 1 tablespoon raisins and another slice of bread. [*POINTS*: 5]) **cappuccino fat-free yogurt,** 8 ounces	**Banana Waffles With Praline Sauce,** (Toast 2 [4-inch] whole-grain frozen waffles and top with ¼ cup sliced banana, 1 tablespoon chopped pecans, and 2 tablespoons fat-free caramel sundae syrup. [*POINTS*: 7] **fat-free milk,** 1 cup	**Mexican Omelet** (Combine 2 eggs, 2 tablespoons of water, and a dash *each of* salt and pepper; stir. Pour into a small nonstick skillet; cook over medium heat 1 minute or until almost set. Sprinkle 3 tablespoons shredded reduced-fat sharp Cheddar cheese, 2 tablespoons diced red bell pepper, and 1 tablespoon chopped green onion over omelet; fold in half. [*POINTS*: 6] **cooked hash-brown potatoes,** 1 cup **orange juice,** 1 cup
LUNCH	**Spinach-Bean Salad** (Combine 2 cups torn spinach, ½ cup *each of* sliced mushrooms and drained canned black beans, ¼ cup sliced red onion, and 1 hard-cooked egg, sliced. Drizzle with 2 tablespoons fat-free Italian dressing. [*POINTS*: 5]) **fat-free milk,** 1 cup	**Stuffed Potato** (Stuff 1 [8-ounce] baked potato with ¼ cup salsa, 1 tablespoon *each of* sliced green onions and fat-free sour cream, and 3 tablespoons shredded reduced-fat sharp Cheddar cheese. [*POINTS*: 6]) **tossed green salad,** 2 cups, with 3 tablespoons fat-free red wine vinaigrette	**Open-Faced Ham and Swiss Sandwich** (Spread 1 teaspoon mustard over 1 slice high-fiber whole-wheat bread; top with 1 leaf romaine lettuce, 1 ounce sliced lean ham, and 1 (¾-ounce) slice Swiss cheese. Broil until cheese melts. [*POINTS*: 5]) **Cucumber Salad** (Combine ½ cup *each of* tomato and cucumber chunks and ¼ cup sliced onion; toss with 2 teaspoons vinegar, ½ teaspoon sugar, and a dash of salt and pepper. [*POINTS*: 1]) **fat-free milk,** 1 cup
DINNER	**Penne With Sausage and Pepper** (Brown 4 ounces turkey Italian sausage and ½ cup *each of* slivered onion, red bell pepper chunks, and green bell pepper chunks. Add 1 cup beer; partially cover and simmer 15 minutes. Stir in ½ cup cooked penne pasta [*POINTS*: 7]) **Italian bread,** 2 ounces, toasted with 1 tablespoon light butter	**Herbed-Orange Pork Chop** (Spread 1 tablespoon orange marmalade over 1 [6-ounce] center-cut loin pork chop; sprinkle with ¼ teaspoon *each of* thyme, sage, cinnamon and a dash *each of* cumin and garlic powder. Broil 5 minutes on each side or until done. [*POINTS*: 6]) **cooked couscous,** ½ cup couscous with 1 tablespoon sliced green onions and 1 teaspoon light butter **steamed asparagus,** 12 spears	**Linguine With White Clam Sauce** (Spoon ½ cup bottled white clam sauce over 1 cup hot cooked linguine. [*POINTS*: 6]) **Italian Salad** (Combine 2 cups sliced romaine lettuce, ¼ cup *each of* shredded carrot, chopped tomato, and fat-free croutons. Drizzle with 3 tablespoons fat-free Italian dressing; toss well. [*POINTS*: 1])
SNACK	**pimiento-cheese,** ¼ cup with 4 celery stalks **apple,** 1	**gingersnaps,** 2 **fat-free milk,** 1 cup	**Blueberry Parfait** (Layer 1 cup blueberries alternately with 1 cup of frozen fat-free whipped topping, thawed, and 6 reduced-fat vanilla wafers, crushed, in a parfait glass. [*POINTS*: 4]) **fat-free milk,** 1 cup
POINTS	***POINTS*** for the day: 29 **Exchanges:** 6½ Starch, 5½ Vegetable, 1½ Fruit, 1 Very Lean Meat, 3 Lean Meat, 1 Medium-Fat Meat, 1½ High-Fat Meat, 2 Skim Milk, 1 Fat	***POINTS*** for the day: 29 **Exchanges:** 7½ Starch, 3½ Vegetable, 1½ Fruit, 3 Lean Meat, 1 Medium-Fat Meat, 2 Skim Milk, 1½ Fat	***POINTS*** for the day: 30 **Exchanges:** 8 Starch, 4 Vegetable, 3 Fruit, 1 Lean Meat, 3 Medium-Fat Meat, 1 High-Fat Meat, 2 Skim Milk, 1½ Fat

One day's menu provides at least two servings of milk and at least five servings of fruits and/or vegetables.

	MONDAY	TUESDAY	WEDNESDAY	THURSDAY
BREAKFAST	**cooked oatmeal,** 1 cup, with 2 tablespoons raisins and 1 tablespoon brown sugar **strawberries,** 1 cup **fat-free milk,** 1 cup	**Cheese Toast** (Sprinkle 3 tablespoons shredded reduced-fat sharp Cheddar cheese over 1 slice high-fiber whole-wheat bread; broil until cheese melts. [*POINTS*: 2]) **fat-free milk,** 1 cup **apple,** 1	**Breakfast Wrap** (Combine 1 large egg and 1 tablespoon water; cook in a nonstick skillet coated with cooking spray over medium heat until set. Spread over 1 [8-inch] flour tortilla; top with 1 slice Canadian bacon, halved, and roll up. [*POINTS*: 6]) **papaya chunks,** 1 cup **fat-free milk,** 1 cup	**whole-wheat English muffin,** 1 (2-ounce), split and toasted with 1 teaspoon light butter **vanilla fat-free yogurt,** 8 ounces **blueberries,** 1 cup
LUNCH	**hamburger,** 1 small, fast food **green salad,** 2 cups, with 2 tablespoons fat-free Italian dressing	**Mexican Pizza** (Top 1 [8-inch] flour tortilla with ¼ cup *each of* fat-free refried beans, chopped tomato, and shredded reduced-fat sharp Cheddar cheese. Broil 2 minutes or until cheese melts. Top with ½ cup shredded lettuce, 2 tablespoons salsa, and 1 tablespoon *each of* chopped fresh cilantro, sliced ripe olives, and fat-free sour cream. [*POINTS*: 6])	**Mushroom Marinara Pasta** (Sauté ½ cup sliced mushrooms in a nonstick skillet 3 minutes; stir in ½ cup low-fat pasta sauce. Toss with 1 cup hot cooked pasta; sprinkle with 2 tablespoons grated Parmesan cheese. [*POINTS*: 5]) **green salad,** 2 cups, with 2 tablespoons fat-free balsamic vinaigrette **seedless red grapes,** 1 cup	**roasted chicken breast,** 3 ounces **Broccoli Salad** (Combine 1 cup small broccoli florets, ¼ cup shredded reduced-fat sharp Cheddar cheese, 2 tablespoons raisins, 2 teaspoons *each of* reduced-fat mayonnaise and fat-free sour cream, and ½ teaspoon Dijon mustard; toss well. [*POINTS:* 6]) **apple,** 1
DINNER	**Pork Tenderloin With Papaya Salsa** (Combine ¼ cup *each of* chopped papaya and chopped fresh pineapple, and 1 teaspoon *each of* chopped fresh cilantro and fresh lime juice; toss well. Serve with 3 ounces sliced roasted pork tenderloin. [*POINTS*: 4]) **Pecan Rice Pilaf** (Combine 1 cup hot cooked brown rice and 2 tablespoons *each of* chopped carrot, sliced green onions, and toasted pecan pieces. [*POINTS*: 5]) **steamed spinach,** 1 cup	**Cajun Chicken Salad** (Brush 1 [4-ounce skinned, boned chicken breast half with 1 teaspoon *each of* olive oil and white wine vinegar; sprinkle with 1 teaspoon Cajun seasoning. Broil 5 minutes on each side or until done. Chop chicken; toss with 2 cups torn lettuce, ½ cup chopped tomato, and 2 tablespoons *each of* sliced ripe olives and fat-free ranch dressing. [*POINTS*: 8]) **cantaloupe chunks,** 1 cup **French bread,** 2 ounces	**Broiled Grouper With Pecan Sauce** (Brush 1 [6-ounce] grouper fillet with 1 teaspoon *each of* olive oil and lemon juice; broil 5 minutes on each side or until fish flakes easily when tested with a fork. Combine 2 teaspoons each of light mayonnaise and fat-free sour cream, and 1 teaspoon *each of* finely chopped pecans and lemon juice; serve over fish. [*POINTS*: 6]) **cooked couscous,** 1 cup, with 2 tablespoons chopped green onions and 1 teaspoon light butter **steamed zucchini,** 1 cup	**Asian Pork Noodles** (Heat 1 teaspoon dark sesame oil in a nonstick skillet. Add ½ cup red bell pepper strips; sauté 3 minutes. Add 3 ounces diced roasted pork tenderloin, 1 cup hot cooked spaghetti, ¼ cup sliced green onions, and 1 teaspoon *each of* minced fresh cilantro, soy sauce, and creamy peanut butter; stir until peanut butter melts. [*POINTS:* 9]) **steamed carrots,** 1 cup **orange sections,** 1 cup
SNACK	**creme caramel fat-free yogurt,** 8 ounces **reduced-fat vanilla wafers,** 6	**apple pie parfait** (Layer 8 ounces apple pie à la mode fat-free yogurt alternately with 4 gingersnaps, crumbled, in a parfait glass. [*POINTS*: 5])	**cappuccino fat-free yogurt,** 8 ounces	**vanilla fat-free yogurt,** 8 ounces, with 1 tablespoon wheat germ
POINTS	***POINTS*** for the day: 25 **Exchanges:** 7½ Starch, 4 Vegetable, 2½ Fruit, 3 Very Lean Meat, 3 Medium-Fat Meat, 2 Skim Milk, 2 Fat	***POINTS*** for the day: 27 **Exchanges:** 5½ Starch, 3½ Vegetable, 2 Fruit, ½ Very Lean Meat, 2 Medium-Fat Meat, 2 Skim Milk, 2 Fat	***POINTS*** for the day: 27 **Exchanges:** 7 Starch, 4½ Vegetable, 2 Fruit, 5 Very Lean Meat, 2 Lean Meat, 1 Medium-Fat Meat, 2 Skim Milk, 1½ Fat	***POINTS*** for the day: 28 **Exchanges:** 4½ Starch, 3½ Vegetable, 4 Fruit, 3 Very Lean Meat, 3 Lean Meat, 1 Medium-Fat Meat, 2 Skim Milk, 2 Fat

7-DAY MENU PLANNER

WEEK 6

	FRIDAY	SATURDAY	SUNDAY
BREAKFAST	**Papaya Smoothie** (Combine ¾ cup chopped papaya, ¼ cup *each of* chopped fresh pineapple and fat-free milk, and 8 ounces vanilla fat-free yogurt in a blender; process until smooth. [*POINTS*: 3])	**whole-wheat English muffin,** 1 (2 ounce), split and toasted with 1 teaspoon light butter. **lean Canadian bacon,** 1 slice **poached egg,** 1 **fat-free milk,** 1 cup	**Maple-Nut Pancakes** (Top 2 [4-inch] pancakes with 2 tablespoons *each of* toasted walnuts and maple syrup. [*POINTS:* 6]) **fat-free milk,** 1 cup
LUNCH	**Bean Burrito** (Microwave ⅓ cup fat-free refried beans until warm; spread over 1 [8-inch] flour tortilla. Top with ½ cup shredded lettuce, 3 tablespoons shredded reduced-fat sharp Cheddar cheese, and 1 tablespoon fat-free sour cream; roll up. [*POINTS:* 5]) **salsa,** ¼ cup **cantaloupe chunks,** 1 cup **low-fat brownie,** 1 (1½ ounces)	**Roasted Veggie Couscous** (Combine ⅓ cup *each of* cubed eggplant, zucchini, and red bell pepper, and 2 tablespoons fat-free balsamic vinaigrette in a baking dish; stir well. Bake at 400° for 25 minutes or until lightly browned. Toss with 1 cup cooked couscous, ½ cup *each of* torn spinach and chopped tomato, and 2 teaspoons olive oil. Sprinkle with 1 tablespoon grated Parmesan cheese. [*POINTS:* 7]) **papaya,** 1 cup	**Tuna Salad Sandwich** (Combine 2 ounces drained water-packed tuna with 2 tablespoons chopped carrot, 2 teaspoons reduced-fat mayonnaise, 1 teaspoon Dijon mustard, and a dash of celery seeds; spread over 1 slice high-fiber whole-wheat bread. Top with 2 lettuce leaves, 2 tomato slices, and another slice of bread. [*POINTS:* 4]) **cucumber spears,** 1 cup, with 2 tablespoons fat-free ranch dressing **apple pie à la mode fat-free yogurt,** 8 ounces
DINNER	**Broiled Eggplant Parmigiana** (Brush 1 teaspoon *each of* olive oil and balsamic vinegar over 3 eggplant slices; sprinkle with ⅛ teaspoon *each of* salt and pepper. Broil 3 minutes, turning once. Top with ½ cup low-fat pasta sauce; sprinkle with 3 tablespoons grated Parmesan cheese. [*POINTS:* 3]) **green salad,** 2 cups, with 2 tablespoons fat-free balsamic vinaigrette **French bread,** 2 ounces **banana,** 1	**Spicy Chicken Sandwich** (Brush 1 [4-ounce] skinned, boned chicken breast half with 1 teaspoon lemon juice; sprinkle with 1 teaspoon Cajun seasoning. Broil 5 minutes on each side; thinly slice. Spread 2 teaspoons *each of* reduced-fat mayonnaise and Dijon mustard over 1 slice high-fiber whole-wheat bread; top with 2 lettuce leaves, 2 tomato slices, chicken, and another slice of bread. [*POINTS:* 6]) **broccoli florets,** 1 cup, with ¼ cup fat-free ranch dressing **fat-free milk,** 1 cup	**broiled filet mignon steak,** 3 ounces **Wilted Spinach Salad** (Sauté ½ cup sliced mushrooms and 1 bacon slice, chopped, in a nonstick skillet until bacon is crisp; remove from heat. Stir in 2 tablespoons fat-free balsamic vinaigrette. Toss warm mushroom mixture with 2 cups fresh spinach leaves. [*POINTS:* 5]) **orange sections,** 1 cup
SNACK	**Lemon Ice Box Dessert** (Layer 4 graham crackers, crushed, alternately with 8 ounces lemon fat-free yogurt in a 10-ounce custard cup. Top with 2 tablespoons frozen reduced-calorie whipped topping, thawed. [*POINTS:* 5])	**popcorn,** 94% fat-free microwave-popped, 1 large bag **apple,** 1	**S'mores** (Top 4 (2½-inch) graham crackers each with 1 medium marshmallow; broil until marshmallows are lightly browned. Top with 1 tablespoon fat-free hot fudge topping. [*POINTS:* 4])
POINTS	***POINTS*** for the day: 25 **Exchanges:** 7 Starch, 5 Vegetable, 3 Fruit, 1 Very Lean Meat, 1 Lean Meat, 1 Medium-Fat Meat, 3 Skim Milk, 2½ Fat	***POINTS*** for the day: 29 **Exchanges:** 10 Starch, 3½ Vegetable, 2 Fruit, 3 Very Lean Meat, 1½ Lean Meat, 1 Medium-Fat Meat, 2 Skim Milk, 2½ Fat	***POINTS*** for the day: 29 **Exchanges:** 8½ Starch, 4½ Vegetable, 1 Fruit, 2 Very Lean Meat, 3 Lean Meat, 2 Skim Milk, 3½ Fat

One day's menu provides at least two servings of milk and at least five servings of fruits and/or vegetables.

	MONDAY	TUESDAY	WEDNESDAY	THURSDAY
BREAKFAST	**high-fiber whole-wheat bread,** 1 slice, toasted, with 1 tablespoon jelly and 1 teaspoon light butter **poached egg,** 1 **grapefruit,** ½ **fat-free milk,** 1 cup	**bran muffin,** 4 ounces **strawberries,** 1 cup **fat-free milk,** 1 cup	**cooked oatmeal,** 1 cup, with 2 tablespoons raisins, 2 teaspoons sugar **grapefruit,** ½ **fat-free milk,** 1 cup	**Swiss Omelet** (Combine 1 egg, 1 egg white, 2 tablespoons of water, and a dash *each of* salt and pepper; stir. Pour into a small nonstick skillet; cook over medium heat 1 minute or until almost set. Sprinkle 3 tablespoons shredded Swiss cheese and 1 tablespoon chives over omelet; fold in half. [*POINTS*: 4]) **strawberries,** 1 cup **fat-free milk,** 1 cup
LUNCH	**Tuna Salad Tomato Cup** (Combine 4 ounces drained water-packed tuna and 1 tablespoon *each of* reduced-fat mayonnaise and pickle relish; stir well. Cut a tomato into 4 wedges, cutting to, but not through, bottom of tomato; stuff with tuna salad. [*POINTS:* 6]) **cucumber spears,** 1 cup **melba toast,** 6 rounds **fat-free milk,** 1 cup **cantaloupe chunks,** 1 cup	**Roast Beef Sandwich** (Spread 2 teaspoons horseradish mustard over bottom half of 1 [2-ounce] hamburger bun. Fill with 2 ounces shaved deli roast beef, 2 tomato slices, 4 cucumber slices, and ¼ cup alfalfa sprouts. [*POINTS:* 7]) **watermelon chunks,** 1 cup	**Chef's Salad** (Top 2 cups torn lettuce with 1 ounce shaved deli roast beef, 3 tablespoons shredded reduced-fat sharp Cheddar cheese, ¼ cup *each of* shredded carrot and sliced cucumber, and 2 tomato wedges. Serve with 3 tablespoons fat-free Italian dressing. [*POINTS*: 4]) **apple,** 1	**Turkey-Vegetable Sandwich** (Spread 2 teaspoons reduced-fat mayonnaise over 1 slice high-fiber whole-wheat bread; top with 1 ounce roasted turkey, 1 [¾-ounce] slice Swiss cheese, 2 tomato slices, 1 lettuce leaf, and another slice of bread. [*POINTS:* 5]) **pretzel sticks,** 45 **seedless green grapes,** 1 cup
DINNER	**cheese pizza,** ⅛ of a 12-inch pizza **mixed greens,** 2 cups, with 2 tablespoons fat-free Italian dressing **low-fat brownie,** 1 (1½ ounces)	**broiled shrimp,** 4 ounces **cooked corn on the cob,** 1 small ear **Coleslaw** (Combine 1 tablespoon reduced-fat mayonnaise and 1 teaspoon white wine vinegar; stir well. Add 1 cup very thinly sliced green cabbage; toss well. [*POINTS:* 1]) **corn bread,** 2 ounces	**Beef-Vegetable Stir-fry** (Combine 4 ounces thinly sliced flank steak and ½ cup *each of* thinly sliced cabbage, carrots, mushrooms, and snow peas. Toss with 3 tablespoons soy sauce. Stir-fry in a large nonstick skillet coated with cooking spray 3 minutes or until vegetables are crisp-tender; stir in 1 teaspoon dark sesame oil. [*POINTS*: 11]) **cooked long-grain rice,** ½ cup **pineapple chunks,** 1 cup	**pinto beans,** 1 cup **Sour Cream Mashed Potatoes** (Mash ½ cup boiled cubed potato with 2 tablespoons fat-free sour cream, 1 tablespoon chopped fresh chives, and dash *each of* salt and pepper. [*POINTS:* 2]) **stewed okra and tomatoes,** 1 cup **steamed yellow squash,** 1 cup
SNACK	**popcorn,** 94% fat-free microwave-popped, 1 large bag	**vanilla fat-free yogurt,** 8 ounces **banana,** 1	**pretzel sticks,** 45 **fat-free milk,** 1 cup	**banana,** 1, with 1 tablespoon peanut butter **fat-free milk,** 1 cup
POINTS	***POINTS*** for the day: 28 **Exchanges:** 8 Starch, 3 Vegetable, 2 Fruit, 4 Very Lean Meat, 3 Medium-Fat Meat, 2 Skim Milk, 3½ Fat	***POINTS*** for the day: 26 **Exchanges:** 6 Starch, 2½ Vegetable, 3 Fruit, 4 Very Lean Meat, 2 Lean Meat, 2 Skim Milk, 1 Fat	***POINTS*** for the day: 30 **Exchanges:** 6 Starch, 3 Vegetable, 4 Fruit, 4 Lean Meat, 2 Skim Milk, 1 Medium-Fat Meat, 1 Fat	***POINTS*** for the day: 26 **Exchanges:** 6½ Starch, 5 Vegetable, 3 Fruit, 3 Very Lean Meat, 2½ High-Fat Meat, 2 Skim Milk

7-DAY MENU PLANNER

WEEK 7

	FRIDAY	SATURDAY	SUNDAY
BREAKFAST	**Fruit Smoothie** (Combine 1 banana and 8 ounces vanilla fat-free yogurt in a blender; process until smooth; top with 2 tablespoons toasted wheat germ. [*POINTS*: 5])	**shredded wheat,** 2 large biscuits, with 1 tablespoon brown sugar **blueberries,** 1 cup **fat-free milk,** 1 cup	**whole-wheat bagel,** 1 (2-ounce), with 2 tablespoons tub-style light cream cheese and 1 ounce smoked salmon **strawberries,** 1 cup **fat-free milk,** 1 cup
LUNCH	**Tomato-Cheese Sandwich** (Spread 2 teaspoons reduced-fat mayonnaise over 1 slice high-fiber whole-wheat bread; top with 4 slices tomato, 1 [¾-ounce] slice Swiss cheese, and another slice of bread. [*POINTS*: 6]) **pickle,** 1 medium **graham crackers,** 2 (2½-inch) **fat-free milk,** 1 cup	**Pasta Salad** (Combine 1 cup cooked fusilli, ¼ cup *each of* chopped carrot, bell pepper, broccoli, and tomato, and 3 tablespoons *each of* fat-free ranch dressing and shredded reduced-fat sharp Cheddar cheese. Toss well. [*POINTS*: 7]) **apple,** 1	**roasted chicken breast,** 3 ounces **baked sweet potato,** 8 ounces, with 2 tablespoons raisins, 1 tablespoon brown sugar, and 2 teaspoons light butter **steamed green beans,** 1 cup **apple pie à la mode fat-free yogurt,** 8 ounces
DINNER	**Chicken Shish Kebabs** (Cut 1 [4-ounce] skinned, boned chicken breast half into 1-inch pieces. Combine chicken, ½ cup fat-free Italian dressing, and ¼ cup *each of* bell pepper squares, onion chunks, small mushrooms, and cherry tomatoes; marinate in refrigerator 1 hour. Thread on skewers and grill or broil 8 minutes or until chicken is done. [*POINTS*: 4]) **cooked couscous,** ½ cup **watermelon chunks,** 1 cup	**grilled salmon,** 4 ounces **Stuffed Potato** (Top 1 [8-ounce] baked potato with 1 tablespoon *each of* light butter and fat-free sour cream, 1 cooked bacon slice, chopped, and 2 tablespoons chopped fresh chives. [*POINTS*: 7]) **steamed broccoli,** 1 cup	**Barbecued Pork Chop** (Brush 1 [4 ounce] boned pork chop with 1 tablespoon barbecue sauce. Grill 10 minutes or until done. [*POINTS*: 5]) **grilled zucchini,** 1 cup **grilled corn on the cob,** 1 small ear, with 1 teaspoon light butter
SNACK	**Banana Split** (Top ½ cup reduced-fat, vanilla ice cream with ½ cup sliced banana and 1 tablespoon *each of* strawberry jam and fat-free hot fudge topping. [*POINTS*: 6])	**reduced-fat vanilla wafers,** 6 **fat-free milk,** 1 cup	**Peach Crisp** (Place 1 cup sliced peaches in a 10-ounce custard cup coated with cooking spray. Combine 1½ teaspoons *each of* regular oats, all purpose flour, brown sugar, and light butter; crumble over peaches. Bake at 350° or until topping is browned. [*POINTS*: 3])
POINTS	***POINTS*** for the day: 27 **Exchanges:** 8 Starch, 2 Vegetable, 3 Fruit, 3 Very Lean Meat, 1 High-Fat Meat, 2 Skim Milk, ½ Fat	***POINTS*** for the day: 28 **Exchanges:** 7½ Starch 3 Vegetable, 2 Fruit, 4 Lean Meat, 1 Medium-Fat Meat, 2 Skim Milk, 2 Fat	***POINTS*** for the day: 26 **Exchanges:** 6½ Starch, 4 Vegetable, 4 Fruit, 3 Very Lean Meat, 1 Lean Meat, 3 Medium-Fat Meat, 2 Skim Milk, 2½ Fat

One day's menu provides at least two servings of milk and at least five servings of fruits and/or vegetables.

	MONDAY	TUESDAY	WEDNESDAY	THURSDAY
BREAKFAST	**Breakfast Burrito** (Whisk together 1 large egg, 1 large egg white, and 1 tablespoon fat-free milk. Cook in a nonstick skillet coated with cooking spray until firm. Spoon onto 1 [8-inch] flour tortilla. Sprinkle with 3 tablespoons shredded reduced-fat sharp Cheddar cheese; roll up. [*POINTS:* 6]) **strawberries,** 1 cup **fat-free milk,** 1 cup	**bran flakes,** 1½ cups **fat-free milk,** 1 cup **banana,** 1	**cooked oatmeal,** 1 cup, with 2 tablespoons raisins and 1 tablespoon cinnamon-sugar **fat-free milk,** 1 cup	**whole-wheat bagel,** 1 [2 ounce], with 1 tablespoon tub-style light cream cheese **orange sections,** 1 cup **fat-free milk,** 1 cup
LUNCH	**canned tomato soup,** 1 cup, sprinkled with 3 tablespoons grated Parmesan cheese **saltines,** 6, with 1 tablespoon peanut butter **apple,** 1	**Fresh Veggie Sandwich** (Top 1 slice high-fiber whole-wheat bread with 2 tablespoons mashed avocado, 1 small tomato, sliced, ½ cup alfalfa sprouts, ¼ cup sliced cucumber, ⅛ teaspoon *each of* salt and pepper, and another slice of bread. [*POINTS:* 4])	**Stuffed Veggie Potato** (Split 1 [8-ounce] baked potato and stuff with ¼ cup steamed broccoli florets, yellow squash, red bell pepper, shredded reduced-fat sharp Cheddar cheese, and 1 tablespoon *each of* chopped green onions and fat-free sour cream. [*POINTS:* 8]) **strawberries,** 1 cup	**Tomato-Avocado Sandwich** (Top 1 slice high-fiber whole-wheat bread with. 2 tablespoons mashed avocado, 3 tablespoons shredded reduced-fat sharp Cheddar cheese, 1 small tomato, sliced, ⅛ teaspoon *each of* salt and pepper, and another slice of bread. [*POINTS:* 5]) **carrot sticks,** 1 cup **fat-free milk,** 1 cup **blueberries,** ½ cup
DINNER	**Chickpea Stew** (Heat 1 teaspoon olive oil in a nonstick skillet. Add 1 garlic clove, minced, and ¼ cup *each of* chopped onion and carrot; sauté 3 minutes. Stir in 1 cup thinly sliced fresh spinach; cook 2 minutes. Add ¾ cup canned tomato purée, ⅓ cup drained, canned chickpeas, and ¾ teaspoon curry powder. Spoon over 1 cup cooked couscous. [*POINTS:* 7]) **seedless green grapes,** 1 cup	**broiled flounder fillet,** 4 ounces **Orange-Scented Couscous** (Bring ¼ cup *each of* water and orange juice to a boil. Stir in ⅓ cup uncooked couscous, 2 tablespoons chopped green onions, 1 tablespoon slivered almonds, and ⅛ teaspoon salt. Remove from heat; cover, and let stand 5 minutes. [*POINTS:* 6]) **steamed broccoli,** 1 cup	**Spicy Steak Fajitas** (Combine 2 tablespoons lime juice and 4 ounces thinly sliced flank steak. Heat 1 teaspoon olive oil in a nonstick skillet; sauté steak 1 minute. Add ¼ cup *each of* sliced red bell pepper, green bell pepper, and onion, and ½ teaspoon each of crushed red pepper and chili powder; sauté 3 minutes. Spoon onto 1 [8-inch] flour tortilla. Serve with ¼ cup salsa, 2 tablespoons fat-free sour cream, and 1 tablespoon mashed avocado. [*POINTS:* 8]) **orange sections,** 1 cup	**broiled lamb,** 3 ounces **cooked couscous,** 1 cup **Pear-Walnut Salad** (Drizzle 1 peeled, sliced ripe pear with 1 tablespoon honey. Sprinkle with 1 tablespoon *each of* blue cheese and chopped toasted walnuts. [*POINTS:* 5])
SNACK	**blackberry pie fat-free yogurt,** 8 ounces	**banana,** 1, with 1 tablespoon peanut butter **fat-free milk,** 1 cup	**lemon chiffon fat-free yogurt,** 8 ounces	**seedless green grapes,** 1 cup
POINTS	***POINTS*** for the day: 26 **Exchanges:** 9 Starch, 2½ Vegetable, 3 Fruit, 1½ Very Lean Meat, 1 Lean Meat, 2 Medium-Fat Meat, ½ High-Fat Meat, 2 Skim Milk, 1 Fat	***POINTS*** for the day: 25 **Exchanges:** 8 Starch, 4 Vegetable, 2½ Fruit, 4 Very Lean Meat, ½ High-Fat Meat, 2 Skim Milk, 2 Fat	***POINTS*** for the day: 26 **Exchanges:** 6½ Starch, 2½ Vegetable, 4 Fruit, 3 Lean Meat, 1 Medium-Fat Meat, 2 Skim Milk, 1½ Fat	***POINTS*** for the day: 28 **Exchanges:** 8 Starch, 2 Vegetable, 4½ Fruit, 3 Lean Meat, 1 Medium-Fat Meat, ½ High-Fat Meat, 2 Skim Milk, 2 Fat

7-DAY MENU PLANNER

WEEK 8

	FRIDAY	SATURDAY	SUNDAY
BREAKFAST	**Fruit and Cinnamon Quesadilla** (Spread 2 tablespoons tub-style light cream cheese over 1 [8-inch] flour tortilla; top with ⅓ cup thinly sliced strawberries and 1 tablespoon sugar. Sprinkle with a dash of cinnamon; fold in half. Cook in a nonstick skillet coated with cooking spray 2 minutes on each side. [*POINTS:* 5]) **fat-free milk,** 1 cup	**Banana-Peanut Butter Smoothie** (Combine 1 cup fat-free milk, 1 tablespoon peanut butter, and 1 peeled banana in a blender; process until smooth. [*POINTS:* 6]) **high-fiber whole-wheat bread**, 1 slice, toasted	**Mushroom and Cheese Omelet** (Combine 1 egg, 1 egg white, 2 tablespoons water, and a dash *each of* salt and pepper; pour into a small nonstick skillet and cook over medium heat 1 minute or until almost set. Top with ¼ cup sliced mushrooms and 3 tablespoons shredded reduced-fat sharp Cheddar cheese; fold in half. [*POINTS:* 4]) **whole-wheat bagel,** ½ [2 ounce], with 1 teaspoon light butter **orange juice,** ½ cup
LUNCH	**hamburger,** 1 small, fast food **green salad,** 2 cups, with 2 tablespoons fat-free Italian dressing	**Spinach-Egg Sandwich** (Combine 1 hard-cooked egg, chopped, 1 tablespoon reduced-fat mayonnaise and ½ teaspoon Dijon mustard; stir well. Spread over 1 slice high-fiber whole-wheat bread; top with ¼ cup fresh spinach and another slice of bread. [*POINTS:* 5]) **carrot sticks,** 1 cup	**Chicken Salad Sandwich** (Chop 1 chicken breast half from dinner on Friday. Combine with 2 tablespoons *each of* chopped carrot, green onions, and reduced-fat mayonnaise, 1 teaspoon Dijon mustard, and a dash of celery seeds; spread over 1 slice high-fiber whole-wheat bread. Top with 2 lettuce leaves, 2 tomato slices, and another slice of bread. [*POINTS:* 9]) **cucumber spears,** 1 cup **fat-free milk,** 1 cup
DINNER	**Honey-Lemon Chicken** (Brush 2 [4-ounce] skinned, boned chicken breast halves each with 1 tablespoon *each of* lemon juice and honey. Sprinkle with ⅛ teaspoon *each of* salt and pepper. Broil 5 minutes on each side. Reserve 1 chicken breast half for lunch on Sunday [*POINTS:* 4]) **steamed new potatoes,** 1 cup **Spinach With Walnuts** (Sauté 2 cups fresh spinach and 1 tablespoon chopped walnuts in 1 teaspoon oil in a nonstick skillet. Top with 1 tablespoon Parmesan cheese. [*POINTS:* 3])	**Seared Salmon Steak** (Brush 1 [6-ounce] salmon fillet with 1 tablespoon lemon juice and 1 teaspoon Greek seasoning blend. Cook in a nonstick skillet coated with cooking spray over medium-high heat for 3 minutes on each side. [*POINTS:* 6]) **Artichoke Linguine** (Combine 1 cup cooked linguine, ½ cup canned quartered artichoke hearts, 2 tablespoons chopped ripe olives, 1 tablespoon lemon juice, and ½ teaspoon olive oil; toss well. [*POINTS:* 6])	**Beef and Bean Tortilla** (Cook 3 ounces ground round and ¼ cup chopped onion in a nonstick skillet until browned, stirring to crumble. Stir in ¼ cup fat-free refried beans and 3 tablespoons *each of* salsa and shredded reduced-fat sharp Cheddar cheese. Spoon over 1 [8-inch] flour tortilla. Serve with ¼ cup salsa and 1 tablespoon fat-free sour cream. [*POINTS:* 6]) **mango chunks,** 1 cup
SNACK	**Mixed Fruit Parfait** (Layer 1 [8-ounce] container vanilla fat-free yogurt alternately with ½ cup *each of* blueberries and sliced strawberries in a parfait glass. [*POINTS:* 3])	**Tropical Smoothie** (Combine 1 cup fat-free milk, ¾ cup peeled cubed mango or papaya, and 1 peeled banana in a blender; process until smooth. [*POINTS:* 5])	**blueberry fat-free yogurt,** 8 ounces
POINTS	***POINTS*** for the day: 25 **Exchanges:** 7 Starch, 4 Vegetable, 3 Fruit, 3 Very Lean Meat, ½ Lean Meat, 2 Medium-Fat Meat, 2 Skim Milk, 3 Fat	***POINTS*** for the day: 29 **Exchanges:** 5 Starch, 2½ Vegetable, 2½ Fruit, 5 Lean Meat, 1 Medium-Fat Meat, ½ High-Fat Meat, 2 Skim Milk, 1 Fat	***POINTS*** for the day: 28 **Exchanges:** 4½ Starch, 2½ Vegetable, 3 Fruit, 4 Very Lean Meat, 2 Lean Meat, 3 Medium-Fat Meat, 2 Skim Milk, 1½ Fat

One day's menu provides at least two servings of milk and at least five servings of fruits and/or vegetables.

	MONDAY	TUESDAY	WEDNESDAY	THURSDAY
BREAKFAST	**Cinnamon Toast** (Spread 1 teaspoon light butter over 1 slice high-fiber whole-wheat bread; sprinkle with 1 teaspoon cinnamon-sugar. Broil until toasted. [*POINTS:* 1]) **banana,** 1 **fat-free milk,** 1 cup	**1% low-fat cottage cheese,** ⅓ cup **raisin bread,** 1 slice, toasted, with 1 teaspoon light butter **strawberries,** 1 cup **fat-free milk,** 1 cup	**frozen whole-grain waffles,** 2 (4-inch), toasted, with 1 tablespoon maple syrup and 2 teaspoons light butter **vanilla fat-free yogurt,** 8 ounces **grapefruit,** ½	**cantaloupe,** ¼ melon **English muffin,** ½ (1 ounce), with 1 teaspoon jam **fat-free milk,** 1 cup
LUNCH	**pepperoni pizza,** ⅛ of a 12-inch pizza **garden salad,** 2 cups, with 2 tablespoons fat-free creamy ranch dressing **cappuccino fat-free yogurt,** 8 ounces	**Vegetarian Pitas** (Combine ¼ cup *each of* chopped tomato, shredded lettuce, shredded carrot, and alfalfa sprouts, and 2 tablespoons raisins; toss well. Cut 1 [2-ounce] whole-wheat pita in half; stuff with vegetable mixture. Drizzle 2 tablespoons fat-free creamy ranch salad dressing over each half. [*POINTS:* 5]) **seedless green grapes,** 1 cup **fat-free milk,** 1 cup	**canned reduced-fat, reduced-sodium New England clam chowder,** 1 cup **saltine crackers,** 6 **pear,** 1	**Barley and Bean Salad** (Combine 1 cup *each of* chopped cucumber and chopped tomato, ½ cup cooked barley, ¼ cup drained canned red kidney beans, and 2 teaspoons *each of* olive oil and red wine vinegar; toss well. [*POINTS:* 8]) **kiwifruit,** 1
DINNER	**Spice-Crusted Chicken Breast** (Combine ¾ teaspoon *each of* ground coriander and cumin, and ⅛ teaspoon *each of* salt and pepper; sprinkle over both sides of 1 [4-ounce] skinned, boned chicken breast half. Broil 5 minutes on each side or until done. [*POINTS:* 3]) **Roasted Beans and Peppers** (Place 1 cup trimmed green beans and 1 cup julienne-cut red bell pepper on a baking sheet. Drizzle with 1 teaspoon olive oil; bake at 500° for 8 minutes or until lightly browned. [*POINTS:* 2]) **cooked brown rice,** 1 cup	**broiled lamb chop,** 3 ounces **cooked couscous,** 1 cup, with 1 tablespoon minced fresh mint and 2 teaspoons light butter **steamed carrots,** 1 cup	**Onion-Zucchini Frittata** (Sauté 1 cup *each of* chopped onion and zucchini in a small nonstick skillet over medium heat until tender. Combine 1 egg, 1 tablespoon fat-free milk, ⅛ teaspoon *each of* salt and pepper; stir well. Pour over vegetables; cover and cook until firm. Sprinkle with 3 tablespoons shredded reduced-fat sharp Cheddar cheese. [*POINTS:* 5]) **Beet Salad** (Combine 1 cup mixed salad greens, 1 cup sliced beets, and 1 tablespoon fat-free red wine vinaigrette; toss well. [*POINTS:* 1]) **dinner roll,** 2 ounces, with 1 teaspoon light butter	**Hobo Fish Dinner** (Layer 1 sliced small baking potato, 1 sliced small onion, 1 sliced carrot, and an 8-ounce halibut fillet on a 1 [8-inch] square of heavy foil. Sprinkle with ⅛ teaspoon *each of* salt, pepper, and dried dill. Wrap foil to form a tightly sealed pouch; bake at 450° for 30 minutes or until done. [*POINTS:* 9]) **raspberry sorbet,** ½ cup
SNACK	**Brownie Sundae** (Top 1 [1½-ounce] low-fat brownie with ¼ cup reduced-fat ice cream and 1 tablespoon fat-free hot fudge topping. [*POINTS:* 3])	**Frozen Vanilla Parfait** (Layer ½ cup reduced-fat ice cream and 3 tablespoons graham cracker crumbs in a parfait glass. [*POINTS:* 4])	**fat-free milk,** 1 cup **low-fat brownie,** 1 (1½-ounce)	**banana,** 1 **fat-free milk,** 1 cup
POINTS	***POINTS*** for the day: 25 **Exchanges:** 8½ Starch, 4 Vegetable, 1 Fruit, 3 Very Lean Meat, 2 Medium-Fat Meat, 2 Skim Milk, 4 Fat	***POINTS*** for the day: 29 **Exchanges:** 8 Starch, 3 Vegetable, 3 Fruit, 1 Very Lean Meat, 3 Lean Meat, 2 Skim Milk, 2 Fat	***POINTS*** for the day: 30 **Exchanges:** 8 Starch, 4 Vegetable, 2 Fruit, 1 Very Lean Meat, 2 Medium-Fat Meat, 2 Skim Milk, 3 Fat	***POINTS*** for the day: 28 **Exchanges:** 6 Starch, 3 Vegetable, 3 Fruit, 7½ Very Lean Meat, 2 Skim MIlk, 2 Fat

7-DAY MENU PLANNER

WEEK 9

	FRIDAY	SATURDAY	SUNDAY
BREAKFAST	**Egg Sandwich** (Scramble 1 egg in a small nonstick skillet over medium heat. Spoon egg onto 1 slice high-fiber whole-wheat bread; top with 1 slice *each of* fat-free American processed cheese, tomato, and another slice of bread. [*POINTS:* 4]) **orange juice,** 1 cup **fat-free milk,** 1 cup	**bran flakes,** 1½ cups **banana,** ½ **fat-free milk,** 1 cup	**cooked cream of wheat cereal,** 1 cup, with 1 tablespoon brown sugar **fat-free milk,** 1 cup **strawberries,** 1 cup
LUNCH	**cooked chicken breast,** 3 ounces **steamed green beans,** 1 cup **steamed carrots,** 1 cup **cream-style corn,** ½ cup **corn bread,** 2 ounces, with 1 teaspoon light butter	**baked ham,** 3 ounces **Spinach Mushroom Salad** (Combine 2 cups torn spinach, ½ cup *each of* sliced mushrooms and sliced red onion, 1 sliced hard-cooked egg, and 2 teaspoons chopped cooked bacon. Toss with 2 tablespoons fat-free French dressing. [*POINTS:* 4]) **cantaloupe chunks,** 1 cup	**Peanut Butter and Banana Sandwich** (Spread 1 tablespoon peanut butter over 1 slice high-fiber whole-wheat bread; top with 1 sliced banana and another slice bread. [*POINTS:* 6]) **carrot and celery sticks,** 1 cup **blueberry fat-free yogurt,** 8 ounces
DINNER	**broiled flank steak,** 3 ounces **baked potato,** 8 ounces, with 2 teaspoons light butter and chives **steamed broccoli,** 1 cup	**broiled shrimp,** 4 ounces **coleslaw,** 1 cup coleslaw mix, with 1 tablespoon fat-free coleslaw dressing **cooked corn on the cob,** 1 small ear **apple,** 1	**Greek Linguine** (Toss 1 cup hot cooked linguine with ½ cup chopped spinach, ½ cup drained canned chickpeas, 2 tablespoons raisins, 2 teaspoons olive oil, ¼ teaspoon crushed red pepper, and ⅛ teaspoon salt. [*POINTS:* 10]) **Romaine-Artichoke Salad** (Combine 1 cup sliced romaine lettuce and ½ cup drained canned quartered artichoke hearts; toss with 1 tablespoon fat-free red wine vinaigrette. Top with 1 teaspoon grated Parmesan cheese. [*POINTS:* 1])
SNACK	**Coffee Shake** (Combine 1 cup fat-free milk, 4 ice cubes, 2 teaspoons *each of* sugar and instant coffee granules; process in blender until smooth. [*POINTS:* 2]) **seedless green grapes,** 1 cup	**reduced-fat vanilla wafers,** 6, with 1 tablespoon peanut butter **fat-free milk,** 1 cup **peanut butter,** 1 tablespoon	**apple,** 1, cut into wedges, with 2 tablespoons fat-free caramel syrup
POINTS	***POINTS*** for the day: 26 **Exchanges:** 6½ Starch, 6½ Vegetable, 3 Fruit, 4 Very Lean Meat, 3 Lean Meat, 1 Medium-Fat Meat, 2 Skim Milk, 1 Fat	***POINTS*** for the day: 25 **Exchanges:** 5½ Starch, 4 Vegetable, 2½ Fruit, 4 Very Lean Meat, 3 Lean Meat, 1 Medium-Fat Meat, ½ High-Fat Meat, 2 Skim Milk, ½ Fat	***POINTS*** for the day: 27 **Exchanges:** 9 Starch, 4 Vegetable, 4 Fruit, 1 Very Lean Meat, ½ High-Fat Meat, 2 Skim Milk, 2 Fat

LOW-FAT INGREDIENT SUBSTITUTIONS

Needed Ingredient	Substitutions
FATS AND OILS	
Butter or margarine	Reduced-calorie margarine or margarine made with canola, corn, peanut, safflower, or soybean oil; reduced-calorie stick margarine in baked products
Mayonnaise	Fat-free, reduced-fat, or low-fat mayonnaise
Oil	Safflower, soybean, corn, canola, or peanut oil in reduced amount
Salad dressing	Fat-free or oil-free dressing
Shortening	Soybean, corn, canola, or peanut oil in amount reduced by one-third
DAIRY PRODUCTS	
Cheeses: American, Cheddar, colby, Edam, or Swiss	Cheeses with 5 grams of fat or less per ounce like reduced-fat and part-skim cheeses
Cheese, cottage	Fat-free or 1% low-fat cottage cheese
Cheese, cream	Fat-free, ⅓-less-fat cheese, or tub-style light cream cheese
Cheese, ricotta	Fat-free, light, or part-skim ricotta cheese
Cream, sour	Low-fat or fat-free sour cream; low-fat or fat-free yogurt
Cream, whipping	Chilled fat-free evaporated milk or fat-free half-and-half
Ice cream	Fat-free or low-fat frozen yogurt; fat-free or low-fat ice cream; sherbet; sorbet
Milk, whole	Fat-free, low-fat, or reduced-fat milk
MEATS, FISH, POULTRY, AND EGGS	
Bacon	Canadian bacon; turkey bacon; lean ham
Beef, ground	Extralean or ultralean ground beef; freshly ground raw turkey
Beef, lamb, pork, or veal	Chicken, turkey, or lean cuts of meat trimmed of all visible fat
Luncheon meat	Skinned, sliced turkey or chicken breast; lean ham; lean roast beef
Poultry	Skinned poultry
Tuna packed in oil	Tuna packed in water
Turkey, self-basting	Turkey basted with fat-free broth
Egg, whole	2 egg whites or ¼ cup fat-free egg substitute
MISCELLANEOUS	
Fudge sauce	Fat-free fudge sauce or chocolate syrup
Nuts	Reduce amount one-third to one-half, and toast
Soups, canned	98% fat-free or reduced-fat, reduced-sodium condensed cream soups

VEGETABLE COOKING CHART

Vegetable	Servings	Preparations	Cooking Instructions
Asparagus	3 to 4 per pound	Snap off tough ends. Remove scales, if desired.	To steam: Cook, covered, on a rack above boiling water 8 to 12 minutes. To boil: Cook, covered, in a small amount of boiling water 6 to 8 minutes or until crisp-tender.
Broccoli	3 to 4 per pound	Remove outer leaves and tough ends of lower stalks. Wash; cut into spears.	To steam: Cook, covered, on a rack above boiling water 15 to 18 minutes.
Carrots	4 per pound	Scrape; remove ends, and rinse. Leave tiny carrots whole; slice large carrots, or cut into strips.	Cook, covered, in a small amount of boiling water 8 to 10 minutes (slices) or 12 to 15 minutes (strips).
Cauliflower	4 per medium head	Remove outer leaves and stalk. Wash. Leave whole, or break into florets.	Cook, covered, in a small amount of boiling water 10 to 12 minutes (whole) or 8 to 10 minutes (florets).
Corn	4 per 4 large ears	Remove husks and silks. Leave corn on the cob, or cut off tips of kernels, and scrape cob with dull edge of knife.	Cook, covered, in boiling water to cover 10 minutes (on cob) or in a small amount of boiling water 8 to 10 minutes (cut).
Green beans	4 per pound	Wash; trim ends, and remove strings. Cut into 1½-inch pieces.	Cook, covered, in a small amount of boiling water 12 to 15 minutes.
Potatoes	3 to 4 per pound	Scrub; peel, if desired. Leave whole, slice, or cut into chunks.	To cook: Cook, covered, in a small amount of boiling water 30 to 40 minutes (whole) or 15 to 20 minutes (slices or chunks). To bake: Bake at 400° for 1 hour or until done.
Snow peas	4 per pound	Wash; trim ends, and remove tough strings.	Cook, covered, in a small amount of boiling water 3 to 5 minutes. Or cook over high heat in reduced-calorie margarine or in pan coated with cooking spray 3 to 5 minutes, stirring constantly.
Squash, summer	3 to 4 per pound	Wash; trim ends. Leave whole, slice, or chop.	To steam: Cook, covered, on a rack over boiling water 10 to 12 minutes (sliced or chopped). To boil: Cook, covered, in a small amount of boiling water 8 to 10 minutes (slices) or 15 minutes (whole).
Squash, winter *(including acorn, butternut, hubbard, and spaghetti)*	2 per pound	Rinse; cut in half, and remove all seeds.	To boil: Cook, covered, in boiling water 20 to 25 minutes. To bake: Place cut side down in shallow baking dish; add ½ inch water. Bake, uncovered, at 375° for 30 minutes. Turn and season, or fill; bake 20 to 30 minutes or until tender.

GUIDE TO FOOD STORAGE

Follow this guide for food storage, and you can be sure that what's in your freezer, refrigerator, and pantry is fresh-tasting and ready to cook.

IN THE FREEZER

(At -10° to 0° F)

DAIRY

Cheese, hard	3 months
Cheese, soft	2 weeks
Egg substitute	6 months
Egg whites	6 months
Egg yolks	8 months
Ice cream, sherbet	1 month

FRUITS AND VEGETABLES

Commercially frozen fruits	1 year
Commercially frozen vegetables	8 to 12 months

MEATS, POULTRY, AND SEAFOOD

Beef, Lamb, and Veal	
Ground, uncooked, and all cuts, cooked	3 months
Roasts and steaks, uncooked	9 months
Pork	
Ground, uncooked, and all cuts, cooked	3 months
Roasts and chops, uncooked	6 months
Poultry	
All cuts, cooked	1 month
Boneless or bone-in pieces, uncooked	6 months
Seafood	
Bass, perch, trout, and shellfish	3 months
Cod, flounder, and halibut	6 months

IN THE REFRIGERATOR

(At 34° to 40° F)

DAIRY

Buttermilk, low-fat	1 to 2 weeks
Cheese, grated Parmesan	1 year
Cheeses, Cheddar and Swiss	3 to 4 weeks
Cream cheese, ⅓-less-fat and reduced-fat	2 weeks
Eggs and egg substitute	1 month
Margarine	1 month

MEATS, POULTRY, AND SEAFOOD

Beef, Lamb, Pork, and Veal	
Ground and stew meat, uncooked	1 to 2 days
Roasts, uncooked	2 to 4 days
Steaks and chops, uncooked	3 to 5 days
Chicken, Turkey, and Seafood	
All cuts, uncooked	1 to 2 days

FRUITS AND VEGETABLES

Apples, beets, cabbage, carrots, celery, citrus fruits, eggplant, and parsnips	2 to 3 weeks
Apricots, berries, peaches, pears, plums, asparagus, cauliflower, cucumbers, mushrooms, okra, peas, peppers, salad greens, and summer squash	2 to 4 days
Corn, husked	1 day

IN THE PANTRY

Keep these at room temperature for six to 12 months.

BAKING AND COOKING STAPLES

Baking powder
Biscuit and baking mix
Broth, canned
Cooking spray
Honey
Mayonnaise, regular, light, and nonfat (unopened)
Milk, canned evaporated skimmed
Milk, nonfat dry powder
Mustard, prepared (unopened)
Oils, olive and vegetable
Pasta, dried
Peanut butter, reduced-fat
Rice, instant and regular
Salad dressings, bottled (unopened)
Seasoning sauces, bottled
Tuna, canned

FRUITS, LEGUMES, AND VEGETABLES

Fruits, canned
Legumes (beans, lentils, peas), dried or canned
Tomato products, canned
Vegetables, canned

METRIC EQUIVALENTS

The recipes that appear in this cookbook use the standard United States method for measuring liquid and dry or solid ingredients (teaspoons, tablespoons, and cups). The information in the following charts is provided to help cooks outside the U.S. successfully use these recipes. All equivalents are approximate.

EQUIVALENTS FOR DIFFERENT TYPES OF INGREDIENTS

A standard cup measure of a dry or solid ingredient will vary in weight depending on the type of ingredient. A standard cup of liquid is the same volume for any type of liquid. Use the following chart when converting standard cup measures to grams (weight) or milliliters (volume).

Standard Cup	Fine Powder (ex. flour)	Grain (ex. rice)	Granular (ex. sugar)	Liquid Solids (ex. butter)	Liquid (ex. milk)
1	140 g	150 g	190 g	200 g	240 ml
¾	105 g	113 g	143 g	150 g	180 ml
⅔	93 g	100 g	125 g	133 g	160 ml
½	70 g	75 g	95 g	100 g	120 ml
⅓	47 g	50 g	63 g	67 g	80 ml
¼	35 g	38 g	48 g	50 g	60 ml
⅛	18 g	19 g	24 g	25 g	30 ml

LIQUID INGREDIENTS BY VOLUME

¼ tsp	=							1 ml
½ tsp	=							2 ml
1 tsp	=							5 ml
3 tsp	=	1 tbls			=	½ fl oz	=	15 ml
		2 tbls	=	⅛ cup	=	1 fl oz	=	30 ml
		4 tbls	=	¼ cup	=	2 fl oz	=	60 ml
		5⅓ tbls	=	⅓ cup	=	3 fl oz	=	80 ml
		8 tbls	=	½ cup	=	4 fl oz	=	120 ml
		10⅔ tbls	=	⅔ cup	=	5 fl oz	=	160 ml
		12 tbls	=	¾ cup	=	6 fl oz	=	180 ml
		16 tbls	=	1 cup	=	8 fl oz	=	240 ml
		1 pt	=	2 cups	=	16 fl oz	=	480 ml
		1 qt	=	4 cups	=	32 fl oz	=	960 ml
						33 fl oz	=	1000 ml = 1 liter

DRY INGREDIENTS BY WEIGHT

(To convert ounces to grams, multiply the number of ounces by 30.)

1 oz	=	¹⁄₁₆ lb	=	30 g
4 oz	=	¼ lb	=	120 g
8 oz	=	½ lb	=	240 g
12 oz	=	¾ lb	=	360 g
16 oz	=	1 lb	=	480 g

LENGTH

(To convert inches to centimeters, multiply the number of inches by 2.5.)

1 in	=			=	2.5 cm		
6 in	=	½ ft		=	15 cm		
12 in	=	1 ft		=	30 cm		
36 in	=	3 ft	= 1 yd	=	90 cm		
40 in	=			=	100 cm	=	1 meter

COOKING/OVEN TEMPERATURES

	Fahrenheit	Celsius	Gas Mark
Freeze Water	32° F	0° C	
Room Temperature	68° F	20° C	
Boil Water	212° F	100° C	
Bake	325° F	160° C	3
	350° F	180° C	4
	375° F	190° C	5
	400° F	200° C	6
	425° F	220° C	7
	450° F	230° C	8
Broil			Grill

General Recipe Index

POINTS® Recipe Index

All recipes, including those in the Weekly Menu Planners, are listed under the ***POINTS*** value for the recipe.

4 POINTS

5 POINTS

7 POINTS

8 POINTS

9 POINTS

10 POINTS

11 POINTS

CONTRIBUTORS

EDITORIAL DEVELOPMENT
Regan Miller Jones, R.D.

INDEXER
Mary Ann Laurens

PHOTOGRAPHER
Howard L. Puckett

PHOTO STYLISTS
Melanie J. Clarke
Lorrie Hulston
Missie Neville
Ashley J. Wyatt

TEST KITCHENS STAFF
Natalie E. King
Leigh Mullinax
Alyssa Ouverson
Kathleen Royal Phillips
Kate M. Wheeler, R.D.

FEATURE WRITERS
Katherine Alford
Mindy Keyes Black
Elisabeth Flynn
Jennifer Greer
Margaret Littman
Bill Marsano
Martha Thomas
Jim Travisano
Joe Watts
Kimberly Weeks
Tracey Zemitis

RECIPE DEVELOPERS
Patti Bess
Jack Bishop
David Bonom
Holly B. Clegg
Jim Fobel
Alyson M. Haynes
Nancy Hughes
Lorrie Hulston
Regan Miller Jones
Elizabeth Tyler Luckett
Marcy Marceau
Marge Perry
Kathleen Royal Phillips
Kay Reed
Victoria Abbot Riccardi
Julia Dowling Rutland
Beth K. Shields
Jan A. Smith
Elizabeth J. Taliaferro
Dugan Vacca
Lynn Walters
Kenneth Wapner
Joe Watts
Joy Zacharia, R.D.